A Laboratory Manual and Study Guide

for

HUMAN ANATOMY

Third Edition

D1396503

Barbara H. Kalbus
Kenneth G. Neal
Margaret A. Wilson

Long Beach City College
Long Beach, California

ILLUSTRATED BY
Robert G. Bush
PHOTOGRAPHS BY
Ann C. Kern

Burgess Publishing

A Division of Burgess International Group, Inc.

© 1986 by Burgess Publishing
Previous editions © 1970, 1973 by Barbara H. Kalbus and Kenneth G. Neal
ISBN 8-8087-5616-8
Printed in the United States of America

Burgess Publishing
7110 Ohms Lane
Minneapolis, Minnesota 55435

J I H G F E D C B A

PREFACE

This manual has been designed to be used by students to develop laboratory skills, to become familiar with the methods of science, and to learn the significant concepts of anatomy. We have attempted to provide students with opportunities to apply what has been learned in lectures and in the laboratory, to make the laboratory interesting for the student, and to reduce preparation time on the part of the instructor.

The inclusion of detailed orientation for students and discussions providing background for the assigned material saves valuable time in preparing and performing laboratory activities for both the student and the instructor.

We feel that the following features will greatly facilitate the study of anatomy in the laboratory:

1. The section on **Orientation and Suggestions for Students** provides general directions for laboratory procedures.
2. The numerous illustrations, photographs and diagrams clarify the laboratory directions.
3. Each exercise includes a discussion (when appropriate) and a procedure with detailed instructions. As a general rule, no additional orientation or oral instructions are required.
4. The **Questions** section for each chapter (located at the end of the manual) is designed to be removed from the manual for answering questions, and for submitting for evaluation.
5. Anatomical studies involve the dissection of the cat, sheep heart, sheep brain, and the sheep eye. Original drawings and photographs are included with the instructions for dissection, which greatly facilitate the identification of structures in the specimen.
6. Most of the illustrations and photographs can serve as self-tests and each includes a key.
7. Each major unit includes a relatively comprehensive **self-test** (with key) that covers lecture, laboratory, and practical applications.

The cat is emphasized in the manual, and it may be desirable to limit all dissection to this single animal. In addition, detailed instructions for the dissection of certain organs of the sheep that are included may be readily adapted to beef or other mammalian structures.

All of the exercises in this manual have been used under laboratory conditions over the past several years by the authors and many other instructors throughout the United States.

Barbara H. Kalbus

Kenneth G. Neal

Margaret A. Wilson

ACKNOWLEDGMENTS

It is with deep appreciation that we acknowledge the skill of Robert Bush in drawing most of the illustrations in this manual. We also want to thank Ann Kern for the excellent series of photographs included in this edition.

Our gratitude also to Linda Neal for her diligence and attention to detail as she ably assisted in the editing of the manual and had complete responsibility for providing photo-ready copy of the manuscript. Rebecca van Harrevelt spent many hours at the computer composing copy for this text and double-proofed everything she did--her concern for accuracy has been a real asset.

Sharon Noble composed most of the headlines and tables. Barbara Kalbus performed the majority of the dissections used by our photographer and Margaret Wilson reviewed the entire book and rewrote sections where necessary. Kenneth Neal edited the project.

The Authors

CONTENTS

	Page
Preface	iii
Acknowledgments	iv
Orientation and Suggestions for Students	1

Chapter I. Body Organization and Terminology 6

Ex. I-A. Organization of the Body as a Whole ...	6
Ex. I-B. Anatomic Terminology	7
Ex. I-C. Major Organ Systems	11
Self-Test: Body Organization and Terminology ...	12
Questions for Chapter I	241

Chapter II. Basic Microscopy 14

Ex. II-A. Structure of the Microscope	14
Ex. II-B. Microscope Drawings	15
Ex. II-C. Orientation of Images Viewed through the Compound Microscope	17
Ex. II-D. Thread Slide	18
Self-Test: Basic Microscopy	20
Questions for Chapter II	245

Chapter III. Cells, Mitosis, Tissues, and Skin ... 21

Ex. III-A. The Structure of a Cell Observed under the Light Microscope Compared to that Observed with an Electron Microscope	21
Ex. III-B. Mitosis	21
Ex. III-C. Epithelial Tissue	25
Ex. III-D. Connective Tissue	27
Ex. III-E. Muscular Tissue	34
Ex. III-F. Nerve Tissue	36
Ex. III-G. The Skin	37
Self-Test: Cells, Mitosis, Tissues, and Skin ...	39
Questions for Chapter III	247

Chapter IV. The Skeletal System 41

Ex. IV-A. Composition and Structure of Bone	41
Ex. IV-B. The Appendicular Skeleton	43
Ex. IV-C. The Axial Skeleton	53
Ex. IV-D. The Fetal Skeleton	66
Ex. IV-E. Joints	67
Self-Test: The Skeletal System	69
Questions for Chapter IV	251

Chapter V.   The Muscular System 72

    Ex. V-A.   The Gross Anatomy of the Major Super-
            ficial Human Muscles 72
    Ex. V-B.   The External Anatomy of the Cat 72
    Ex. V-C.   Skinning the Cat 77
    Ex. V-D.   The Musculature of the Cat 80
    Self-Test: Muscular System 116
    Questions for Chapter V 255

Chapter VI.   The Digestive System 118

    Ex. VI-A.   Anatomy of the Human Digestive
             System 118
    Ex. VI-B.   Dissection of the Digestive System
             of the Cat 118
    Self-Test: The Digestive System 135
    Questions for Chapter VI 259

Chapter VII.   The Respiratory System 138

    Ex. VII-A.   Anatomy of the Human Respiratory
              System 138
    Ex. VII-B.   Dissection of the Cat Respiratory
              System 139
    Self-Test: The Respiratory System 146
    Questions for Chapter VII 261

Chapter VIII.   The Circulatory System 148

    Ex. VIII-A.   Structure of an Artery, Vein, and
               a Lymph Vessel Valve 148
    Ex. VIII-B.   Gross Anatomy of the Human
               Circulatory System 149
    Ex. VIII-C.   The Dissection of the Sheep Heart .. 149
    Ex. VIII-D.   The Dissection of the Circulatory
               System of the Cat 159
    Self-Test: The Circulatory System 173
    Questions for Chapter VIII 263

Chapter IX.   The Nervous System 176

    Ex. IX-A.   Anatomy of the Nervous System 176
    Ex. IX-B.   The Dissection of the Sheep Brain 177
    Ex. IX-C.   The Dissection of the Cat CNS 185
    Ex. IX-D.   The Dissection of the Cat Peripheral
             Nervous System 186
    Self-Test: The Nervous System 189
    Questions for Chapter IX 267

Chapter X. Sense Organs 192

   Ex. X-A. Gross Anatomy of the Human Eye 193
   Ex. X-B. Dissection of the Sheep Eye 193
   Ex. X-C. Anatomy of the Ear 197
   Self-Test: Sense Organs 200
   Questions for Chapter X 271

Chapter XI. The Urinary System 203

   Ex. XI-A. Anatomy of the Human Urinary
          System 203
   Ex. XI-B. Dissection of the Urinary System
          of the Cat 206
   Self-Test: The Urinary System 210
   Questions for Chapter XI 275

Chapter XII. The Endocrine System 212

   Ex. XII-A. Endocrine Glands 212
   Ex. XII-B. Dissection of the Endocrine Glands
           of the Cat 213
   Self-Test: The Endocrine System 215
   Questions for Chapter XII 277

Chapter XIII. The Reproductive System 217

   Ex. XIII-A. The Human Male Reproductive
            System 217
   Ex. XIII-B. The Human Female Reproductive
            System 219
   Ex. XIII-C. The Endometrial (Menstrual)
            Cycle 227
   Ex. XIII-D. The Placenta 228
   Ex. XIII-E. Embryology 229
   Ex. XIII-F. Dissection of the Reproductive
            System of the Cat 233
   Self-Test: The Reproductive System 238
   Questions for Chapter XIII 281

ORIENTATION AND SUGGESTIONS FOR STUDENTS

A. Introduction

The laboratory experience can be the most rewarding part of the course, if a student approaches it with an appropriate attitude - namely, with the **desire for knowledge,** an **interest in the development of skills and techniques,** and a **willingness to be subject to the discipline of the laboratory.** The latter is especially important in the development of habits essential to good scientific work. Such discipline and training is required in virtually all areas of science, and may be lifesaving in many cases. The development of scientific attitudes is the result of thinking and acting in a scientific manner. Carelessness, sloppiness, tardiness, preconceived ideas, and inefficiency may be accepted in some areas of human endeavor, but not in science.

Critically observe all specimens which you are asked to study. Your own observations should provide answers to most of the questions that arise during the laboratory. **Learn to think independently.** The instructor will offer helpful suggestions, but should not be expected to be a source of ready answers to each of your questions. No one can learn for you.

B. Laboratory Supplies

In the spaces provided, check the supplies your instructor indicates are to be provided by you.

1. ___ 3H pencil
2. ___ 4H pencil
3. ___ red pencil
4. ___ blue pencil
5. ___ manila folder
6. ___ box of colored pencils
7. ___ lens paper
8. ___ dissecting kit
9. ___ biology filler paper
10. ___ 6 inch ruler
11. ___ eraser
12. _____

C. Assignments

All, or most, of the assignments will be given in advance of the laboratory. The student is expected to read the introductions, as well as to preview procedures, **before** the date of the assigned laboratory. In addition, a brief orientation will be given at the beginning of the laboratory.

D. General Laboratory Rules

There are reasons for every rule imposed upon the student. If these are not readily apparent to you, **ask your instructor for an interpretation.** Since the laboratory environment and situation varies somewhat from school to school, and since methods employed may also vary from instructor to instructor, some of the following rules may not apply. On the other hand, your instructor may invoke still additional rules.

1. **Be on time.** Instructions are given at the beginning of laboratory. It is your responsibility to be present to receive them.
2. Bring your text-book, laboratory manual, and supplies to the laboratory.
3. Do not leave the laboratory early without permission of the instructor.
4. Visitors are not allowed except by special permission.
5. All work to be handed in should be arranged in sequence and placed in a manila folder. Write your name, class, day and hour class meets, and (if one is assigned) your section number on the index portion of the folder.
6. Before leaving, check to see if you have done the following:
   a. Cleaned the laboratory desk.
   b. Turned out the desk lamp.
   c. Returned microscope slides to their proper location.
7. Keep the sinks in your area clean. Do not put solid matter, such as dissectable materials, in the sinks. Waste baskets are for solids, sinks are for liquids.
8. Don't waste time at the beginning of the laboratory period. Whenever possible, begin work as soon as you enter the room.
9. Always keep in mind the meaning of the work you are doing.
10. Acknowledge the fact that extra time on laboratory work is often necessary.
11. Don't hesitate to consult your instructor, if you have any problems with the course.

E. Care of Preserved Specimens

1. CAT

The cat is packaged in a plastic bag containing a liquid preservative. After opening the bag, pour any extra fluid into the sink. At the conclusion of any laboratory involving the dissection of the cat, two or three thicknesses of paper towels moistened with tap water should be used to cover the specimen where the skin was removed. The cat should then be placed in the storage cabinet. This procedure will ordinarily keep the specimen in good condition throughout the course.

2. ORGANS (e.g., sheep eye, heart, kidney, brain, etc.)

Each specimen should be wrapped in a double thickness of moistened paper towels and placed in the plastic bag with the cat, or in individual plastic bags.

An alternate method is to place the organs in a 5% solution of formaldehyde. The latter solution is sufficiently concentrated to maintain the preserved state of the organs for the period of time they are being used.

F. Written Work

At the end of the manual there are 13 sections (a section for each chapter) entitled **Questions.** To facilitate the recording of answers, remove the Questions section from the manual when they are assigned. Anwers to questions should always be written neatly and legibly. Use either number 2 pencil or ink (blue or black only) in writing answers to the questions. When completed, write your name on each page and place your assignments in a labeled manila folder (see Section D, No. 5). Do not clip or staple the pages together.

G. Laboratory Tests

As one aspect of evaluation of work done in the laboratory, your instructor may give laboratory tests. The frequency of such tests will be announced by the instructor. The following methods are often employed in testing in the laboratory.

1. Practical

This type of test may include actual specimens (e.g., bones), microscope slides, drawings, and questions. There are several ways in which such a test may be given. One method commonly used involves the establishment of from 30 to 40 test stations. One or more specimens, a microscope with a slide in focus, a diagram or drawing with structures to be identified, or a card containing written questions is located at each station. The student is provided with an answer sheet and stands at a specified station. At the signal to begin, the student answers the questions (usually from three to five) asked at that station. The time alloted for this task varies from 45 seconds to 1 1/2 minutes. When time is called, the student moves to the next station, and so forth, until the test is completed.

2. Orals

In this type of test, the student is asked to bring a specimen he has dissected to the instructor, who then asks the student to identify selected structures. The student may also be asked to give functions of the structures identified. In some cases, models may be used for giving oral tests.

3. Written Tests

These may take a variety of forms (short answer, identification, essay, etc.). These tests are designed to determine the student's understanding of the work performed in the laboratory.

H. Vocabulary

Your ability to communicate and to comprehend and to reason and to interpret depends upon the acquisition of a functional vocabulary. This is especially true of any science course, wherein the vocabulary practically constitutes a "foreign language." It is therefore important for you to develop an understanding of all unfamiliar words with which you come in contact in the process of your reading and investigations. Define all new words in terms **you** understand. Practice pronouncing the words. Make a conscious effort to use the new words until, by constant reinforcement, they are firmly entrenched in your mind.

I. Self Tests

At the end of each chapter is a true-false self-test. (See Directions for Self-Test in Chapter I). Each test item includes a key word, words, or phrase that is in **Bold Type**. If the test item is false, the **Bold** portion should be corrected to make the statement true. In general, the self-tests cover material found in texts, covered in lecture, and applied in the laboratory. Keys are located at the end of each self-test.

1. **Suggestions for Using the Self-Tests**
   a. Take them as a **pretest** before studying the material covered.
      (1) Write your answers on a separate sheet of paper, but do not correct them at this time.
      (2) This procedure will provide you with clues as to what to look for in your reading of the text, what to listen for in lecture, and what to watch for in the laboratory.
   b. After you have had an opportunity to study the material covered, take the self-test again (**post-test**).
      (1) Correct your pretest and post-test by using the key at the end of the test.
      (2) Compare the results of the post-test with those you achieved on the pretest to determine how much you actually learned.
   c. Other suggestions:
      (1) Always try to determine the reason why a given statement is or is not true. Merely knowing the answer to the statement may provide very little depth.
      (2) Any words in a statement that are not understood should be defined from a suitable reference.
      (3) Try to correlate the concepts indicated in the statements with the material presented in lectures, discussions, the text, and laboratory.

2. **Limitations of Self-Tests**
   a. They may be a useful tool, but they are not comprehensive.
   b. Since courses vary in their emphasis of certain concepts, this must be taken into consideration when the self-tests are used.
   c. Tests usually sample bits of a student's knowledge-- never the whole. Study-type tests, such as the self-tests in this manual, merely provide a basis for learning subject matter and showing trends in achievement.
   d. Analysis of questions missed on a self-test may often imply that the student needs to study the entire block of knowledge from which the question was derived.
   e. If not used as suggested (e.g., as a supplement to other learning devices), the student may fail to attain the depth and insights essential for this course.

J. Illustrations as Self-Tests

Many drawings in this manual are designed so that they may be used as self-tests. Prestudy of similar illustrations in the textbook, references, wall charts, as well as the prestudy of models and specimens, is one way to prepare the student for the self-tests. The student may then try to identify the parts indicated on an illustration (writing the answers on a separate piece of paper). The answers may then be checked with the keys found in the chapter.

Chapter I
BODY ORGANIZATION
AND TERMINOLOGY

Ex. I-A. Organization of the Body as a Whole

DISCUSSION

The human body is made up of **cells.** Cells that have similar specializations and are united in the performance of a particular function form a **tissue.** Tissues, in turn, make up an **organ,** which may be defined as several tissues grouped into a structural unit having a special function. A set or series of organs united in a common function is referred to as a **system.** While it is possible to distinguish individual parts (e.g., a cell, a tissue, or an organ) in the human organism, these parts function as an integrated whole.

In doing the following exercises, and throughout your study of anatomy, keep the following question constantly before you: How does this part of the human body fit in with the concept of the body as an integrated whole?

Part 1. Cavities of the body

PROCEDURE

1. Using your text and reference books for orientation, locate the following cavities of the body on the dissectable torso:

    a. cranial   e. abdominal
    b. nasal   f. pelvic
    c. buccal (oral) g. ventral
    d. thoracic   h. dorsal

2. Under each label on Figure I-1, indicate the major structures found in the cranial, thoracic, abdominal, pelvic, and vertebral cavities. Use anatomic charts, your text, and references to aid you in this activity.

Part 2. Regions of the body

PROCEDURE

1. Locate the following nine regions of the body on the dissectable torso and on your own body: **epigastric, umbilical, hypogastric (pubic),** right and left **hypochondriac,** right and left **lumbar (lateral),** and the right and left **inguinal (iliac).** Use your text and other references for orientation.

2. Use Figure I-1 as a self-test for the nine body regions. See Section J, p. 5 (Illustrations as Self-Tests) for a suggested approach. Under each label, write the major structure or structures underlying the region.

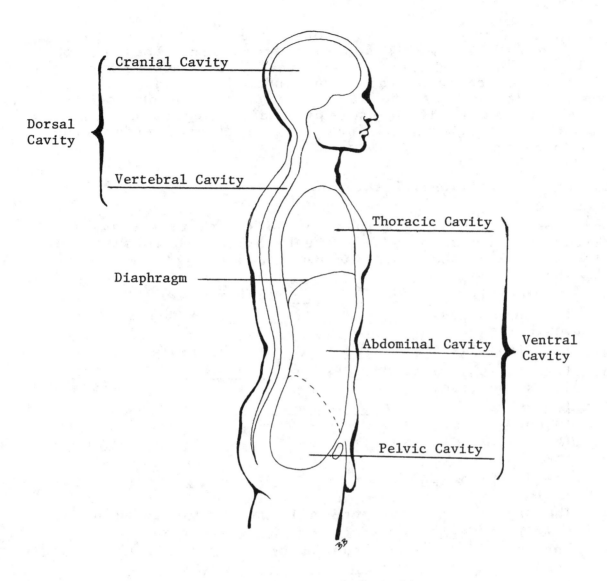

Figure I-1: Body Cavities

Ex. I-B. Anatomic Terminology

DISCUSSION

Terminology used in locating various structures of the human body is vital to any precision in the study of anatomy. Directional terms and the planes of the body are essential tools that will be used repeatedly throughout the course. Build a firm foundation by learning the meaning of the terms, then reinforce your understanding of them by applying them whenever possible.

In lower animals the **ventral** surface (belly) faces downward while the **dorsal** surface (back) faces upward. Since man assumes an upright position, the ventral surface is forward, and the term ventral is, in humans, synonymous with the word **anterior**. Furthermore, dorsal is synonymous with **posterior** in humans. In an animal, such as a dog, the head is anterior, while in humans the head is **superior (cephalic).** The tail of the dog is posterior while the coccygeal vertebrae in humans are **inferior** (or **caudal).** The term **caudad** (or caudal) may be used to describe either the tail portion of the dog or the lower part of a human. The term **cephalad** (or cephalic) may be used to describe the cranial (or head) portion of either the dog or of a human.

Part 1. Using Directional Terms
PROCEDURE

1. Self-test: without referring to the key that follows, use directional terms to fill in the blank spaces. Assume the structures are located in the human body.

    a. The head is _____ to the neck.

    b. The foot is _____ to the ankle.

    c. The umbilicus is _____ to the lumbar vertebrae.

    d. The fibula is _____ to the tibia.

    e. The vertebral column is _____ to the digestive tract.

    f. The ulna is on the _____ side of the forearm.

    g. The elbow (olecranon process) is _____ to the shoulder.

    h. The kneecap (patella) is _____ to the ankle.

    i. The layer of the peritoneum lining to the abdominal cavity is called the _____ layer.

    j. The layer of the peritoneum covering the internal organs is called the _____ layer.

Key

a. superior (cranial, cephalic)	f. medial
b. inferior (distal)	g. distal
c. anterior (ventral)	h. proximal (superior)
d. lateral	i. parietal
e. posterior (dorsal)	j. visceral

Part 2. Planes of the Body
PROCEDURE

1. Examine Figure I-3 showing the planes of the body. Identify the planes of the body on yourself and your lab partner.

2. Answer the questions involving a knowledge of the planes of the body under Questions for Chapter I.

KEY TO FIGURE I-2

1. right hypochondriac
2. right lumbar (lateral)
3. right inguinal (iliac)
4. epigastric
5. left hypo- chondriac
6. umbilical
7. left lumbar (lateral)
8. left inguinal (iliac)
9. hypogastric

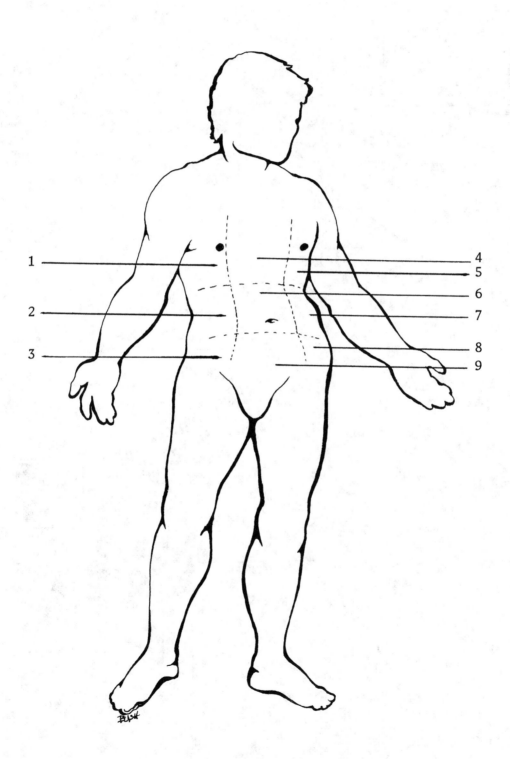

Figure I-2: Regions of the Body

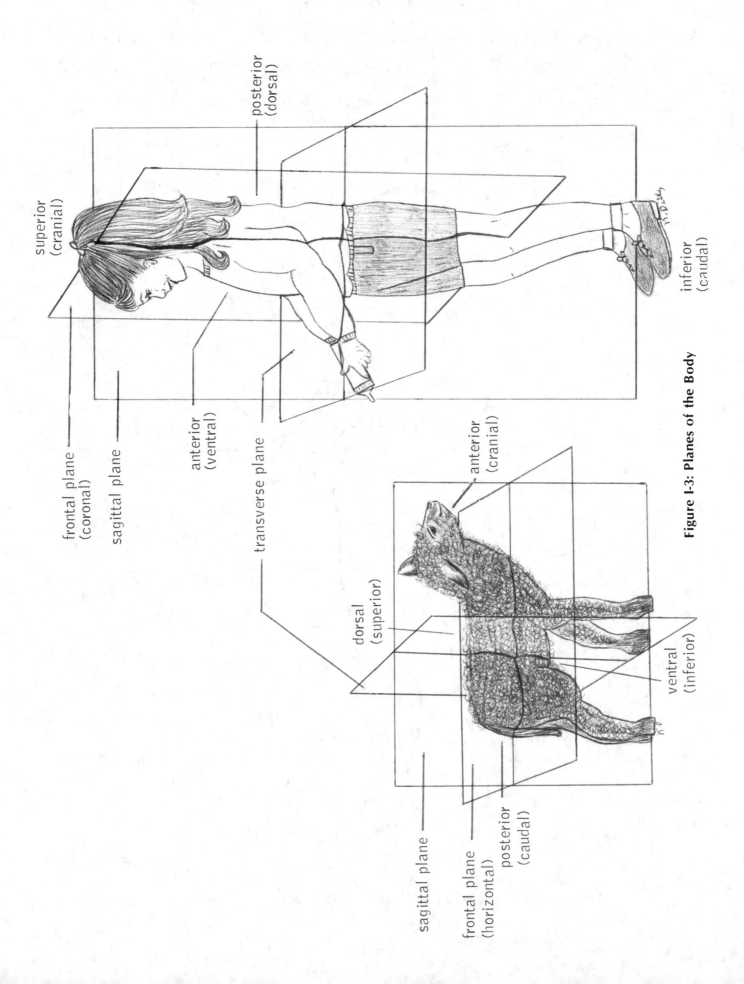

Figure I-3: Planes of the Body

Ex. I-C. Major Organ Systems

DISCUSSION

An organ system is an arrangement of closely related organs concerned with the same function. The following are examples of organ systems: **Integumentary, Skeletal, Muscular, Digestive, Respiratory, Circulatory, Nervous, Excretory** (which includes the **Urinary**), **Endocrine**, and **Reproductive.**

PROCEDURE

1. Place each of the following in the appropriate system or systems:

   gastrocnemius _____   sweat glands_____

   brain _____   lungs _____

   heart _____   kidneys _____

   ovaries _____   skin _____

   femur _____   colon _____

   thyroid _____   sternum _____

   aorta _____   testes _____

   esophagus _____   trachea _____

   spinal cord _____   pituitary _____

   parotid glands_____   urethra _____

   trapezius _____   larynx _____

   cerebellum _____   rectum _____

2. Indicate which of the following is a cell, which a tissue, which an organ, and which an organ system.

   leukocyte _____   cartilage _____

   brain _____   pancreas _____

   liver _____   skin _____

   gall bladder _____   spleen _____

   epithelium _____   kidney _____

   erythrocyte _____   duodenum _____

   deltoid _____   neuron _____

   monocyte _____   eye _____

   larynx _____   heart _____

   tibia _____   blood _____

3. Answer the questions concerning organ systems under Questions for Chapter I.

SELF-TEST: BODY ORGANIZATION AND TERMINOLOGY

DIRECTIONS

The following statements are either true or false. If a test item is false, the portion in bold type should be altered to make the statement true. When taking the self-test, it is suggested that the answers be written on a separate sheet of paper. This simplifies using these tests for review where it is usually undesirable to have the answers exposed. Answers may be checked by referring to the key at the end of the test. For more extensive suggestions concerning the use of self-tests, their functions and limitations, see Section I (Self-Tests) under Orientation and Suggestions for Students.

1. The **midsagittal** plane divides the body into a top and bottom half.
2. **Sagittal and coronal** planes divide the body into upper and lower parts.
3. The knee is **proximal** to the foot.
4. The part of the nervous system found within the **dorsal cavity** is called the central nervous system.
5. In relation to the mandible, the maxilla is **inferior**.
6. **Proximal** is a term meaning the part located farthest from the midline.
7. **Visceral** is applied to organs located within the body cavities.
8. A cut through the body, or body structures, dividing it (or them) into front and back portions, is called a **transverse cut.**
9. The hands are the **proximal** portion of the upper extremities.
10. The spinal cord and brain are found within the **ventral** cavity.
11. When an individual stands in anatomic position the radius is **mesial** in position.
12. A part of the body located on or at the surface is said to be **peripheral.**
13. In the anatomical position, the arms are at the side with the palms of the hands **supinated.**
14. With reference to the esophagus, the stomach is **inferior.**
15. Two terms that apply to the back part of humans are **posterior and ventral.**
16. The large intestine is located within the **abdominal and pelvic cavities.**
17. **Homeostasis** is a term which means relative uniformity of cellular environment.
18. The spleen is found within the **mediastinum.**
19. The lungs are located in the **thoracic cavity.**
20. The liver is in the **abdominal cavity.**
21. A sagittal section is on or parallel to the **coronal suture.**
22. The surface of a cat's body that forms its back is known as the **ventral** surface.
23. In man, the back of the body may be called either the **dorsal or the posterior** surface.

24. The **anterior** end of a cat's body is the one to which the head is attached.
25. When you lie on your ventral surface you are said to be in a **supine** position.
26. Fingerprints are made by pressing the **palmar** surfaces of the fingers against an object.
27. Any part of the body which is away from the midline is said to be **mesial** in location.
28. The **abdomen** may be divided into four sections called quadrants.
29. The part of the appendage that lies farthest from the trunk is the **caudal** portion.
30. The crest of the hip bone is **dorsal** to the vertebrae.
31. The pain of appendicitis is frequently felt in the **lower left** quadrant of the abdomen.
32. The female gonads are located within the **vertebral cavity**.
33. The **buccal cavity** opens into the oropharynx.

KEY

1. transverse	10. dorsal	22. dorsal
2. transverse	11. lateral	25. prone
5. superior	15. posterior	27. lateral
6. lateral	and dorsal	29. distal
8. frontal	18. abdominal	30. lateral
(coronal)	cavity	31. lower right
9. distal	21. sagittal	32. pelvic cavity

Chapter II
BASIC MICROSCOPY

Ex. II-A. Structure of the Microscope

PROCEDURE

1. Examine the drawing of the microscope (Figure II-1). Compare this drawing with your microscope and learn the names and functions of all parts indicated by the instructor.

2. Use of the microscope:
   a. When it is necessary to lift the microscope, hold the **arm** with one hand, and add support at the **base** with the other hand.
   b. Place the microscope on the desk with the arm facing you.
   c. Since tilting results in poor light regulation and unwanted movement in fresh preparations, do not tilt this instrument unless instructed to do so.
   d. Always begin by cleaning the **ocular** (eyepiece), **objectives, slide,** and **mirror** (when present), with **lens paper**.
   e. Focusing procedure:
      (1) Turn the **revolving nosepiece** until the low power objective (10X) clicks into position over the hole in the **stage** of the microscope. **Always begin with the low power objective.**
      (2) Place the slide to be used on the stage of the microscope with the specimen to be observed centered (as nearly as possible) over the hole. Secure the slide under the **slide clips**.
      (3) For light control, which is essential in good microscopy, make certain that the **iris diaphragm** is opened to maximum size. If your microscope does not have a built in illuminator, arrange the microscope lamp and concave side of the mirror so that a maximum amount of light is reflected through the tube of the microscope. This adjustment is made while you are looking through the eyepiece. To regulate light intensity, adjust the iris diaphragm. The mirror should not be disturbed except to insure maximum light.
      (4) Usually a stop is present on the microscope which will prevent the low power objective from striking the slide. Determine if this is true of your instrument by lowering the 10X objective as close to the slide as possible without touching it, or until the tube can be lowered no farther.
      (5) To avoid eyestrain and subsequent headaches, it is best to look through the microscope with both

eyes open. Practice makes this a simple proce- dure.

(6) Look through the eyepiece and turn the coarse ad- justment knob to **slowly** raise the objective from the slide, until the specimen comes into focus. The image should then be brought into sharp focus with the **fine adjustment knob.** This knob should also be used for observing the specimens in depth.

(7) Move the slide to find the specific area you de- sire to view in more detail. Since the quality of slides and individual portions of the slides may vary, always select a slide (or area of the slide) for study that seems typical.

(8) The microscope is **parfocal.** This means that when the high power objective is brought into position in place of the low power objective, the object will be in focus, or almost in focus, **provided** you make certain that the material to be viewed is centered and in sharp focus before turning from low power.

(9) With the high power objective in position and us- ing the **fine adjustment knob,** slowly raise the objective until the image comes into view. If no image comes into view, it may be necessary to slowly lower the objective. **Never** focus downward with the coarse adjustment knob when using high power.

(10) Unless otherwise directed, drawings should be made using the high power objective.

(11) Always return the slide to the correct position in the slide box after use.

Ex. II-B. Microscope Drawings

DISCUSSION

Drawings are a valuable means of recording and checking the results of your observations. A drawing should indicate the accuracy and detail of all observations made. Properly com- pleted drawings provide a basis for reviewing material you have observed under the microscope. They also provide evidence to the instructor that you have seen the significant structures.

The practice slides used in this exercise may consist of assorted tissues on damaged slides. It is not the purpose of this exercise to identify the various tissues; the student should, however, use these slides to learn how to use the mi- croscope and to learn how to make a drawing.

PROCEDURE

1. Select one or more of the practice slides and, using the procedure indicated in Ex. II-A, practice focusing (on both low and high power) until you are thoroughly familiar with the technique.

2. On one of the practice slides, locate two or three cells and draw them in accordance with the following specifications. (This is the procedure to be used on any drawings requested, unless instructions to the contrary are given).

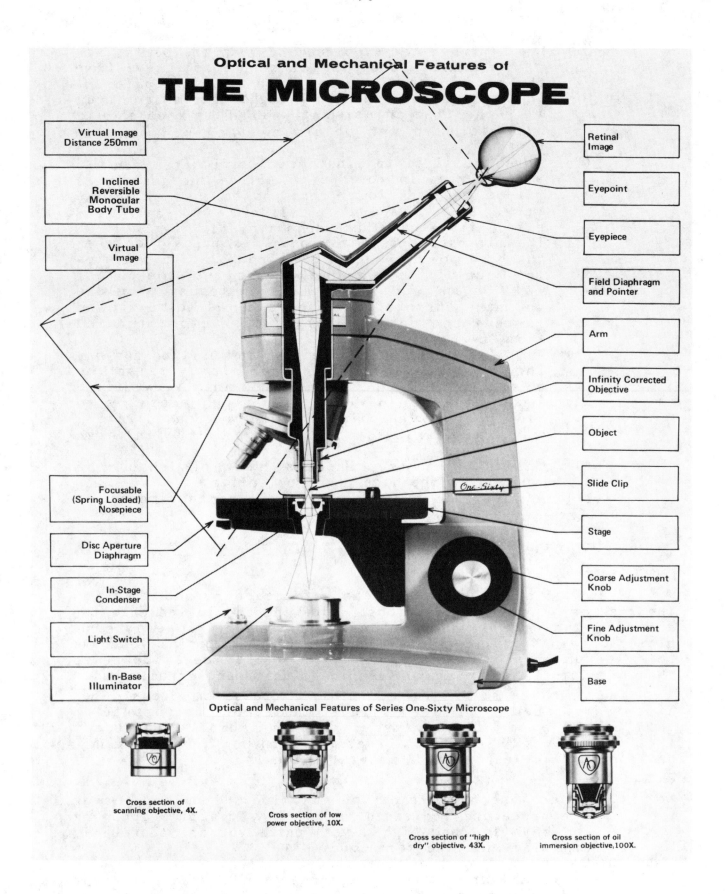

Optical and Mechanical Features of
THE MICROSCOPE

Virtual Image Distance 250mm

Inclined Reversible Monocular Body Tube

Virtual Image

Focusable (Spring Loaded) Nosepiece

Disc Aperture Diaphragm

In-Stage Condenser

Light Switch

In-Base Illuminator

Retinal Image

Eyepoint

Eyepiece

Field Diaphragm and Pointer

Arm

Infinity Corrected Objective

Object

Slide Clip

Stage

Coarse Adjustment Knob

Fine Adjustment Knob

Base

Optical and Mechanical Features of Series One-Sixty Microscope

Cross section of scanning objective, 4X.

Cross section of low power objective, 10X.

Cross section of "high dry" objective, 43X.

Cross section of oil immersion objective, 100X.

Figure II-1: The Microscope (Courtesy of American Optical Corp.)

a. Make all drawings on Biology Filler (or plain white) paper.

b. In the upper right hand corner of the page print your name. Under your name, print the title of the course and the section number of your laboratory.

c. In the upper left hand corner, print the exercise number and, under this, the date the work was done.

d. Centered at the top of the page, print the title of the exercise.

e. As a general rule, do not include drawings of more than one exercise on a page. Use only one side of the page.

f. Drawings must be large and neat, with the size of the cells in correct proportion to the drawing as a whole. When making the drawing, use firm continuous lines-not several indistinct, discontinuous lines. Individual drawings should not be boxed off in squares, rectangles, or circles.

g. Draw only what is actually observed, but always look for a typical view of the structure being observed.

h. An appropriate subtitle, which identifies the specific drawing, should be placed under each drawing. The subtitle, when appropriate, should include the magnification and type of section - such as cross section (**x.s.** or **c.s.**), longitudinal section (**l.s.**), tangential section (**t.s.**), whole mount, fresh mount, or smear.

i. The drawings should be approximately centered on the page (or slightly to the left) with the labels to the right, except where excessive crowding makes this impractical.

j. Print all labels on lines **drawn with a ruler** parallel to the top and bottom margins of the page. None of the label lines should cross each other. The label line should be touching either the edge or be within the structures indicated. Arrows should not be used.

k. Use brackets to enclose related labels. For example, the parts of the nucleus should be labeled separately, and then bracketed to indicate nucleus.

l. Be accurate in your spelling (look up the word if you are in doubt).

Ex. II-C. Orientation of Images Viewed through the Compound Microscope

Part 1. Letter "e" Slide
PROCEDURE

1. Obtain a prepared slide containing the printed letter "e" under the cover glass. Note that you can read the letter with the naked eye.

2. Draw the letter as it normally apprears on the slide (DRAWING A).

3. Place the slide on the stage of the miscroscope so that the letter is in the same relative position as when observed in No. 2.

4. Look in the microscope under low power and draw the letter as it appears to you (DRAWING B).

---------------(DRAWING A)---------------   ----------(DRAWING B)----------

5. Move the slide so that the letter appears in the upper left corner of the field. Now, center the letter while looking through the microscope. In which directions did you move the slide? _____

Part 2. Newspaper Slide

PROCEDURE

1. Obtain a newspaper slide (approximately 1 in. x 3 in. piece with printing on its surface).

2. Draw an asymmetrical letter as it normally appears on the paper slide (DRAWING A).

3. Place the slide on the stage of the microscope so that the asymmetrical letter is in the same relative position as when observed in No. 2.

4. Look in the microscope under low power and draw the letter as it appears to you (DRAWING B).

---------------(DRAWING A)---------------   ----------(DRAWING B)----------

5. Move the slide so that the letter appears in the upper left corner of the field. Now, center the letter while looking through the microscope. In which directions did you move the slide? _____

Ex. II-D. Thread Slide

DISCUSSION

This exercise requires careful technique. It demonstrates the fact that objects viewed through a microscope are three-dimensional, and that detail exists at varying levels which can only be observed by careful manipulation of the fine adjustment knob.

PROCEDURE

1. Obtain a prepared slide containing three colored, crossed threads.
2. Begin with the slide slightly out of focus **below** the three threads.
3. Using the fine adjustment knob, adjust the body tube of the microscope upward until the bottom thread comes into focus, then the middle thread, then the upper thread. Repeat this procedure until you have determined the correct sequence of the threads. (Use the low power objective, then check the results with the high power objective).
4. Record your observations in the spaces provided below.

   a. Color of thread on bottom _____ Slide Letter ____

   b. Color of the middle thread _____

   c. Color of thread on top _____

5. Have the instructor check your results.

   Approved _____

SELF-TEST: BASIC MICROSCOPY

DIRECTIONS: See Chapter 1, Self-Test, p. 12

1. The **nosepiece** of the microscope is a device for holding two or more readily interchangeable objectives.
2. **Parfocal** refers to objectives or lenses on a nosepiece that focus at the same position.
3. The **iris diaphragm** controls the amount of light passing through the object.
4. A **larger** portion of a specimen is seen with a high power objective than a low power objective.
5. More detail of the specimen can be observed using a **high power objective** than with a **low power objective**.
6. The ability of a lens to distinguish the fine detail in the structure of a specimen is known as its **magnification** power.
7. A microscope that includes both objective and eyepiece lenses is called a **compound** microscope.
8. If an object is observed with a microscope having a 5X eyepiece and a 20X objective, it is magnified **50** times.
9. When using the high power objective, the **coarse adjustment knob** is used for focusing.
10. A micrometer is **1000 times** smaller than a millimeter.
11. A cell is 100 micrometers long. It would require approximately **1000** such cells to stretch an inch when the cells are placed end to end.
12. The **higher** the power of the objective, the easier it is to locate the specimen to be observed.
13. Light rays bend as they pass from the atmosphere into water. This phenomenon is known as **refraction**.
14. By using a lens of the proper shape, light rays can be made to converge to a point known as the **focus**, from which point they go on to form an image beyond.
15. An electron microscope converges **light rays** to focus by means of electromagnets or an electrostatic field.
16. A possible abbreviation for a longitudinal section is **t.s.**
17. Selective regulation of light intensity **is essential** to good microscopy.
18. The diameter of an erythrocyte is about 8 micrometers. Therefore **100** erythrocytes would be visible if lined up across a microscope field 400 micrometers wide.

KEY

4. smaller	9. fine adjustment knob	15. electron beams
6. resolving	11. 250	16. l.s.
8. 100	12. lower	18. 50

Chapter III
CELLS, MITOSIS, TISSUES, AND SKIN

Ex. III-A. The Structure of a Cell Observed under the Light Microscope Compared to that Observed with an Electron Microscope

DISCUSSION

Cells are highly diversified, both structurally and functionally, but all living cells have certain things in common. This part of the exercise provides an introduction to structures that almost all cells have in common.

PROCEDURE

1. Except for the nucleus, few of the structures of a cell are visible with the light microscope. Figure III-1 illustrates cellular structures visible in a properly stained slide. Most of these structures may also be observed in the cells making up tissues. Figure III-1 may be used as a self-test (see Section J, p 5 for suggested approach).

KEY TO FIGURE III-1

1. plasma
   membrane
2. centriole
3. centrosphere

4. cytoplasm
5. mitochondrion
6. nuclear
   membrane

7. chromatin
8. nucleolus
9. nucleoplasm
10. nucleus

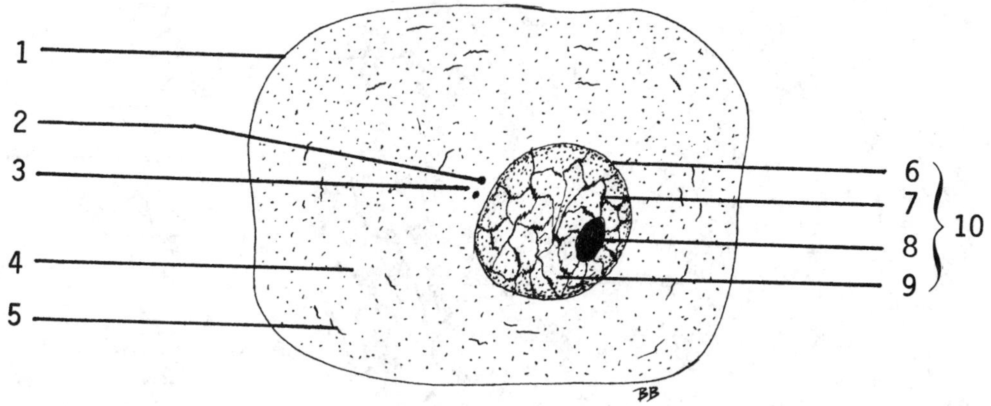

Figure III-1: Structure of Cell (observed under the light microscope)

2. Figure III-2 illustrates the structure of a generalized cell as viewed with an electron microscope. Figure III-2 may be usesd as a self-test.

Ex. III-B. Mitosis

DISCUSSION

Mitosis is a systematic sequence of events resulting in the production of two daughter cells with the same number of chromosomes as the initiating or parent cell. Each of the two

KEY TO FIGURE III-2

1. golgi apparatus
2. mitochondria
3. lipid droplets
4. plasma membrane
5. lysosome
6. centrosphere
7. centrioles
8. nuclear membrane
9. vacuole
10. nucleus
    (nuclearplasm)
11. endoplasmic reticulum
12. nucleoli
13. ribosomes
14. glycogen inclusions
15. pinocytic vesicle
16. cytoplasm

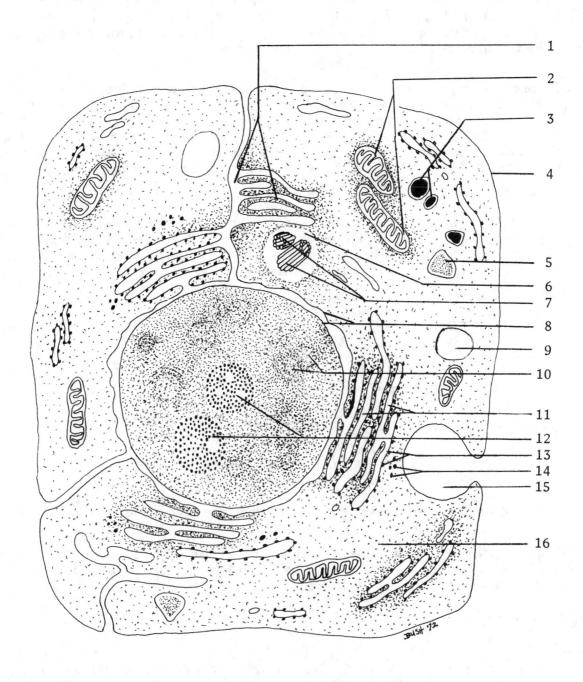

Figure III-2: Generalized Cell (as viewed with an electron microscope)

daughter cells contains identical sets of chromosomes and genes. Genes provide the basis for inheritance. They are the "blueprints" which determine what an organism will become (both structurally and functionally). These determinations take place within the cells as a result of many biochemical reactions initiated either directly or indirectly by the substance of the genes - deoxyribonucleic acid (DNA).

Through mitosis the number of somatic cells is increased during the growth of the body. Mitosis is also the means by which worn-out cells of the body are replaced.

The blastula, which is an early stage of embryological development, shows all of the various phases of animal mitosis. In this exercise the whitefish blastula is used because these slides are readily available and the phases of mitosis that occur are the same as those in humans.

PROCEDURE

1. Select a prepared slide of the whitefish blastula and focus under the low power objective.
2. Now, using the high power objective, explore the slide and locate the following stages of mitosis: **interphase, prophase, metaphase, anaphase, telophase,** and **daughter cells.**
3. As each stage of mitosis is located, compare it with Figure III-4. Note the characteristics that identify each stage of mitosis.
4. Figure III-4 may be used as a self-test.

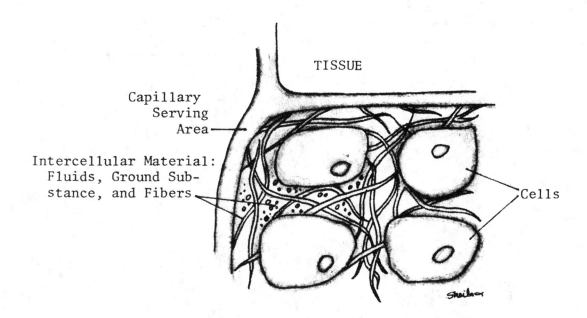

Figure III-3: All tissues are composed of cells and a matrix and must be served by a capillary bed.

KEY TO FIGURE III-4

A. interphase
B. early prophase
C. prophase
D. metaphase
E. metaphase cell cut
   through equator
F. anaphase

G. early telophase
H. late telophase
I. daughter cells
1. nucleus
2. nuclear membrane
3. cytoplasm
4. plasma membrane

5. astral rays
6. centrosphere
7. chromatin
8. chromosomes
9. chromosomes at equator
10. spindle fibers
11. cleavage furrow

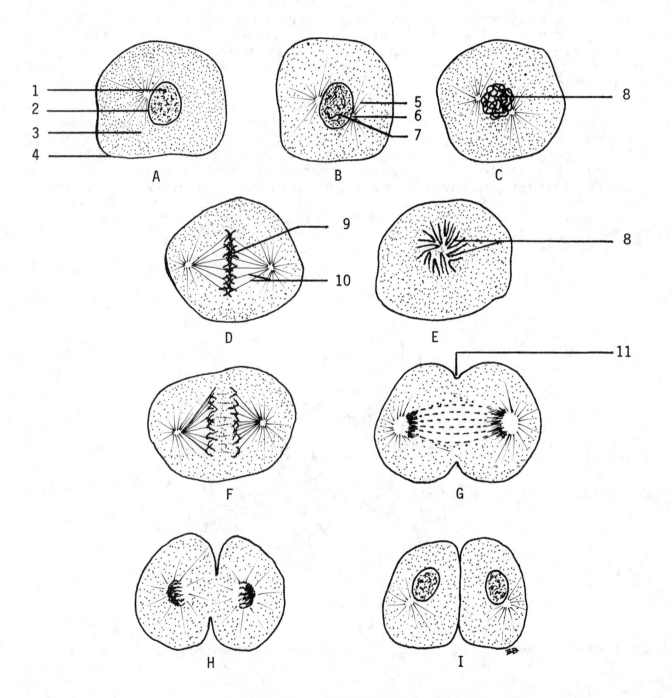

Figure III-4: Mitosis (as observed in whitefish blastula)

Ex. III-C. Epithelial Tissue

DISCUSSION

Epithelial tissues are specialized to protect, absorb, and secrete. They cover the free external and internal surfaces of the body. Secretory epithelium usually exists in the form of glands, which are groups of epithelial cells that have grown down into the underlying tissue from a surface epithelial membrane.

Preliminary study should precede examination of tissues under the microscope. The drawings of epithelial tissues (Figures III-5, 6, 7, 8, and 9) have been made from prepared slides similar to the ones used in the laboratory. Use these, and other reference material, as a guide. In studying tissues, think in terms of the characteristic appearance of the cells making up the tissues, as well as the locations and functions of each tissue.

Part 1. Simple Squamous Epithelial Tissue (cheek cell smear)

DISCUSSION

The cells of this tissue are shaped like flat plates or scales. This tissue lines the heart, blood vessels and lymph vessels where it is called endothelium. It also makes up the wall of the air sacs (alveoli) of the lung and the part of the kidney that filters the blood (glomerulus).

EPITHELIAL TISSUES

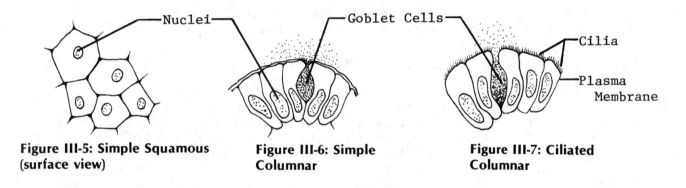

Figure III-5: Simple Squamous (surface view)   **Figure III-6: Simple Columnar**   **Figure III-7: Ciliated Columnar**

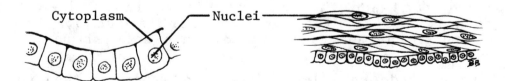

Figure III-8: Simple Cuboidal   **Figure III-9: Stratififed Squamous**

The following procedure involves the use of the surface cells of stratified squamous epithelial tissue lining the mouth. Such cells are comparable to simple squamous epithelial tissue.

PROCEDURE

1. With the broad end of a toothpick, scrape the lining of your cheek two or three times to collect some of the cells from the mucous membrane. Move the toothpick across a clean slide to leave a thin layer of the collected material on it.
2. Allow the preparation to air dry, then cover the smear with 2-3 drops of 1% methylene blue stain.
3. After **one minute** gently rinse the slide in cold tap water to remove excess dye. Do this by holding the slide under a slow-running tap or by flooding it two or three times by means of a medicine dropper. Gently blot (**do not rub**) the slide dry with a paper towel.
4. Examine the slide under both low and high power objectives of your microscope. **Draw** from 3-6 cells just as they appear under your microscope and label all the parts you can identify. The epithelial cells should be drawn at least 1 inch in diameter. You may also observe the presence of bacteria (usually bacilli) on the slide. Include these (if present) in your drawing.

ALTERNATE PROCEDURE: Amphibian (Frog) Skin

1. Select a prepared slide of frog skin. The frog skin is two cells thick and the structure of the cells can be readily seen.
2. Locate an area on the slide where the cells appear to be one cell thick. **Draw** from 3-6 squamous epithelial cells as seen under high power and label the parts. The cells have only one nucleus per cell. If another nucleus is visible, it belongs to the second layer of cells. Do not include it in your drawing.

Part 2. Simple Columnar Epithelial Tissue

DISCUSSION

As the name implies, the cells of this tissue are taller than they are wide. Simple columnar epithelium makes up the outer layer of the **villi** in the cross-sectional view, and has the appearance of fingerlike projections. Simple columnar epithelium also lines the stomach and the large intestine; the epithelium of the GI tract is not ciliated. **Ciliated columnar epithelium** is a modified type of epithelial tissue which contains cilia on the surface of each cell. It lines the upper respiratory tract and the uterine (Fallopian) tubes. **Goblet cells** are unicellular glands which secrete mucus; these are found in both simple and ciliated columnar epithelium.

PROCEDURE

1. Obtain a slide entitled "simple columnar epithelium, intestine."
2. Locate the villi on low power and select an area where a single row of individual columnar cells may be seen clearly. Then turn to high power and observe the details of the cells.
3. Draw from 3 to 6 cells (at least 1/2 inch wide) and label all the parts you can identify. Include a goblet cell.

4. Your drawing should show clearly the shape, size, and location of the nucleus, the parts of the nucleus, the brush border, and any additional structures you can identify.

Part 3. Simple Cuboidal Epithelial Tissue

DISCUSSION

The cells of this tissue are almost cube shaped. This tissue is found in many glands.

PROCEDURE

1. Select a prepared slide and locate the cuboidal epithelial tissue under the microscope.
2. Draw from 3-6 cuboidal cells as observed under the high power objective and label the parts.

Part 4. Stratified Squamous Epithelial Tissue

DISCUSSION

This tissue is layered (in strata) to protect the underlying tissues. The deepest cells are almost cube-shaped, but they become more and more flattened as the surface is approached. At the surface the cells are completely flat (similar to simple squamous epithelium). The tissue varies from a few to many layers thick, depending on its location. It makes up the outer layer of the skin (epidermis) and lines the mouth, esophagus and vagina.

PROCEDURE

1. Locate the tissue on low power and move the slide until a relatively thin area is found. Select an area which shows some of the detail of individual cells.
2. Using the high power objective draw a section, at least four cells wide, from the deepest layer of the tissue to the surface.

Ex. III-D. Connective Tissue

DISCUSSION

Connective tissues are specialized for providing support and holding other tissues together. They are characterized by a much larger content of intercellular substances (the matrix) than other tissues.

Part 1. Areolar (Loose) Connective Tissue

DISCUSSION

This tissue is distributed quite extensively throughout the body. It is one of the tissues of the subcutaneous layer and is found around blood vessels, nerves and between organs. It consists of white **collagenous** fibers, yellow **elastic** fibers, assorted tissue cells and a semi-fluid to fluid ground substance. The fibers and the fluid (tissue fluid) constitute the **matrix**. Before veiwing a slide of areolar tissue, examine Figure III-10 and other reference material for orientation.

PROCEDURE

1. Obtain a slide of areolar connective tissue.
2. Locate the tissue on low power; then turn to high power to distinguish the different types of fibers and cells.

3. To distinguish between the two kinds of fibers, look for differences in thickness. The **white collagenous fibers** occur in parellel bundles and thus resemble slightly wider bands. The yellow elastic fibers are single, thin strands which may branch.

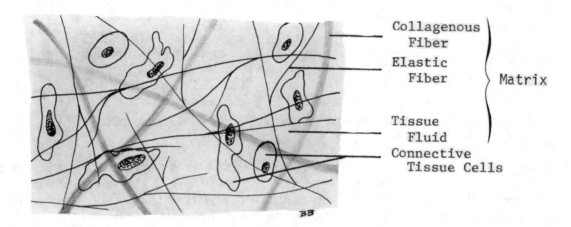

Collagenous Fiber

Elastic Fiber

} Matrix

Tissue Fluid

Connective Tissue Cells

Figure III-10: Areolar Connective Tissue

4. **Fibroblasts** will be found among the fibers in the matrix. The elongated or star-shaped bodies of the fibroblasts send out sharp processes. However, the cytoplasm of these cells is difficult to see without careful light regulation, although the dark-staining nuclei are relatively easy to observe. **Macrophages** (histiocytes) are usually elongated, spinal-shaped cells.
5. Draw a section of the slide including the following: **matrix, collagenous fibers, elastic fibers,** and **connective tissue cells.** Label all structures drawn.

Part 2. Adipose Tissue

DISCUSSION

Fat cells are scattered singly or in groups in areolar tissue. A mature fat cell contains one large drop of fat. The cytoplasm is reduced to a thin rim surrounding the drop of fat. When fat cells form in large numbers and crowd out other cells, areolar tissue is transformed into adipose tissue. Adipose tissue is found in the subcutaneous layer, around the heart, kidney, blood vessels and nerves.

Examine Figure III-11 and other reference material before viewing a prepared slide of adipose tissue.

PROCEDURE

1. Obtain a slide containing adipose tissue.
2. Locate the tissue on low power, then examine it under the high power objective. (If the tissue has been stained, the cells will appear black if **osmic acid** was used, or orange if **Sudan III** was used).
3. Draw from 3-6 cells and label all of the parts.

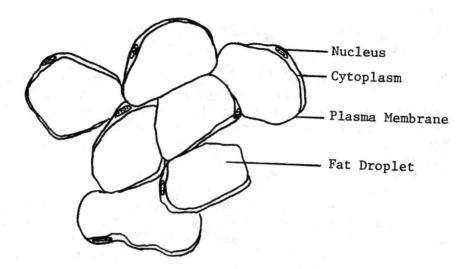

Figure III-11: Adipose Tissue

Part 3. Hyaline Cartilage
DISCUSSION

Hyaline cartilage forms the tracheal rings, part of the larynx and nose, the covering of the articular surfaces of bones, the costal cartilages and most of the fetal skeleton. Each **chondrocyte** (cartilage cell) is enclosed within a space called a **lacuna.** The chondrocyte usually completely fills this cavity. There may be as many as four cells in a lacuna in mature cartilage. No blood vessels are found in cartilage and the cells are nourished by the **perichondrium,** a fibrous membrane covering the cartilage.

Fibrous cartilage (white fibrocartilage) differs from hyaline cartilage in that it has many collagenous (white) fibers within the matrix. This cartilage forms the symphysis pubis and the intervertebral discs.

Elastic cartilage (yellow fibrocartilage) differs from hyaline cartilage in that it has elastic fibers in the matrix. It is found in the external ear, the Eustachian tube, parts of the larynx, etc.

Examine Figure III-12 of hyaline cartilage before viewing the prepared slide under the microscope.

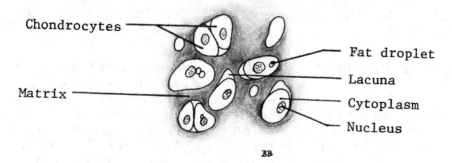

Figure III-12: Hyaline Cartilage

PROCEDURE

1. Obtain a slide of hyaline cartilage.
2. Locate the tissue first on low power, then observe it on high power.
3. On the basis of your observations, draw and label a segment of this tissue which includes the matrix, lacunae, and chondrocytes. You should be able to observe nuclei and other structures in the cells.
4. Which tissues can be observed on either side of the strip of cartilage?
5. Demonstrations:
   a. Examine the slide under the microscope showing fibrous cartilage, noting the characteristics indicated in the preceding discussion.
   b. Look at the slide under the microscope showing elastic cartilage. Note the characteristics indicated in the preceding discussion.

Part 4. Osseous (Bony) Tissue

DISCUSSION

The **shaft (diaphysis)** of a typical long bone consists of a cortex of **compact (dense)** osseous tissue, with an inner lining of **cancellous (spongy)** bony tissue. Spongy bone consists of plates and bars forming a network which is well adapted for providing mechanical support. It lacks Haversian canals and related structures that are found in compact bone.

Most of the mass of a bone is made up of layers (**lamellae**) of calcified **interstitial substance** (or bone matrix). The lamellae are arranged differently in compact than in spongy bone tissue. Found in the interstitial substance are **lacunae** (cavities) which are completely filled with osteocytes (bone cells). Very fine apertures are found in the walls of the lacunae, from which arise minute canals called **canaliculi**. The latter penetrate the matrix in all directions, branching profusely to form a network in which frequent anastomoses (interconnections) occur. The network thus formed interconnects all the lacunae and Haversian canals.

Within the compact bone of the diaphysis of any long bone are numerous **Haversian canals.** These are cylindrical, vertically branching and anastomosing canals which may contain one or more blood vessels (usually two capillaries). They communicate with each other, the external surface of the bone, and the bone marrow cavity by means of the horizontal **Volkmann's canals.**

Before viewing the slide of ground, compact bone, examine the following three figures showing relationships between gross bone and Haversian systems. Figure III-13 shows a small portion of the diaphysis of a bone and its marrow. It has been magnified to demonstrate both longitudinal and cross-sectional aspects of Haversian systems. Figure III-14 provides a microscopic view of a longitudinal section of Haversian canals. Figure III-15 shows a cross section of two Haversian systems as viewed under the microscope.

PROCEDURE

1. Obtain a slide entitled "Ground Bone" or "Bone, Human."
2. Locate the tissue on low power, then draw while observing under high power. Since the tissue is quite thick, with the cover glass raised, use caution on high power to avoid breaking the slide.
3. Diagram one complete Haversian system. Include a wedge from the center to the edge of the system, drawn in detail. Include the following structures:
    a. **Haversian canal**, the large opening in the center. This may appear empty, may contain remnants of blood vessels, or it may appear dark due to the grinding process.
    b. **Lacunae**, small depressions arranged more or less symmetrically around the Haversian canal. Osteocytes are not present in these lacunae due to the grinding process. Observe the position and shape of the lacunae.
    c. **Canaliculi**, tiny canals that lead to and from the lacunae and Haversian canal. Observe the position, shape, and length of the canaliculi. The canaliculi in the outer ring loop back into the Haversian system.
    d. **Matrix**, the ground substance between the lacunae and canaliculi.
    e. **Lamellae**, the circular layers of bone laid down by the osteocytes. Each lamella is composed of a ring of lacunae and matrix.

KEY TO FIGURE III-13

1. periosteum
2. periosteal vein
3. periosteal artery
4. Haversian system
5. Haversian canal
6. Volkmann's canal
7. medullary artery
8. marrow cavity

KEY TO FIGURE III-14

1. Haversian canal
2. Volkmann's canal
3. lacuna

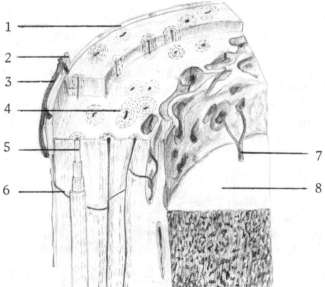

Figure III-13: Cross Section of Diaphysis (magnified)

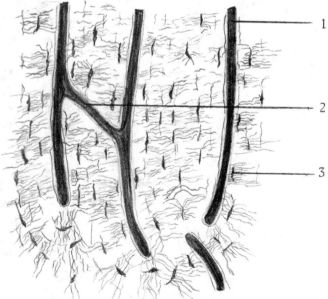

Figure III-14: Longitudinal Section through Compact Bone (430X)

KEY TO FIGURE III-15

1. matrix   3. canaliculus   5. lamella
2. Haversian canal   4. lacuna containing osteocyte

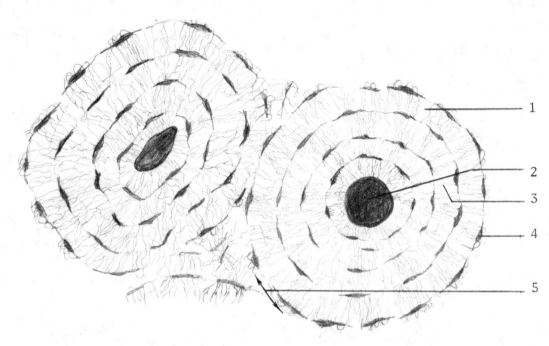

Figure III-15: Cross Section through Two Haversian Systems

Part 5.   Blood

DISCUSSION

The slide to be examined consists of a thin smear of blood stained with either Wright's stain or Giemsa's stain. With these dyes, granules in the cytoplasm of various kinds of leukocytes are differentially stained. The nuclei of the leukocytes are stained purple and the erythrocytes are stained a pale red color.

The following outline provides some of the identifying characteristics of the cells that may be observed on the prepared slide:

A.   **Erythrocytes** (red blood cells). The great majority of the cells you will observe will be of this type. They are small, **biconcave** discs. Many vertebrates have nucleated red cells (e.g., amphibians such as frogs and salamanders); however the erythrocytes of mammals are **anucleate.**

B.   **Leukocytes** (white blood cells):

1.   **Lymphocytes** (20-25% of all leukocytes). These are found in large numbers in lymph nodes and lymph as well as in the circulating blood. They have a large, single nucleus which is approximately spherical in shape and surrounded by a narrow band of cytoplasm.

2. **Monocytes** (3-8% of all leukocytes). These cells are usually the largest of the leukocytes. They contain a single, nonlobed, nucleus which is frequently curved in the form of a crescent. Monocytes contain more cytoplasm than lymphocytes.
3. **Granulocytes.** The cytoplasm of these cells contains numerous granules, which may vary in density and coarseness depending on the type. They are distinguished on the basis of the color they stain with various dyes. These differentiating stains are included in Wright's stain.
   a. **Neutrophils** (60-70% of all leukocytes). They are also called **polymorphonuclear** leukocytes because their nuclei consists of several (usually three to five) lobes. Upon careful observation (high power) it will be noted that the lobes are interconnected. The granules in the cytoplasm are relatively fine grained, stain with a neutral dye, and appear faint red in color.

KEY TO FIGURE III-16

A.   erythrocytes (red blood cells)
B-1. macrolymphocyte
B-2. microlymphocyte
C.   monocytes
D.   neutrophils ⎫
E.   eosinophil ⎬ **granulocytes** ⎫ **leukocytes**
F.   basophil   ⎭
G.   thrombocytes (platelets)

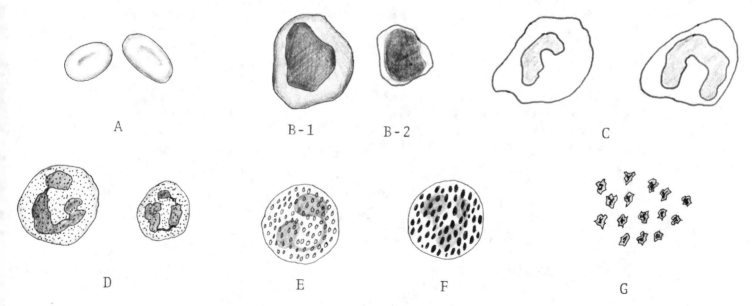

A   B-1   B-2   C

D   E   F   G

Figure III-16: Human Blood Cells

    b. **Eosinophils** (2-4% of all leukocytes). The dense granules of these cells, seen in the cytoplasm, are stained red by the eosin in Wright's stain. The nucleus is usually bilobed, but this may be difficult to observe due to the dense granular cytoplasm.

    c. **Basophils** (0.5-1% of all leukocytes). These cells contain such coarse granules that they all but blot out the nucleus. The granules take a basic dye and appear to be blue or purple in color.

4. **Thrombocytes (Platelets).** Platelets are much smaller than erythrocytes. They are derived from the fragmentation of the cytoplasm of large cells called **megakaryocytes** (100 micrometers in diameter) found in the bone marrow.

PROCEDURE

1. Obtain a slide of a human blood smear.
2. For orientation, refer to the drawings of blood cells (Figure III-16) and other references.
3. Note that the great majority of cells on the slide are erythrocytes. Draw two or three of the cells as they appear in different positions.
4. Identify and draw a lymphocyte.
5. Identify and draw a neutrophil.
6. Optional: If time permits, identify and draw an eosinophil, a basophil, a monocyte, and a group of thrombocytes.

Ex. III-E. Muscular Tissue

Part 1. Skeletal (Striated) Muscle

DISCUSSION

    Each skeletal muscle cell is a multinucleate fiber containing many bands called **striations.** They range in length from 1 mm to 12 cm and in diameter from 0.01 to 0.1 mm.

PROCEDURE

1. Obtain a slide showing teased skeletal muscle tissue.
2. Compare a fiber, as seen under high power, with Figure III-17.
3. Draw one muscle fiber as seen in longitudinal section.
4. Label **sarcolemma, sarcoplasm,** and **striations.** Include nuclei if they are visible. Note their size (relative to the striations) and their position.

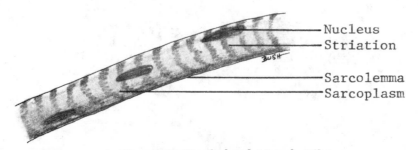

Figure III-17: Skeletal Muscle Fiber

Part 2. Visceral (Smooth) Muscle

DISCUSSION

The cells of this tissue are up to .5 mm in length; each spindle-shaped cell has tapered ends.

PROCEDURE

1. Obtain a slide of teased smooth (visceral) muscle tissue.
2. Compare the cells observed with Figure III-18.
3. Draw two or three representative cells and label all parts identified.

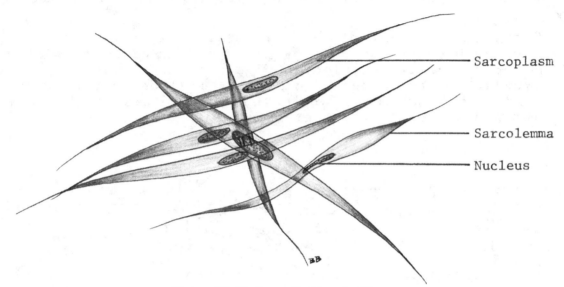

Sarcoplasm

Sarcolemma

Nucleus

Figure III-18: Smooth Muscle Fibers

Part 3. Cardiac Muscle

DISCUSSION

Somewhat fainter striations are observed in this tissue than in skeletal muscle tissue. Also, this tissue contains unique dark bands called **intercalated discs.** The electron microscope has revealed that these discs are placed where two cell membranes abut at the ends of adjacent cardiac fibers. The cardiac fibers form a continuum by repeatedly branching.

PROCEDURE

1. Obtain a slide of cardiac muscle tissue.
2. Compare this tissue, as observed under high power, with Figure III-19.
3. Draw and label three or four fibers showing the branching nature of the tissue, striations, and intercalated discs.

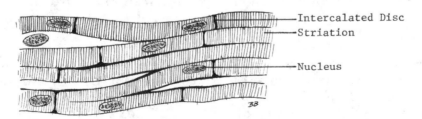

Intercalated Disc
Striation

Nucleus

Figure III-19: Cardiac Muscle Tissue

Ex. III-F. Nerve Tissue

Part 1. Motor Neurons
DISCUSSION

The slide to be examined was prepared by smearing and staining the ventral horn of the spinal cord. The cell bodies of motor neurons in a spinal cord smear are among the largest in the cord. In the process of preparing the slide, **the axon and dendrites of these large cells were broken.** On this slide, neuroglia cells are visible between the separated neurons.

PROCEDURE

1. Obtain a slide entitled "Nerve cells, ox spinal cord."
2. Locate one neuron under low power and compare it with the motor neuron illustrated in Figure III-20.
3. Draw the neuron under high power. Include in your drawing (and label) the **axon, dendrites,** and **nucleus** with **nucleolus** and any other visible parts.

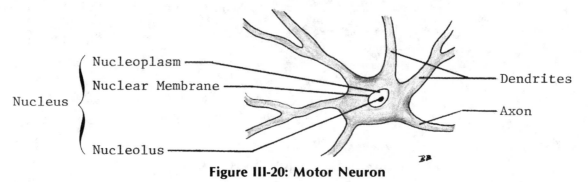

Nucleus { Nucleoplasm / Nuclear Membrane / Nucleolus }

Dendrites

Axon

Figure III-20: Motor Neuron

Part 2. Myelinated (Medullated) Nerve Fiber
DISCUSSION

Myelinated nerve fibers are located in the central nervous system and in peripheral nerves. Their name is derived from the fact that such fibers are surrounded by a pearly white, lipid substance called the **myelin sheath.** In the central nervous system the myelin sheath is formed by **glial cells,** and fibers containing it make up the white matter (gray matter is composed mainly of cell bodies and fibers which usually lack myelin; hence, it is gray in color). In the peripheral nerves, axons of motor neurons are surrounded by sheaths of myelin which are formed by **Schwann cells.** All myelin sheaths are interrupted at regular intervals at points referred to as **nodes of Ranvier.** All nerve fibers outside the central nervous system are covered with the **neurilemma** (sheath of Schwann), whether they are myelinated or not.

PROCEDURE

1. Obtain a slide containing teased myelinated nerve fibers. Locate a fiber that appears to be typical and compare it with Figure III-21.
2. Using the high power objective, draw a segment of the fiber which includes two nodes of Ranvier, neurilemma, nucleus of Schwann cell, myelin sheath, and axis cylinder.

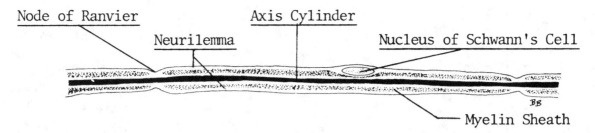

Figure III-21: Myelinated Nerve Fiber

Ex. III-G. The Skin

DISCUSSION

Skin consists of two principal layers: the **epidermis (cuticle)**, and the **dermis (corium** or **true skin)**. The epidermis contains an outer layer of cells which are keratinized (protoplasm replaced by nonliving protein called keratin). These cells are flattened and scalelike and are constantly being lost by the body. This layer of cells is known as the **stratum corneum** or horny layer; the cells are replaced as a result of the mitotic divisions of the inner layer of the epidermis, which is known as the **stratum germinativum.**

The **dermis**, like the epidermis, is variable in its thickness in different parts of the body. For example, it is especially thick over the palms of the hands and the soles of the feet. This portion of the skin is composed of dense irregular connective tissue with numerous elastic fibers. Numerous blood vessels, nerves, and lymphatics pass through the dermis.

Appendages of the skin include hair, nails, **sudoriferous** (sweat) glands, and **sebaceous** (oil) glands.

The **subdermal** tissue (**subcutaneous layer**) contains fat cells, areolar connective tissue, blood vessels, lymphatics, and nerves. These tissues provide a connection between the skin and deeper tissues. Where the connective fibers are loose (such as in the neck) the skin can be moved quite easily. Where the skin is attached more firmly (such as in the palms and soles), only limited movement is possible.

The specialized receptors located within the skin (for receiving such stimuli as cold, heat, touch, pain, etc.) are discussed under the introduction in Chapter X.

PROCEDURE

1. Using Figure III-22 as a guide, examine the structures on the model of human skin.
2. Obtain a slide of human skin. Using references, anatomical charts, the skin model and Figure III-22, explore the slide for the following structures (check off each structure identified).

a. ___ adipose tissue

b. ___ arrector pili muscle

c. ___ blood vessel

d. ___ bulb of hair

k. ___ nerve fiber

l. ___ Pacinian corpuscle

m. ___ pore of sweat gland

n. ___ Ruffini's end organ

e. ___ dermis
f. ___ duct of sweat gland

g. ___ epidermis
h. ___ hair shaft
i. ___ Krause's end bulb
j. ___ Meissner's corpuscle

o. ___ sebaceous gland
p. ___ stratified squamous epithelium
q. ___ stratum corneum
r. ___ stratum germinativum
s. ___ subcutaneous layer
t. ___ sudoriferous gland

KEY TO FIGURE III-22

A. epidermis (stratified squamous epithelium)
B. dermis (true skin)
C. subdermis (subcutaneous tissue)
1. pore of sweat gland
2. stratum corneum (horny layer)
3. stratum germinativum

4. duct of sweat gland
5. hair shaft
6. sebaceous (oil) gland
7. arrector pili muscle
8. hair follicle
9. sudoriferous (sweat) gland
10. bulb of hair (with papilla)
11. adipose tissue

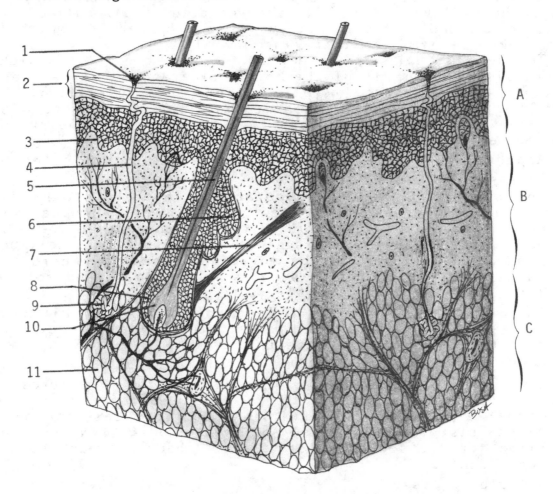

Figure III-22: The Skin (sense organs enlarged to show detail)

SELF-TEST: CELLS, MITOSIS, TISSUES, AND SKIN

DIRECTIONS: See Chapter 1, Self-Test, p. 12

1. A group of cells of similar structure constitutes **an organ.**
2. Epithelial tissue **covers and lines.**
3. Nervous tissue **supports and binds.**
4. Epithelial tissue can be distinguished from connective tissue by **sparseness of intercellular materials.**
5. Goblet cells are unicellular glands found in **certain connective tissues.**
6. Cartilage is a variety of connective tissue which contains **osteocytes** in lacunae.
7. One location of **elastic cartilage** is within the external ear.
8. Skin is **a tissue.**
9. A single layer of flat cells which line the blood vessels is classified as **mesothelium.**
10. **Simple columnar epithelium** lines the stomach and intestines.
11. Stratified squamous epithelium is found, primarily, **covering the outside of the body.**
12. **Pesudostratified ciliated columnar epithelium** is found lining much of the respiratory tract.
13. Cilia are found on the surface of **all epithelial cells.**
14. Goblet cells produce **mucus.**
15. **Mucous membranes** line the alimentary, respiratory, and urogenital tracts.
16. **Serous membranes** line closed body cavities and cover organs which lie within the cavities.
17. **Haversian canals** are minute channels in the matrix of bone tissue extending to lacunae.
18. The Haversian system is a nutritive arrangement of cells in **cancellous** bone.
19. The periosteum is a **fibrous** membrane covering bone.
20. The cell is both the **structural and functional** unit of the body.
21. **All** human cells have cell membranes.
22. The skin contains **stratified squamous epithelium.**
23. The **epidermis** of the skin contains the secreting portions of the sweat glands.
24. The skin contains **striated** muscle fibers.
25. A hair is a product of **epidermal** cells.
26. The dermis contains **fibrous connective tissues.**
27. The upper surface of the epidermis is the **stratum granulosum.**
28. Sensitivity of the skin is determined by sense organs lying in the **epidermis.**
29. Freckles are patches of **melanin.**
30. Some injections with hypodermic needles hurt more than others because **pain receptors may be hit.**
31. **Contractions of arrector pili muscles** pull the hair up and pull the adjacent skin down, causing "goose pimples."
32. The **epidermis** is the thickest layer of skin.

33. The **epidermis** layer of skin is the only layer lacking a direct blood supply.
34. The epidermis consists **only of dead cells.**
35. **Sebaceous glands** lubricate the skin and keep it from cracking.
36. Wrinkles are the result of **creases formed where the skin is habitually folded.**
37. The skin has friction ridges **over its entire surface.**
38. **Melanocytes** are specialized cells in the lower part of the epidermis which produce melanin.
39. When chromosomes line up in the center of the spindle during mitosis, it is the **anaphase.**
40. The nuclear membrane disappears during the **metaphase** of mitosis.
41. The chromosomes consist of a pair of chromatids held together by a centromere in the **prophase** of mitosis.
42. During metaphase, the centromeres **divide.**
43. During mitosis, chromosomes appear to be short rods due to **the spiral arrangement of each chromosome.**
44. In the **anaphase** of mitosis, there are individual chromosomes, each with a single centromere.
45. The **nucleus** of a cell contains the Golgi apparatus.
46. Mitochondria are found **in both the cytoplasm and the nucleus of a cell.**
47. Energy is released as the result of enzymatic reactions occurring in **ribosomes.**
48. Tendons consist primarily of **elastic connective tissue.**
49. The golgi apparatus is apparently concerned with **secretion.**
50. **Vacuoles** may serve as a storage place for foods.
51. Deoxyribonucleic acid is found primarily in **cytoplasm.**
52. Secretion in the body **always** involves some form of epithelial tissue.
53. **Mucous membranes** line passageways which open to the outside, whereas **serous membranes** line closed cavities.
54. **Osteoblasts** form the hard intercellular matrix of bone.
55. **Connective tissue** forms the surface of and **epithelial tissue** the underlying layer of mucous, cutaneous, and serous membranes.

KEY

1.	a tissue	32.	dermis
3.	conducts	34.	of living and dead cells
5.	columnar epithelium	37.	mostly hands and feet-- not pronounced elsewhere
6.	chondrocytes		
8.	an organ	39.	metaphase
9.	endothelium	40.	prophase
13.	ciliated columnar cells	45.	cytoplasm
17.	canaliculi	46.	only in cytoplasm
18.	compact (dense)	47.	mitochondria
23.	dermis	48.	white fibrous connective tissue
24.	smooth (visceral)		
27.	stratum corneum	51.	the nucleus
28.	dermis	55.	epithelial tissue; connective tissue

Chapter IV
THE SKELETAL SYSTEM

Ex. IV-A. Composition and Structure of Bone

DISCUSSION

The skeletal system includes the bones and the joints. The study of the bones is termed osteology; that of the joints arthrology. The functions of the skeletal system include the following: protection of internal organs such as the heart and lungs, support of the body, attachment for muscles, storage of calcium and phosphorus, and manufacture of blood cells (hemopoiesis).

The dried bones used in the laboratory have been cleansed of all membranes and muscle tissue. In a fresh bone, a membrane called the **periosteum** surrounds the **diaphysis** (shaft) of a long bone. The periosteum serves for growth in circumference, for repair, and for nutrition of the bone. The **periosteal blood vessels** penetrate into the bone by way of **Volkmann's canals,** carrying blood rich in nutrients and oxygen. A similar membrane, called the **endosteum,** lines the **marrow cavity (medullary cavity).** This membrane, in children, contains cells called **osteoclasts** which destroy bone, enlarging the marrow cavity. The **articular cartilage,** composed of hyaline cartilage, covers the **epiphyses** (ends) of the long bones. This serves to prevent friction at joints. In a sectioned bone of an adult, an **epiphyseal line** can be seen at each end of the bone at the junction between the epiphysis and the diaphysis. This is the remnant of the epiphyseal cartilage, which serves for growth in length of the bone.

In a fresh bone, the shaft of the bone is filled with yellow bone marrow, composed primarily of adipose tissue. The ends of some of the long bones, flat bones, bodies of vertebrae, cranial bones, the sternum, and the ribs contain red bone marrow. This type of marrow manufactures erythrocytes, granulocytes, monocytes, and thrombocytes.

PROCEDURE

1. Examine the sectioned femur. Locate the following struc-
    tures:
    a. **Compact bone.** Note the thick layer of compact bone in
        the shaft and the thin layer covering the epiphyses.
    b. **Cancellous (spongy) bone.** This type is contained in
        the epiphyses; a thin layer of spongy bone lines the
        marrow cavity.
    c. **Marrow cavity.**
    d. **Epiphyseal line.**
2. Use Figure IV-1, a longitudinal section through the femur,
    as a self-test. See Section J, p. 5 (Illustrations as
    Self-Tests) for suggestions in using such figures as self-
    tests.

KEY TO FIGURE IV-1

1. compact bone	3. marrow cavity	5. diaphysis
2. cancellous bone	4. epiphysis	6. epiphyseal line

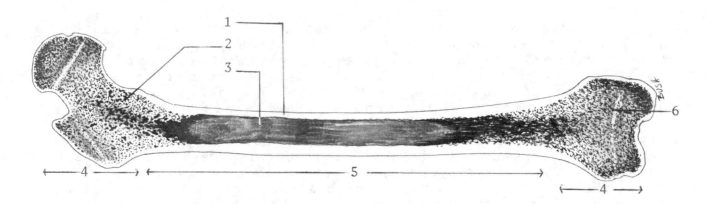

Figure IV-1: Longitudinal Section through Femur

3. Examine the bone that has been soaked in dilute acetic
    acid for several days. The acid dissolves the minerals in
    the bone, leaving only organic materials. Examine the con-
    sistency of the bone. Try to bend the bone.
4. Examine the bone that has been baked at high temperature
    for eight hours. The heat removes the organic materials in
    the bone, leaving the minerals. Note the color of the
    bone. Gently press on the bone. Determine whether this
    bone can be bent.
5. Review the microscopic structure of bone in Ex. III-D,
    Part 4. Study Figure III-13, 14, and 15 (in Ex. III-D) to
    determine how nutrients are transported to the osteocytes
    and to the marrow cavity.

Ex. IV-B. The Appendicular Skeleton

DISCUSSION

The skeleton in a typical adult contains 206 bones, although this number can vary. The skeleton is divided into two parts, the appendicular skeleton and the axial skeleton. The appendicular skeleton is composed of the 126 bones of the appendages and the girdles (shoulder and pelvic), which connect the appendages to the axial skeleton.

PROCEDURE

1. Locate each of the illustrated bones (Figure IV-2 to IV-16) on an articulated skeleton.
2. Compare the parts of the bones indicated in each figure with those in your text and other references and on bones of a disarticulated skeleton.
3. Determine the function of each part indicated by using your text or other references.
4. As you study the bones, whenever possible locate them and their parts on yourself.
5. Each of the illustrations may be used as self-tests. Keys are included for each illustration.

KEY TO FIGURE IV-2

1. acromial extremity   2. sternal extremity
3. conoid tubercle (coracoid tuberosity)

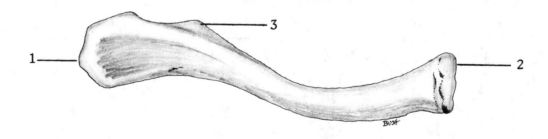

Figure IV-2: Right Clavicle (superior surface, tipped forward)

44

KEY TO FIGURE IV-3

1. superior border
2. supraspinous fossa
3. superior (medial) angle
4. scapular notch
5. spine

6. infraspinous fossa
7. vertebral (medial) border
8. coracoid process
9. acromion process
10. glenoid cavity

11. lateral angle
12. neck
13. axillary border (lateral)
14. inferior angle

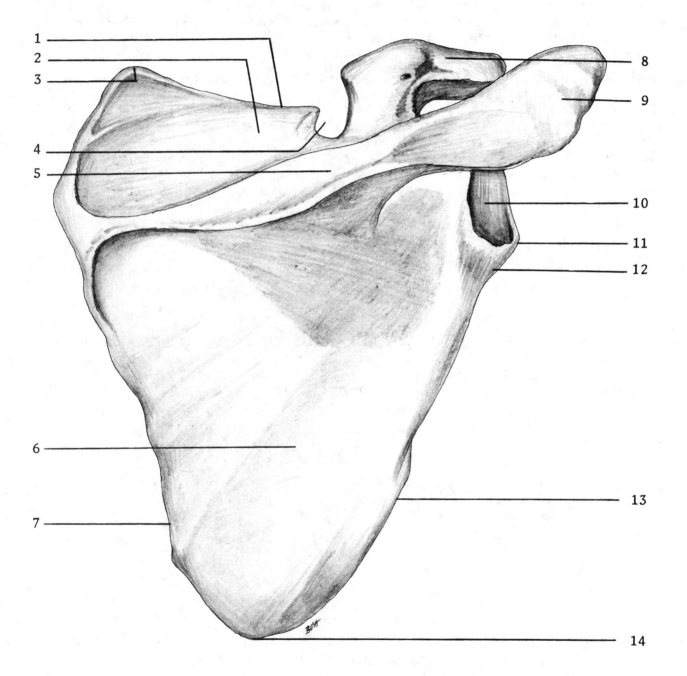

Figure IV-3: Posterior View of the Right Scapula

KEY TO FIGURE IV-4

1. head
2. greater tubercle
3. lesser tubercle
4. bicipital groove
   (intertubercular groove)

5. coronoid fossa
6. radial fossa
7. lateral epicondyle
8. capitulum

9. medial
   epicondyle
10. trochlea

KEY TO FIGURE IV-5

1. head
2. anatomical neck
3. surgical neck

4. deltoid tuberosity
5. groove for radial
   nerve
6. lateral epicondyle

7. olecranon fossa
8. trochlea
9. medial epicondyle

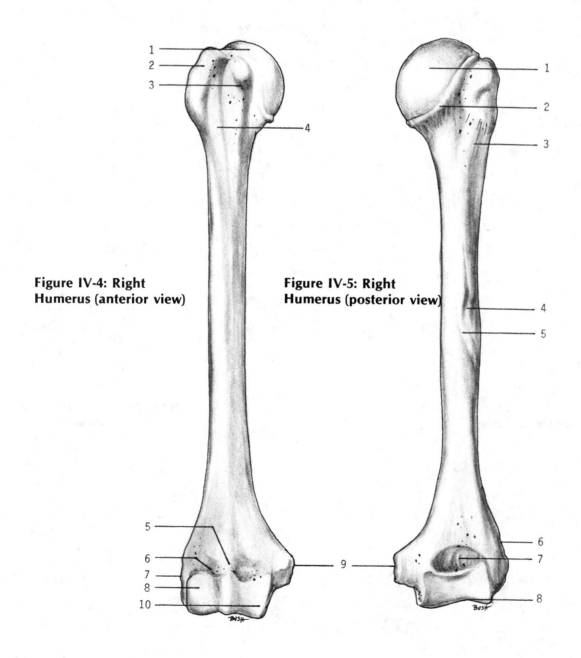

Figure IV-4: Right
Humerus (anterior view)

Figure IV-5: Right
Humerus (posterior view)

KEY TO FIGURE IV-6

1. head   3. radial tuberosity   5. ulnar notch
2. neck   4. styloid process

KEY TO FIGURE IV-7

1. olecranon process   3. coronoid process   5. head
2. trochlear notch   4. radial notch   6. styloid process
   (semilunar notch)

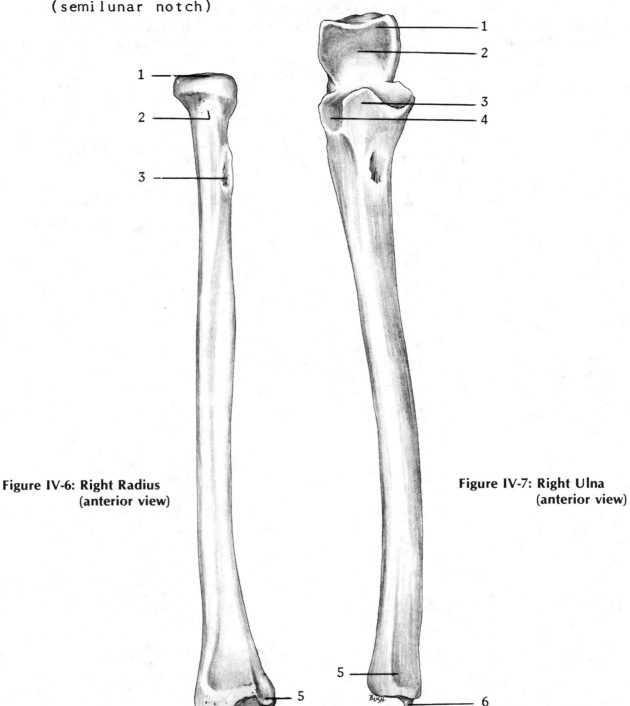

Figure IV-6: Right Radius
(anterior view)

Figure IV-7: Right Ulna
(anterior view)

KEY TO FIGURE IV-8

1. third phalanx
2. second phalanx
3. first phalanx
4. phalanges
5. fifth metacarpal
6. capitate

7. hamate
8. triangular
   (triquetrum)
9. pisiform
10. lunate (semilunar)
11. navicular (scaphoid)

12. lesser multangular
   (trapezoid)
13. greater multangular
   (trapezium)
14. carpals
15. metacarpals

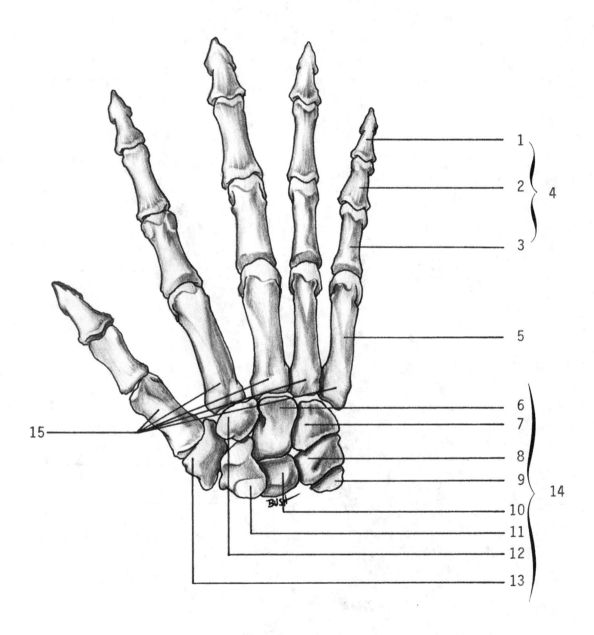

Figure IV-8: Dorsal Surface of Right Hand

48

KEY TO FIGURE IV-9

1. ilium
2. posterior superior iliac spine
3. posterior inferior iliac spine
4. greater sciatic notch
5. ischial spine
6. lesser sciatic notch
7. ischium
8. ischial tuberosity
9. iliac crest
10. anterior superior iliac spine
11. anterior inferior iliac spine
12. acetabulum
13. crest of pubis
14. pubis
15. obturator foramen

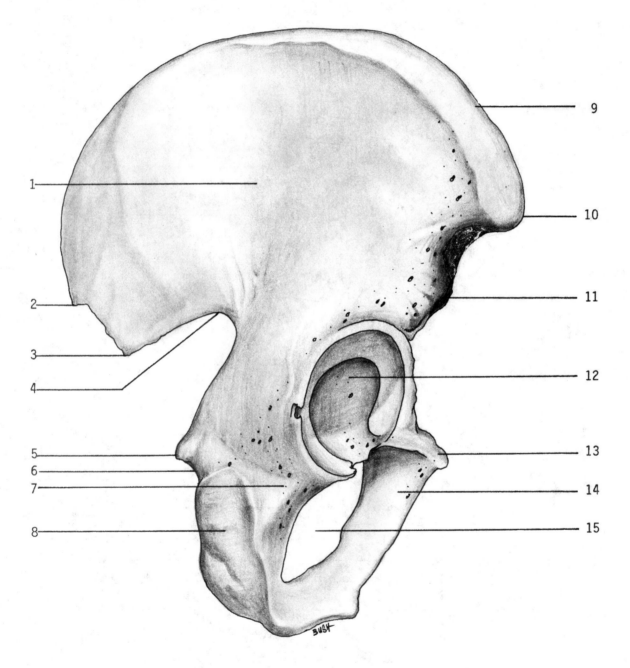

Figure IV-9: Lateral View of the Right Os Coxae

49

KEY TO FIGURE IV-10

1. sacral promontory
2. iliac crest
3. auricular surface on ilium
4. iliac fossa
5. anterior sacral foramen
6. sacrum
7. arcuate line
8. anterior superior iliac spine
9. coccyx
10. brim of pelvis
11. ischial spine
12. pelvic inlet
13. acetabulum
14. superior ramus of pubis
15. pubic symphysis
16. obturator foramen
17. pubic arch

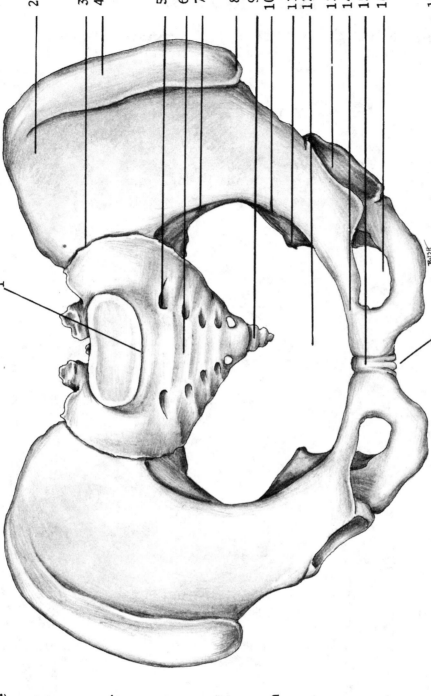

Figure IV-10: The Female Pelvis

KEY TO FIGURE IV-11

1. greater trochanter   3. lateral epicondyle   5. head
2. intertrochanteric line   4. patellar surface   6. neck
                                                  7. medial epicondyle

KEY TO FIGURE IV-12

1. head   4. lesser trochanter   7. lateral condyle
2. greater trochanter   5. linea aspera   8. medial condyle
3. neck   6. intercondyloid fossa

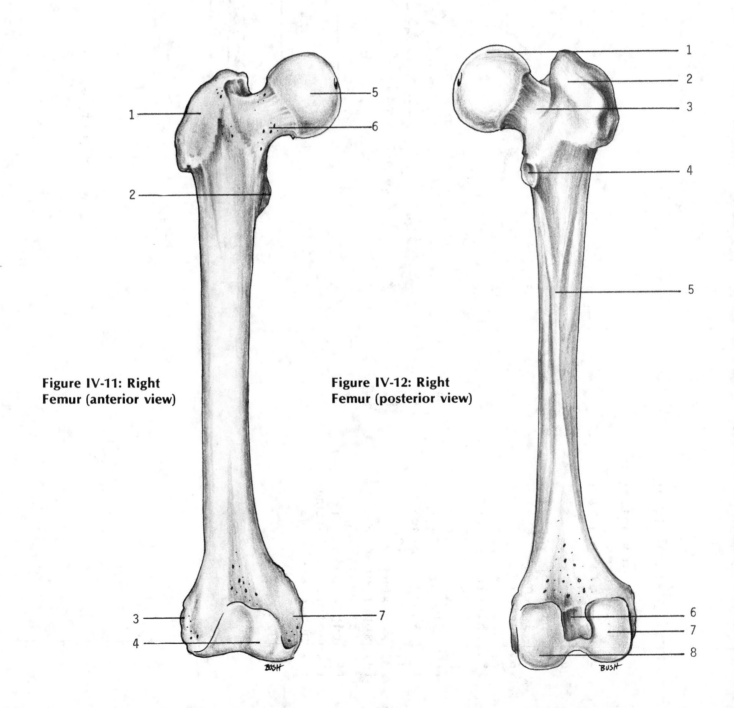

Figure IV-11: Right Femur (anterior view)

Figure IV-12: Right Femur (posterior view)

51

KEY TO FIGURE IV-13

1. styloid process   2. head of fibula   3. lateral malleolus

KEY TO FIGURE IV-14

1. intercondylar   4. tibial tuberosity   7. inferior articular
   eminence   5. anterior crest   surface
2. medial condyle   6. medial malleolus   8. fibular notch
3. lateral condyle

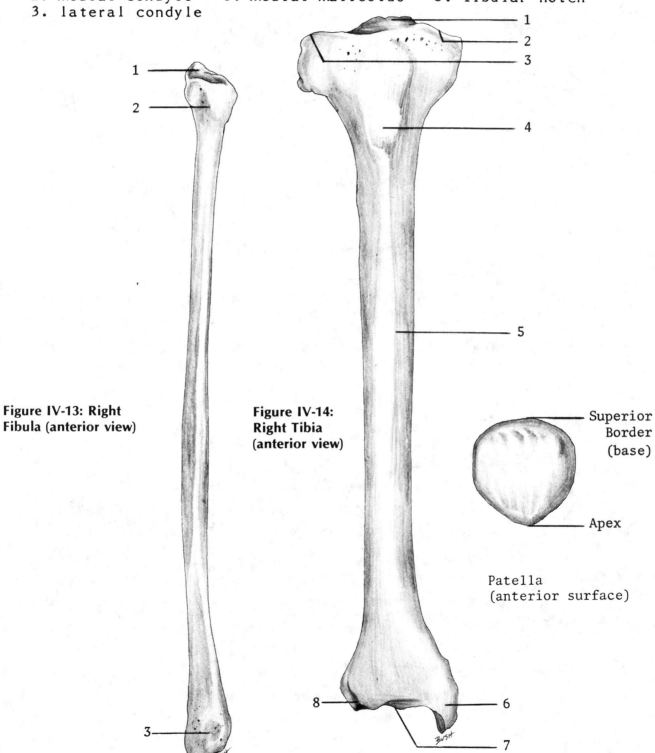

**Figure IV-13: Right
Fibula (anterior view)**

**Figure IV-14:
Right Tibia
(anterior view)**

Superior
Border
(base)

Apex

Patella
(anterior surface)

KEY TO FIGURE IV-15

1. third phalanx
2. second phalanx
3. first phalanx

4. phalanges
5. first metatarsal
6. first (medial) cuneiform

7. navicular
8. talus
9. calcaneus

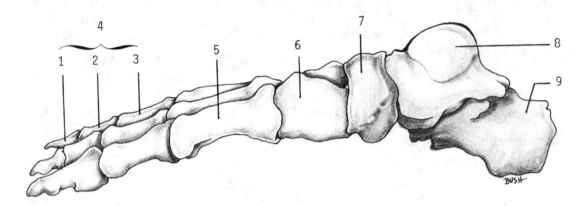

Figure IV-15: Bones of the Right Foot (medial view)

KEY TO FIGURE IV-16

1. third phalanx
2. second phalanx
3. first phalanx
4. phalanges
5. fifth metatarsal

6. metatarsals (metatarsus)
7. third (lateral) cuneiform
8. second (intermediate) cuneiform
9. first (medial) cuneiform

10. cuboid
11. navicular
12. talus
13. calcaneus
14. tarsals

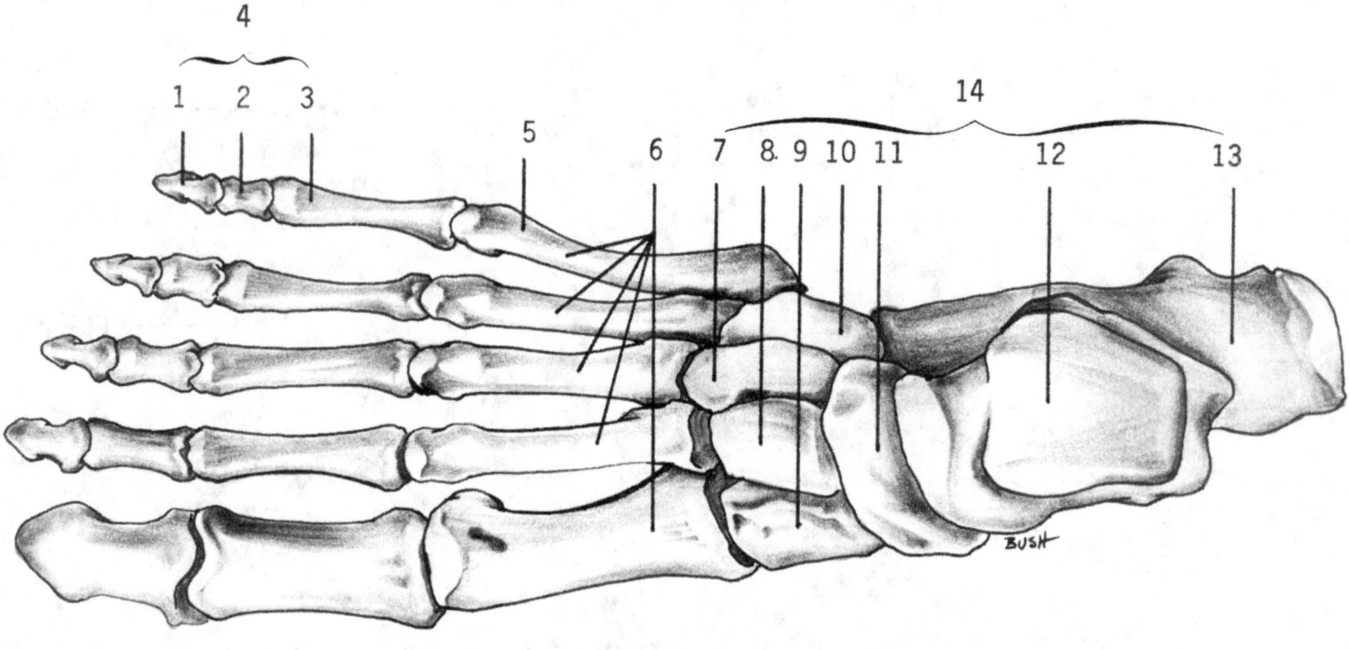

Figure IV-16: Bones of the Right Foot (dorsal surface)

Ex. IV-C. The Axial Skeleton

DISCUSSION

The axial skeleton, composed of 80 bones, includes the bones of the skull, vertebral column, and the thorax.

PROCEDURE

1. Locate each of the illustrated bones (Figure IV-16 to IV-35) on an articulated skeleton. Follow steps 2-5 of the procedure for Ex. IV-B.
2. Practice identifying the bones of the disarticulated skull until you can distinguish each of the separate bones. Verify your identification of the facial bones with the instructor.
3. The student should determine the characteristics of the vertebrae in each region of the vertebral column. Be prepared to identify the region in which any isolated vertebra may be located.

KEY TO FIGURE IV-17

1. sagittal suture
2. supraorbital notch
3. greater wing of sphenoid
4. temporal bone
5. optic foramen
6. superior orbital fissure
7. sphenoid (orbital surface)
8. inferior orbital fissure
9. middle nasal concha
10. infraorbital foramen
11. inferior nasal concha
12. vomer
13. mandible
14. coronal suture
15. parietal bone
16. frontal bone
17. superciliary arch
18. glabella
19. supraorbital margin
20. nasal bone
21. ethmoid
22. lacrimal bone
23. zygomatic plate
24. perpendicular plate of ethmoid
25. maxilla
26. mental foramen

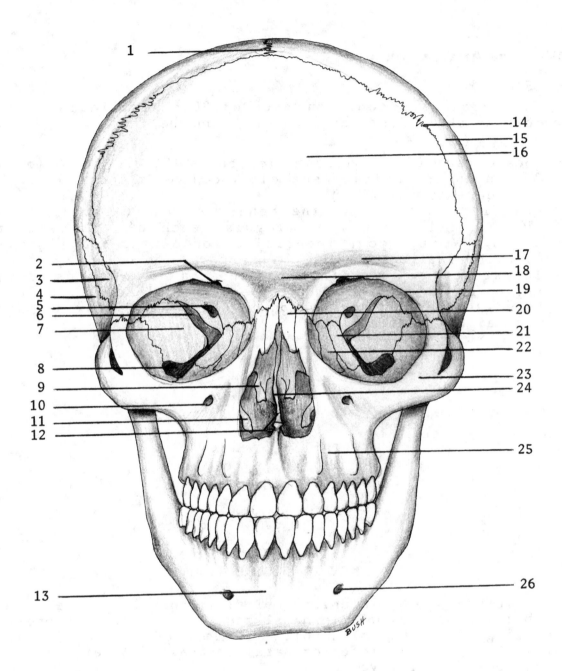

1

14
15
16

17
18
2   19
3   20
4   21
5   22
6
7

8   23
9   24
10
11
12

25

13   26

Figure IV-17: Anterior View of the Skull

KEY TO FIGURE IV-18

1. parietal bone
2. lambdoidal suture
3. squamosal suture
4. temporal bone
5. wormian bone
6. occipital bone
7. mastoid process

8. styloid process
9. coronal suture
10. frontal bone
11. sphenoid bone
12. nasal bone
13. lacrimal bone
14. ethmoid bone

15. zygomatic bone
16. maxilla
17. zygomatic arch
18. external acoustic (auditory) meatus
19. mandible

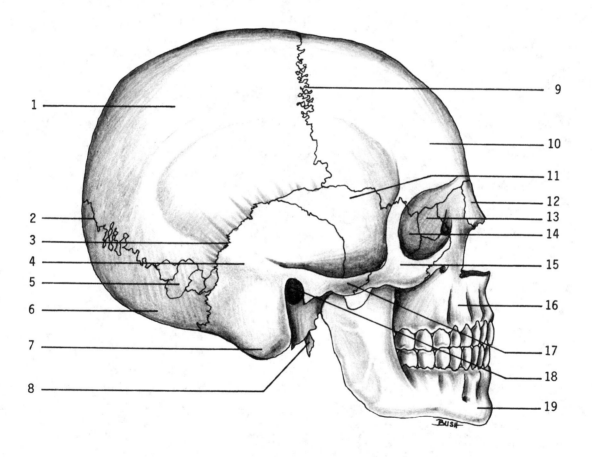

Figure IV-18: The Skull (lateral view)

KEY TO FIGURE IV-19

1. frontal bone
2. sella turcica
3. optic foramen
4. frontal sinus
5. nasal bone
6. perpendicular plate
   of ethmoid
7. sphenoidal sinus
8. vomer
9. palatine process
   of maxilla
10. alveolar process
11. pterygoid process
12. parietal bone
13. internal auditory
    (acoustic)
14. temporal bone
15. jugular foramen
16. occipital bone
17. hypoglossal canal
18. occipital condyle
19. styloid process

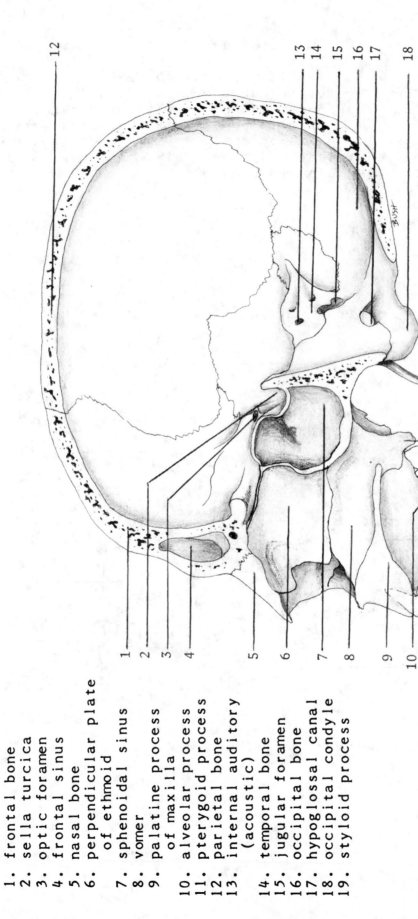

Figure IV-19: Sagittal Section of the Skull

KEY TO FIGURE IV-20

1. perpendicular plate
2. crista galli
3. cribriform plate
4. ethmoidal air cells
5. lamina orbitalis (of left lateral mass)

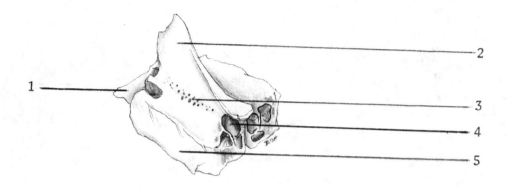

Figure IV-20: Superior View of the Ethmoid

KEY TO FIGURE IV-21

1. optic foramen
2. sphenoid sinus
3. body
4. sella turcica
5. lesser wing
6. superior orbital fissure
7. greater wing
8. foramen rotundum
9. lateral pterygoid process
10. medial pterygoid process

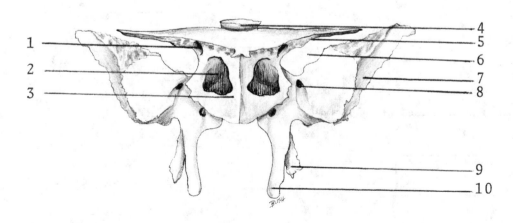

Figure IV-21: Anterior View of the Sphenoid

KEY TO FIGURE IV-22

1. greater wing
2. superior orbital fissure
3. anterior clinoid process
4. foramen rotundum
5. posterior clinoid process
6. foramen ovale
7. foramen spinosum
8. lesser wing
9. optic foramen
10. optic groove
11. sella turcica
12. dorsum sellae

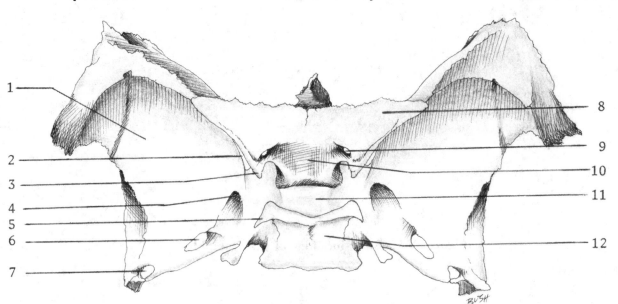

Figure IV-22: Superior View of Sphenoid

KEY TO FIGURE IV-23

1. superior nuchal line
2. condyloid canal
3. occipital condyle
4. hypoglossal canal
5. external occipital protuberance
6. external occipital crest (median nuchal line)
7. inferior nuchal line
8. foramen magnum
9. jugular notch
10. basilar part

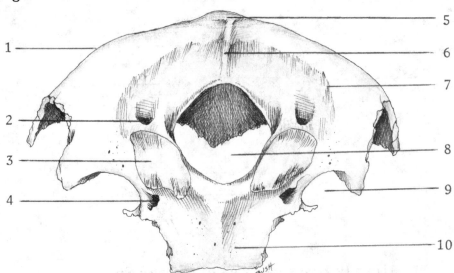

Figure IV-23: Inferior View of the Occipital

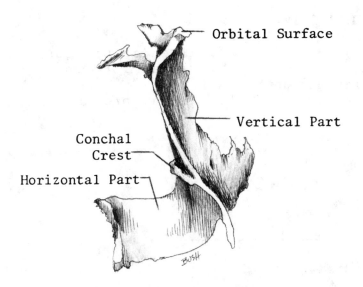

Figure IV-24: Left Palatine

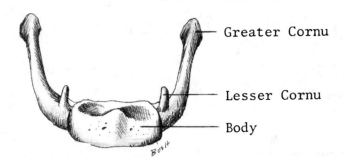

Figure IV-25: Hyoid

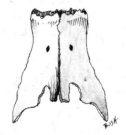

Figure IV-26: Nasal
Bones, outer surface

Figure IV-27: Lacrimal,
lateral aspect

Figure IV-28: Vomer

Figure IV-29: Right Inferior
Nasal Concha, lateral surface

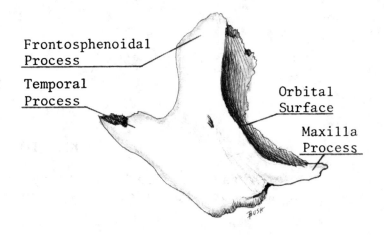

Figure IV-30: Zygomatic (Malar)

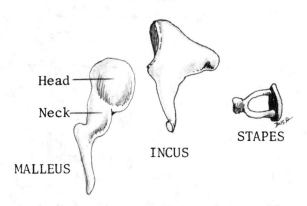

Figure IV-31: Auditory Ossicles

KEY TO FIGURE IV-32

1. coronoid process
2. mandibular notch
3. condyloid process
4. ramus
5. angle
6. mandibular foramen
7. alveolar process
8. mental foramen
9. body
10. mental protuberance

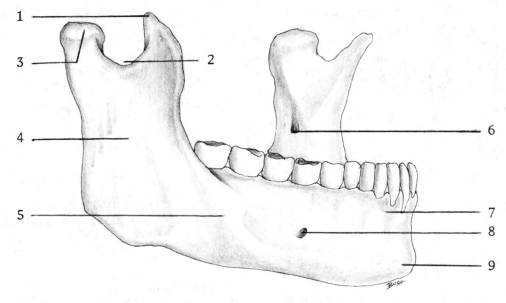

Figure IV-32: The Mandible

KEY TO FIGURE IV-33

1. orbital surface
2. infraorbital groove
3. zygomatic process
4. frontal process
5. infraorbital foramen
6. anterior nasal spine
7. alveolar process

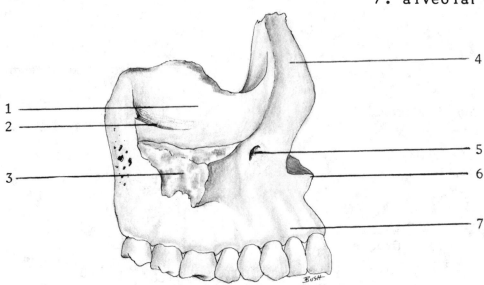

Figure IV-33: Lateral View of the Right Maxilla

KEY TO FIGURE IV-34

1. squama
2. external acoustic meatus
3. mastoid process
4. zygomatic process
5. mandibular fossa
6. styloid process

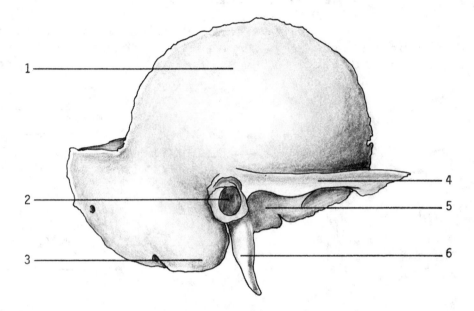

Figure IV-34: The Right Temporal (Lateral Aspect)

KEY TO FIGURE IV-35

1. zygomatic process
2. styloid process
3. external acoustic meatus
4. mastoid process
5. carotid canal
6. petrous portion
7. carotid canal

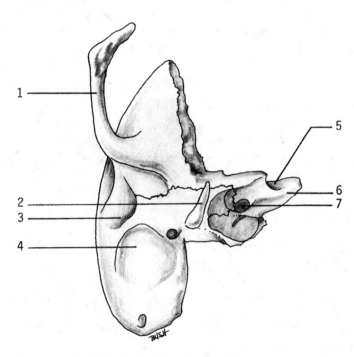

Figure IV-35: The Right Temporal (basal aspect)

KEY TO FIGURE IV-36

1. anterior arch
2. superior articular surface
3. transverse foramen
4. posterior arch
5. transverse process
6. groove for vertebral artery

KEY TO FIGURE IV-37

1. body
2. dens (odontoid process)
3. superior articular surface
4. transverse foramen
5. transverse process
6. lamina
7. bifid spinous process

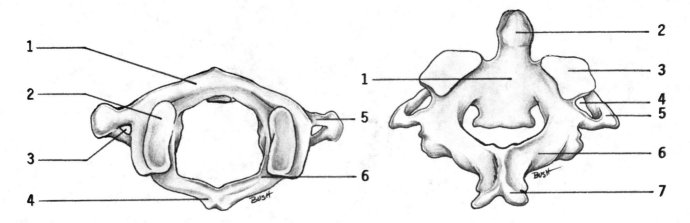

Figure IV-36: The Atlas
(first cervical vertebra)

Figure IV-37: The Axis
(second cervical vertebra)

KEY TO FIGURE IV-38

1. body
2. transverse foramen
3. pedicle
4. transverse process
5. lamina
6. spinous process
7. superior articular process
8. vertebral (spinal) foramen

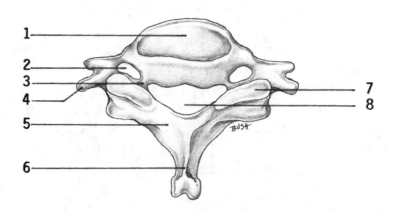

Figure IV-38: Seventh Cervical Vertebra

KEY TO FIGURE IV-39

1. costal demifacet
2. body (centrum)
3. vertebral notch

4. superior articular
   process
5. facet for rib

6. transverse process
7. inferior articular
   process
8. spinous process

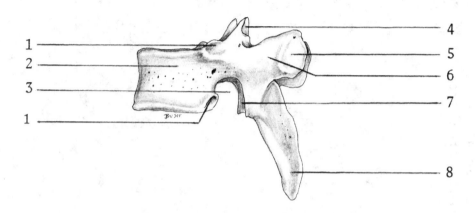

Figure IV-39: A Typical Thoracic Vertebra

KEY TO FIGURE IV-40

1. spinous process
2. inferior articular
   process
3. mamillary process

4. lamina
5. vertebral foramen
6. transverse process

7. superior articular process
8. pedicle
9. body (centrum)

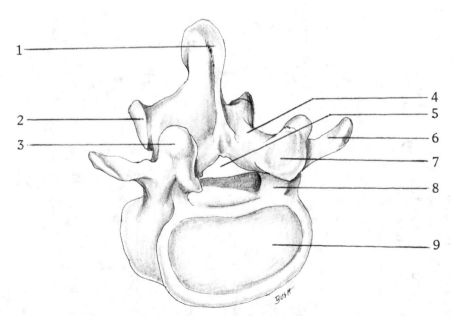

Figure IV-40: A Typical Lumbar Vertebra

KEY TO FIGURE IV-41

1. ala
2. lateral mass
3. pelvic surface
4. articular process
5. auricular surface
6. sacral promontory
7. anterior sacral foramen
8. body of second sacral vertebra (pelvic surface)
9. coccyx

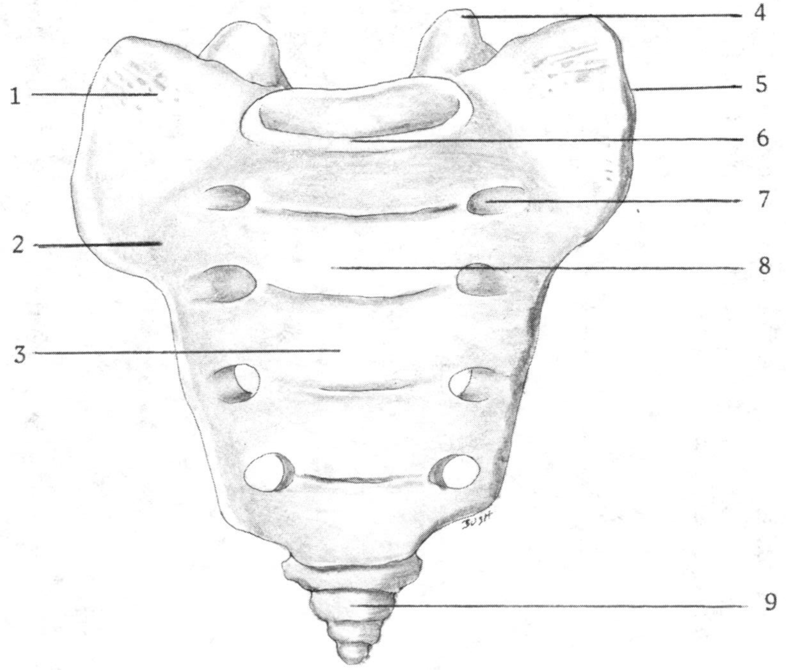

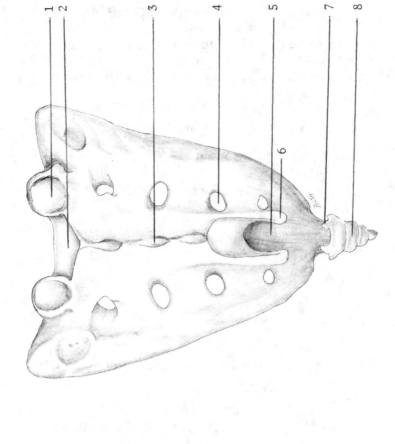

Figure IV-41: The Sacrum and Coccyx (ventral aspect)

KEY TO FIGURE IV-42

1. articular process (for 5th lumbar)
2. sacral canal
3. middle sacral crest
4. lateral sacral crest
5. posterior sacral foramen
6. hiatus
7. cornu of sacrum
8. cornu of coccyx
9. coccyx

Figure IV-42: The Sacrum and Coccyx (dorsal aspect)

KEY TO FIGURE IV-43

A-G = 7 True Ribs
H-L = 5 False Ribs
K-L = 2 Floating Ribs
1. clavicular notch
2. suprasternal notch
   (jugular notch)

3. sternal angle
4. costal notch
5. manubrium
6. costal cartilage
7. rib

8. body (gladiolus)
9. xiphoid (ensiform)
   process
10. intervertebral disc
11. 12th thoracic vertebra
12. floating rib

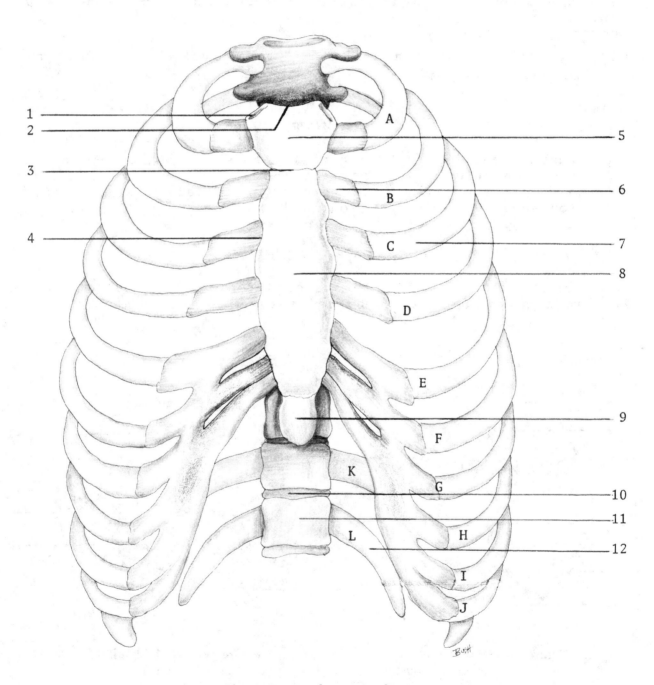

Figure IV-43: The Bony Thorax

Ex. IV-D. The Fetal Skeleton

DISCUSSION

The number of separate bones in the fetus and the child is greater than the 206 in the typical adult skeleton. This is due to the fact that many bones in the adult are composed of several parts fused together; these parts are separate bones in the fetus and child. For example, in a child, the three regions of the os coxae bone (the ilium, ischium, and pubis) form separate bones; in the adult these have united to make one hip bone.

PROCEDURE

1. Use Figure IV-44 and IV-45, two views of the skull at birth, as self-tests.

KEY TO FIGURE IV-44

1. frontal bone	4. sagittal suture	7. lambdoidal
2. frontal suture	5. parietal bone	suture
3. anterior (frontal) fontanel	6. posterior (occipital) fontanel	8. occipital bone

KEY TO FIGURE IV-45

1. coronal suture	3. anterolateral fontanel	5. posterolateral
2. lambdoidal suture	4. squamosal suture	fontanel

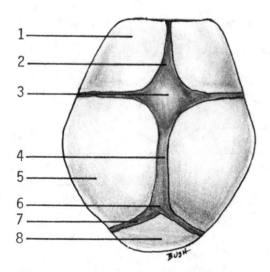

Figure IV-44: Fetal Skull
(Superior surface)

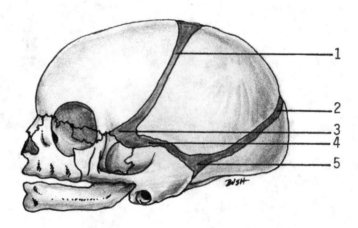

Figure IV-45: Fetal Skull (lateral view)

2. Examine the fetal and adult skeletons, and observe any differences in degree of ossification. Give special attention to the structures listed below, in the fetal skeleton. Compare the bone or process with the corresponding structure in the adult. Record your observations in the Chart under Questions for Chapter IV.

    a. frontal bone
    b. sternum
    c. patella
    d. os coxae

    e. spinous processes of vertebrae
    f. carpals
    g. proximal epiphysis of humerus

3. Determine the sex of the fetal skeleton.

Ex. IV-E. Joints

DISCUSSION

A joint is the site of articulation between two bones. Joints may be divided into three classes, depending on the amount of movement between the articulating bones: **synarthroses** (immovable joints), **amphiarthroses** (slightly movable joints), and **diarthroses** (freely movable joints). Joints may also be divided into five classes, based on the structure of the joint (**synostoses**, **syndesmoses**, **synchondroses**, **symphyses**, and **synovial** joints). Most of the common joints in the body are freely movable joints.

PROCEDURE

1. The instructor will demonstrate a series of x-ray films. This will give you an opportunity to study the bones and joints as they are commonly seen in the hospital or doctor's office.

2. Refer to your text for a diagram of the knee joint; then locate the following structures on a prepared section through a beef knee joint.

    a. synovial membrane
    b. articular cartilage
    c. synovial fluid (joint cavity)

    d. ligaments
    e. tendons
    f. patella

3. List the bones making up the following joints and the type of movements possible for each, in the table under Questions for Chapter IV.

    a. hip joint
    b. knee joint
    c. elbow joint

    d. shoulder joint
    e. wrist joint
    f. interphalangeal joint

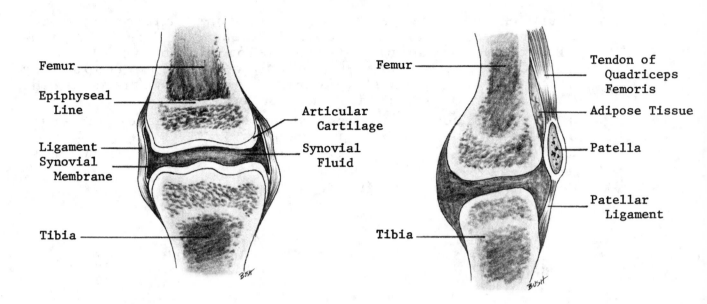

Femur

Epiphyseal
Line

Ligament
Synovial
Membrane

Tibia

Articular
Cartilage

Synovial
Fluid

Femur

Tibia

Tendon of
Quadriceps
Femoris

Adipose Tissue

Patella

Patellar
Ligament

Figure IV-46: Anterior View of Knee Joint

Figure IV-47: Lateral View of Knee Joint

(sagittal section)

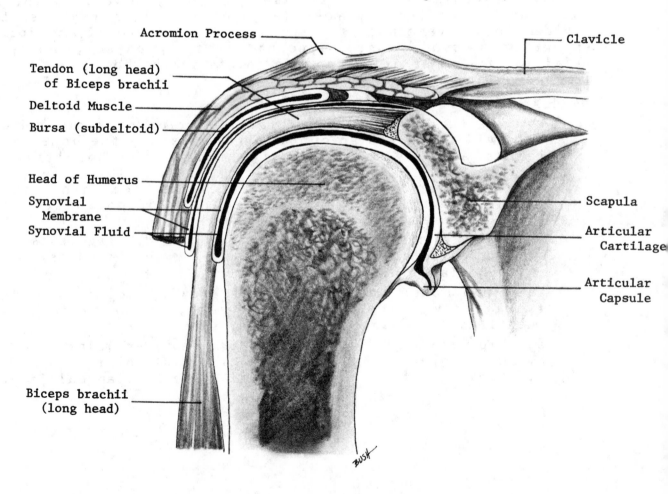

Acromion Process

Tendon (long head)
of Biceps brachii

Deltoid Muscle

Bursa (subdeltoid)

Head of Humerus

Synovial
Membrane

Synovial Fluid

Biceps brachii
(long head)

Clavicle

Scapula

Articular
Cartilage

Articular
Capsule

Figure IV-48: Anterior view of shoulder joint

SELF-TEST: THE SKELETAL SYSTEM

DIRECTIONS: See Chapter 1, Self-Test, p. 12

1. The **malleus** is attached to the tympanic membrane.
2. Bones **lack** blood vessels.
3. The **periosteum** is the membrane responsible for nourishing the bone.
4. A **green-stick** fracture is one wherein the bone breaks the skin.
5. The **pelvic girdle** is actually several bones joined together for the protection of organs in the **pelvic** region.
6. The **floating** ribs provide protection for the heart.
7. The toes contain **a greater** number of bones than do the fingers.
8. The bones of the appendicular skeleton and those of the thorax are formed by the process of **endochondral ossification**.
9. Ossification begins at the **epiphyses** and extends to the **diaphysis**.
10. Spongy bone is found in **flat bones** as well as in **long bones**.
11. The two types of bone formation involve the same processes, except that in endochondral ossification there is an initial period of **destruction of cartilage**.
12. The function of the **trochlea** is to articulate with the ulna.
13. Haversian systems are responsible for nutrition in **compact** bony tissue.
14. Haversian systems are characteristic of **spongy** bone.
15. Red bone marrow is found in the **medullary cavity** of some long bones of the adult.
16. The constricted portion of a long bone is called the **shaft**.
17. **Epiphyses** of bones tend to be **rounded** into condyles, trochanter, heads.
18. The acetabulum is the socket in which the head of the **humerus** articulates.
19. The long bones of the extremities continue to grow during childhood at the **epiphyseal cartilage**.
20. Most of the cranial and facial bones develop by **intramembranous ossification**.
21. Hemopoiesis may occur in the adult in the **ribs and sternum**.
22. The lining of the medullary cavity is called **periosteum**.
23. The primary curves of the vertebral column are the thoracic and **lumbar**.
24. Bending the elbow is an example of **flexion**.
25. Styloid processes are found upon the radius, ulna, and temporal bones, **but not** on the femur.
26. The fusion time of the anterior fontanel of the baby's skull is approximately **18 months**.
27. The **longitudinal arch** extends from the heel to the base of the toes.

28. Touching the little finger with the thumb is called **opposition.**
29. The iliopectineal line is found in the **skull.**
30. The **sella turcica** contains the pituitary gland.
31. The **male** pelvis has a circular pelvic inlet.
32. The **female** pelvis includes wide, flared ilia.
33. Spinal nerves are transmitted by way of **intervertebral foramina.**
34. The spinal cord is located in the **neural arches.**
35. The nasal septum is comprised of the **ethmoid** and **vomer** bones, as well as hyaline cartilage.
36. The air sinuses which open directly into the nasal cavity **do not** include the mastoid sinus.
37. The **secondary curves** of the vertebral column are the cervical and lumbar.
38. Movement of the ankle to turn the sole outward is called **eversion.**
39. When the long strands formed by mesenchymal cells become invested with bone matrix they are called **trabeculae.**
40. The condyles of the occipital bone and the depressions of the **atlas** allow for nodding movements of the head.
41. In turning the head from side to side the **atlas** rotates around a process of the axis called the **dens.**
42. A **foramen** is a tube-shaped passageway.
43. A hollow or depression is called a **cavity.**
44. A small, rounded projection is a **tuberosity.**
45. The viscosity of synovial fluid **is independent** of changes in temperature.
46. **Synchondroses** are freely movable joints.
47. **Circumduction** combines several types of joint movement.
48. **Both** prominent bursae and articular capsules may be present in ball and socket and hinge joints.
49. A **symphysis** joint occurs between bodies of vertebrae.
50. The elbow is an example of a **ball and socket** joint.
51. Swinging the arms around at the shoulder is an example of **circumduction.**
52. The position of the foot when standing on the toes is known as **plantar flexion.**
53. Nodding the head involves **both flexion and extension.**
54. Moving the arms straight out from the sides is called **adduction.**
55. Bending the trunk backwards is an example of **extension.**
56. Moving the thigh forward, as in marching, is an example of **flexion.**
57. Spreading the fingers apart is **adduction.**
58. Turning the palm of the hand up is **pronation.**
59. Shaking the head is **rotation.**
60. A major function of the bony rib cage is to protect the soft organs within the **abdomen.**
61. A **sulcus** is a groove or furrow.
62. Lateral curvature of the spine is called **kyphosis.**
63. A **sprain** is a joint injury with stretching or tearing of the ligaments.
64. Wearing high-heeled shoes is a common cause of **lordosis** in young women.

65. Moving a bone backwards is known as **retraction**.
66. A child was diagnosed as having a green-stick fracture, left femur. The difference between this and an ordinary fracture is that this is a **clean break**.
67. Judging from the diagnosis the patient is a child, because children have more organic matter in their bones than adults, so the bones are more likely to **break clean**.
68. The x-rays showed obvious bands of cartilage near the epiphyses, which meant that this patient's bones **were still growing**.
69. The **periosteum** is important during healing of a fracture because it nourishes the bone and promotes growth and repair.
70. The elbow is actually the **olecranon process**.
71. A depressed skull fracture is a bone **below** normal level that may press on the brain.
72. A simple skull fracture is usually a **shattered** bone.
73. A **craniotomy** was performed on a patient. This is an opening in the cranium to elevate the depressed bone fragment.
74. A **deviated nasal septum**, which means the partition between the nasal cavities is bent to one side, may obstruct breathing.
75. An increase in the thoracic curvature is called **lordosis or swayback**.
76. In a sternal puncture **yellow** marrow is obtained from the sternum.
77. A baby is born who has a spina bifida. This congenital defect is caused by a failure of the **vertebral lamina** to unite.
78. Spina bifida is most likely to occur in the **cervical and thoracic** region.
79. A hole in a bone through which blood vessels or nerves pass is called a **fossa**.
80. A **fovea** is a narrow slit.
81. A long and pointed process is known as a **styloid process**.
82. A **tubercle** is a large roughened process.
83. A rounded polished process for articulation is called a **condyle**.
84. A saddle or spool shaped articular surface is called a **trochanter**.

KEY

2. have	31. female	66. not a clean break
4. compound	34. vertebral canal	67. splinter
6. true	42. meatus	72. a crack in the
7. the same	43. fossa	75. kyphosis or hunchback
9. diaphysis; epiphyses	44. tubercle	76. red
14. compact	45. varies with	78. lumbar and sacral
15. proximal epiphyses	46. diarthroses	79. foramen
16. neck	50. hinge	80. fissure
18. femur	54. abduction	82. tuberosity
22. endosteum	57. abduction	84. trochlea
23. sacral	58. supination	
29. pelvis	60. thorax	
	62. scoliosis	

Chapter V
THE MUSCULAR SYSTEM

Ex. V-A. The Gross Anatomy of the Major Superficial Human Muscles

DISCUSSION

The basic function of muscle is to produce movement of the body or part of the body. In addition, muscles protect the internal organs, maintain posture, and produce large amounts of body heat.

The muscles studied in this exercise are all skeletal muscles. See Chapter III for the histology of skeletal, smooth, and cardiac muscle. The student should learn in this exercise the names of the major superficial muscles of the body.

PROCEDURE

1. Use Figures V-1, V-2, V-3, and V-4 as self-tests. See Section J, p. 5 (Illustrations as Self-Tests) for a suggested approach.
2. Compare the muscles indicated in Figure V-1 and V-2 with similar figures in your text, in references, on anatomic charts, and on the dissectable torso.

Ex. V-B. The External Anatomy of the Cat

DISCUSSION

The cat, **Felis domestica**, is frequently dissected in classes in human anatomy, since it has many features which are similar to humans (both belong to class Mammalia). As the cat is dissected and studied throughout the course, the structures identified should be compared with those of the human.

Dissection is not merely "cutting" the animal, but is a systematic technique of bringing into view structures which, in their normal position, cannot readily be seen. Do not cut or remove any structure unless directed to do so. Never cut a structure before knowing what it is. Always separate structures carefully, especially muscles and blood vessels, by dissecting away connective tissue. Use a dull probe, forceps or scissors rather than a scalpel wherever possible.

You may find that the substances used to preserve the specimen are irritating to your skin. If so, apply "Pro-tek" to your hands (or some similar substance) before dissecting, or wear thin rubber or plastic gloves. Keep your fingers away from your eyes during dissection.

At the conclusion of each laboratory period, clean up the working area thoroughly. Wrap the cat in wet paper towels and replace it in the plastic bag provided. Place a rubber band over the end of the plastic bag. Do not leave any solid material in the sink. Clean and dry the laboratory table and your dissecting instruments.

KEY TO FIGURE V-1

1. platysma
2. serratus anterior
3. iliopsoas
4. inguinal ligament
5. pectineus
6. adductor longus
7. gracilis
8. rectus femoris

9. vastus medialis
10. vastus lateralis
11. gastrocnemius
12. tibialis anterior
13. sternocleidomastoid
14. deltoid
15. pectoralis major
16. biceps brachii

17. brachialis
18. external oblique
19. superficial inguinal
    ring
20. sartorius
21. adductor longus
22. rectus femoris
23. gracilis
24. patella

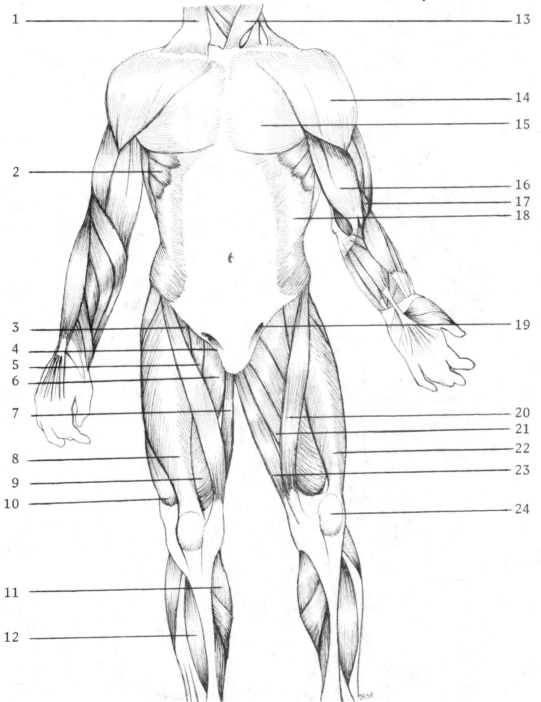

Figure V-1: Anterior View of the Muscles

KEY TO FIGURE V-2

1. adductor magnus
2. gracilis
3. semimembranosus
4. semitendinosus
5. deltoid
6. trapezius

7. triceps brachii
8. latissimus dorsi
9. lumbodorsal fascia
10. gluteus medius
11. gluteus maximus

12. biceps femoris
13. popliteal fossa
14. gastrocnemius
15. soleus
16. Achilles tendon

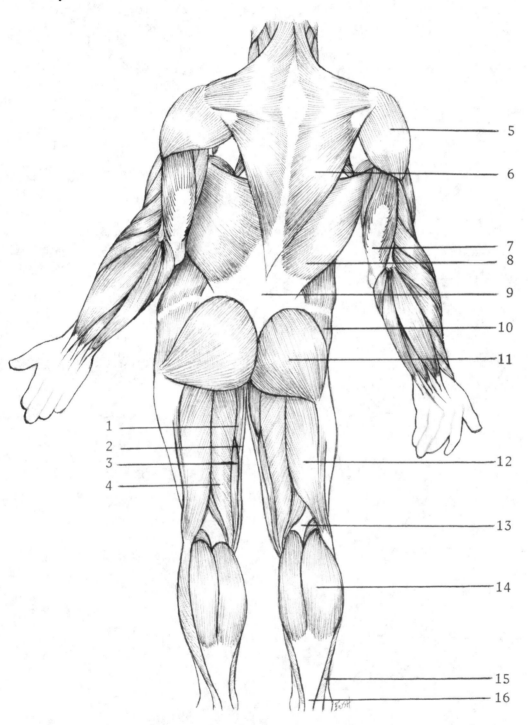

Figure V-2: Posterior View of the Muscles

KEY TO FIGURE V-3

1. frontalis
2. temporalis
3. corrugator
4. orbicularis oculi

5. occipitalis
6. quadratus labii
   superioris
7. zygomaticus

8. masseter
9. buccinator
10. orbicularis oris
11. sternocleidomastoid

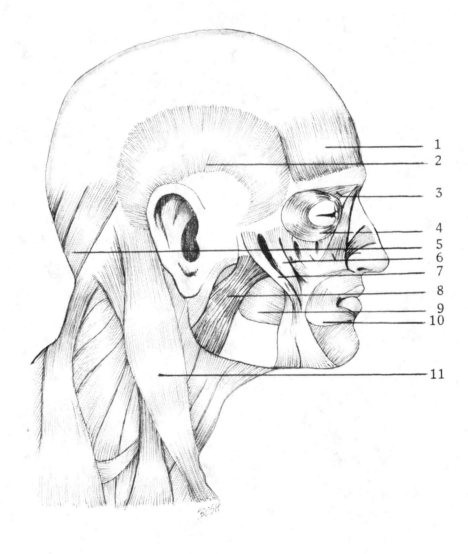

Figure V-3: Lateral View of Major Muscles of Head and Neck

KEY TO FIGURE V-4

1. temporalis
2. frontalis
3. orbicularis oculi

4. zygomaticus
5. quadratus liabii
   superioris

6. orbicularis oris
7. platysma

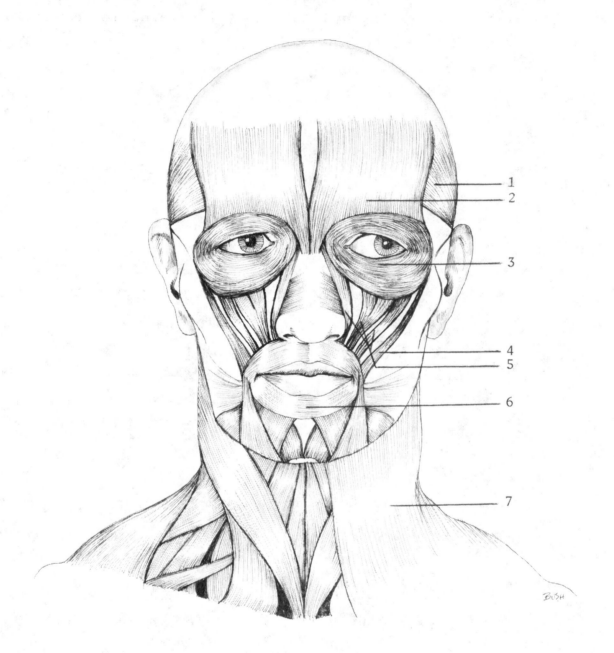

Figure V-4: Anterior View of Major Muscles of the Head and Neck

The terms **right** and **left** always refer to the cat's right and left. In a quadruped, **anterior** or **cranial** refers to the head end; **posterior** or **caudal** to the tail end; **dorsal** or **superior** to the back; **ventral** or **inferior** to the belly. **Lateral** refers to the side; **medial** to the position of a structure nearer the midline of the body (see Figure I-3 in Chapter I). The drawings provided will serve as a guide to your dissection. However, it should be noted that there may be some variation among cats, particularly in the circulatory system.

PROCEDURE

1. Observe the following external features in the cat: head, neck, thorax, abdomen, and tail. Determine the number of pairs of nipples on the trunk. Observe whether the nipples are located on both the male and the female cat.
2. Observe the forelegs and hindlegs of the cat. The foreleg consists of the arm (**brachium**), the forearm (**antebrachium**), the wrist, palm and digits. The hindleg consists of the thigh, shank, foot, and digits. Determine the number of digits on both the foreleg and hindleg.
3. Observe the retractable claws. Locate the friction pads (**tori**) on the bottom of the paws.
4. Examine the skeleton of the cat. Note that the cat walks on its toes (digitigrade method of locomotion) rather than on the soles of the feet (plantigrade method of locomotion).
5. On the head, locate the tactile whiskers (**vibrissae**) around the mouth; the **external nares**; the **auricle** (or **pinna**), which is part of the external ear; and the eyelids (**palpebrae**). Spread the eyelids apart and locate the thin **nictitating membrane** in the medial corner of the eye. This membrane extends laterally over the eyeball, keeping it moist.
6. Determine the sex of your specimen. In both sexes, the **anus**, the opening of the rectum to the outside, is found ventral to the tail. In the male, the **scrotum**, which contains the **testes**, is located anterior to the anus. In the female, the **urogenital aperture** is located just anterior to the anus.

Ex. V-C. Skinning the Cat

PROCEDURE

1. Lay the cat on its ventral surface. Lift up the skin on the dorsal neck region and make a small longitudinal slit in the midline just barely through the the skin. **Do not cut completely through the superficial fascia** beneath the skin into the trapezius muscle. The skin is about 1/4th inch thick.
2. To avoid damaging any muscles, always loosen and lift up the skin before cutting. The skin can be freed by inserting your fingers, forceps or flat end of a scalpel between the skin and the body. Continue the incision down the center of the back to the base of the tail (see Figure V-5).

There is a sheet of deep fascia in the midline between the scapulae that is part of the trapezius muscle. **Be especially careful not to cut through this sheet of deep fascia.**

3. Make additional incisions through the skin around the neck, down the lateral surface of each leg, and around the wrist and ankles (as illustrated in Figure V-5). The skin should be left on the head, tail, feet, and **perineum** (the area between the pubic symphysis and the coccyx).

4. Beginning on the back, gradually separate the skin from the underlying muscles. This can be done easily by pulling the skin back towards you with one hand, and separating the skin from the fascia by gently pressing the fingers of the other hand against the body. Only use a scalpel if absolutely necessary and keep the sharp edge directed towards the skin and away from the body.

5. Note the fine, parallel, brownish muscle fibers that adhere to the undersurface of the skin. This is one of the dermal muscles, the **cutaneous maximus**. This muscle originates from the **latissimus dorsi**, the **pectoralis** group of muscles, and from the **linea alba**, and inserts on much of the skin. Around the armpits (axillary region) it adheres to the latissimus dorsi and to the pectoralis group, and here it should be left on the body of the cat. The cutaneous maximus moves the skin of the cat and is not found in man.

6. The **cutaneous blood vessels** and **nerves** must be cut. These can be seen passing out to the skin. The **mammary glands** should also be removed with the skin. In the female cat these appear as large glandular masses along the ventral surface of the thorax and abdomen.

7. Continue skinning the back as far laterally as possible. In the axillary region separate the cutaneous maximus from the skin and push it toward the body. Then remove the skin from the legs being careful not to damage the **great saphenous vein** on the ventral thigh and leg. If this vein starts to come off with the skin, gently separate it from the skin and push it back towards the body.

8. **Beginning at the ventral surface of the neck** (avoid damage to the external jugular vein), remove the skin down to the wad of fat in the groin. Be careful of the lateral edges of the pectoral muscles as they can be easily torn as the skin is pulled free. Also be careful not to damage muscles if the cat is pregnant or lactating, since the mammary glands adhere to the xiphihumeralis muscles. **Do not** begin at the groin area and pull the skin toward the head since the xiphihumeralis muscle is often severely damaged with this method. (See Figure V-6).

9. If directions have been followed, the skin may now be removed in one piece. Either the skin or moist paper towels may be used to wrap the cat between laboratory periods to prevent drying.

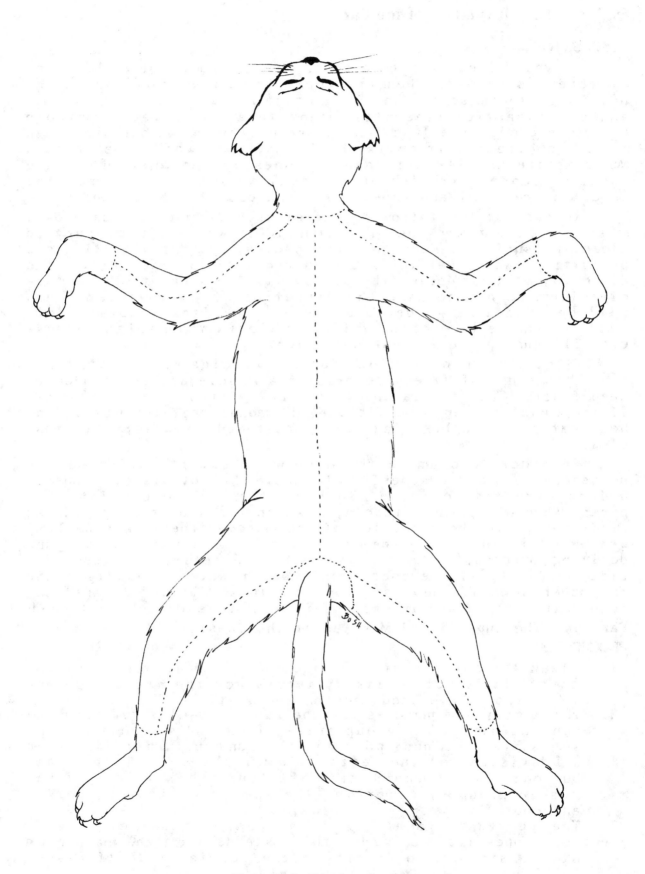

Figure V-5: Skinning the Cat

Ex. V-D. The Musculature of the Cat

DISCUSSION

As you dissect the muscles of the cat, determine the major differences between them and those in man. As you locate the **origin** of the muscle (the site of attachment to a fixed bone) and the **insertion** (the attachment to a more freely movable bone), determine the function of the muscle. Remember that as a muscle contracts, it pulls the insertion towards the origin. Muscles are usually attached to bones by **tendons**, which are bands of dense white fibrous connective tissue. Some muscles insert by means of an **aponeurosis,** a broad flattened tendon.

In each of the following exercises, attempt to locate each muscle before making any incisions. It will be necessary to clean the surface of each of the muscles, by gently pulling off or cutting away superficial fascia and fat, in order to see the direction of the muscle fibers. You will be separating the muscles from each other and the direction of the muscle fibers will be used as a guide. Usually all the fibers of a muscle will run in one direction, while the fibers of an adjacent muscle will run in a different direction.

Do not cut into the fibers of the muscles you are separating. The groups of fibers comprising a muscle are surrounded by deep fascia. This fascia should not be removed from the muscle. If the muscle fibers are visible, it means that the muscle has been cut into, rather than being separated from adjacent muscles.

In order to examine the deep muscles, it is frequently necessary to sever a superficial muscle. Do not bisect a muscle unless directed to do so. To **bisect** means to cut into two parts. When bisecting a muscle, make an incision through it, at right angles to the direction of the muscle fibers, and halfway between the origin and the insertion. In order to see the underlying muscles, it is then necessary to **reflect** the superficial muscle (pull the ends back - one towards the origin and the other towards the insertion). If these directions are followed, the origin and insertion of the muscle will be retained.

Part 1. The Superficial Muscles of the Chest

PROCEDURE

1. Clean the surface of the muscles on the left side of the chest. It is not necessary to dissect the right side unless errors have been made on the left.
2. The **pectoralis** muscles are the large muscles covering the ventral chest. The group arises from the sternum and inserts, for the most part, on the humerus. There are four subdivisions of the pectoralis muscle group in the cat, but only two in man. Locate the four subdivisions of the muscle group by comparing the specimen with Figure V-6 and Photo 1.
3. The **pectoantebrachialis** is a band of parallel fibers, about one-half inch wide, that extends from the manubrium of the sternum to insert on the fascia of the forearm.

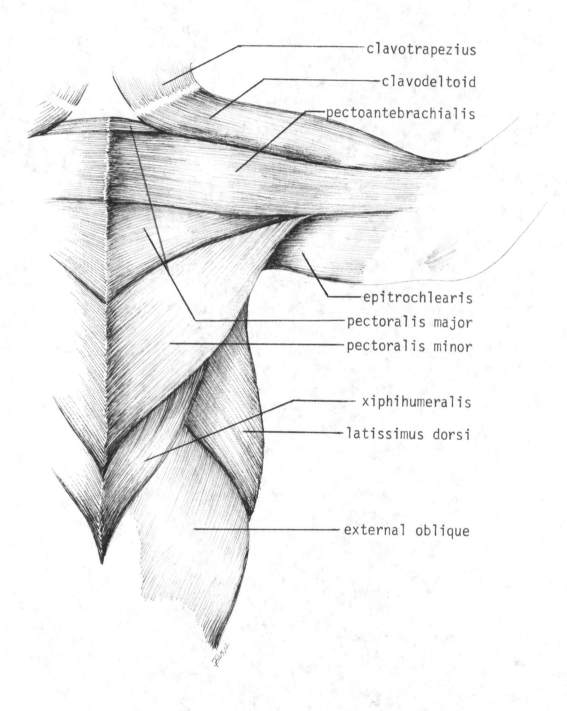

clavotrapezius

clavodeltoid

pectoantebrachialis

epitrochlearis

pectoralis major

pectoralis minor

xiphihumeralis

latissimus dorsi

external oblique

Figure V-6: Ventral View of Chest Musculature

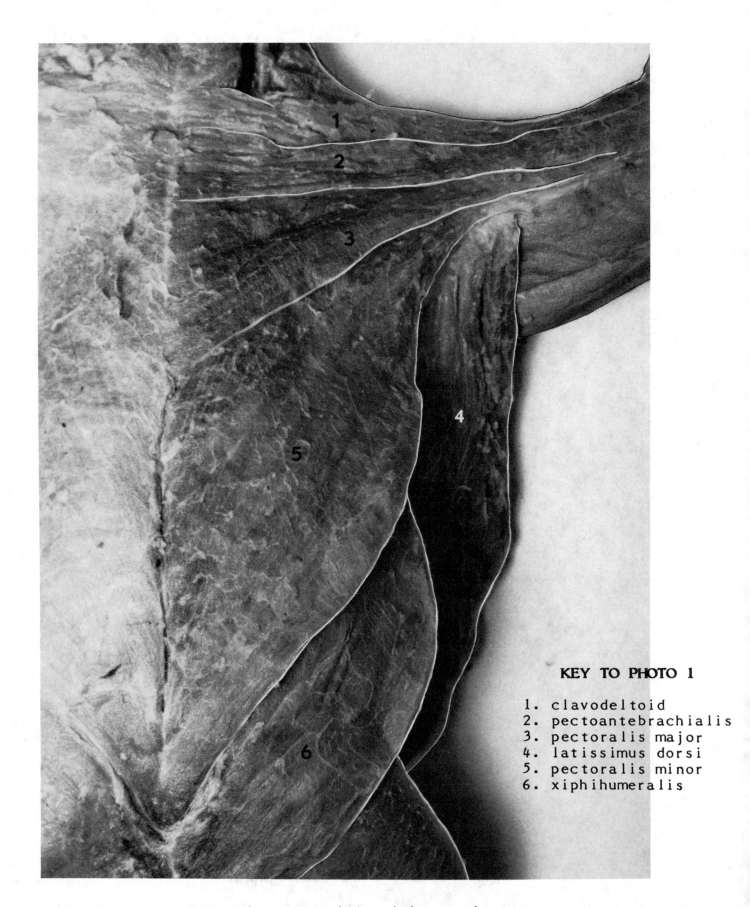

KEY TO PHOTO 1

1. clavodeltoid
2. pectoantebrachialis
3. pectoralis major
4. latissimus dorsi
5. pectoralis minor
6. xiphihumeralis

Photo 1: Ventral View of Chest Muscles

The anterior edge of this muscle is about one-third of an inch from the beginning of the entire pectoralis group; it passes across the rest of the pectoralis. Separate this muscle from the underlying fascia and muscle, then bisect and reflect.

4. The muscle on the shoulder anterior to the pectoantebrachial is the **clavodeltoid** (clavobrachialis). This muscle is part of the deltoid group. Lift up the clavodeltoid and separate it from the connective tissue underneath. You can feel the clavicle on the underside of the medial end of this muscle. The clavodeltoid arises on the clavicle and clavotrapezius and inserts on the ulna with the pectoantebrachialis. It may be considered as a continuation of the clavotrapezius onto the shoulder. Do not bisect this muscle.

5. The **pectoralis major** is the portion of the pectoralis group deep to the pectoantebrachialis and the clavodeltoid. It originates on the upper part of the sternum, and inserts along much of the humerus. It is folded on itself and may appear double. Do not try to separate this muscle into two muscles. The anterior fibers of the pectoralis major parallel those of the pectoantebrachialis.

6. The posterior border of the pectoralis major may be located by noting that the pectoralis minor approaches the major at an angle and then passes underneath it. Loosen the posterior border of the pectoralis major. Separate the muscle from the underlying pectoralis minor as far anteriorly as possible. Bisect and reflect the muscle. Note its wide insertion on the humerus.

7. The **pectoralis minor** lies posterior (and dorsal in part) to the pectoralis major. It originates on the middle portion of the sternum and inserts near the proximal end of the humerus. This muscle is larger than the major in the cat. It is not equivalent to the pectoralis minor in the human. Free this muscle and note that it appears to be divided into two portions; do not separate it along this division. Bisect and reflect the pectoralis minor, being careful not to sever underlying veins and arteries.

8. The **xiphihumeralis**, the fourth subdivision of the pectoralis group, arises from the xiphoid process of the sternum, posterior to the pectoralis minor. The fibers run parallel to the pectoralis minor and eventually pass deep to this muscle to insert on the humerus. The fibers of the xiphihumeralis fuse on the posterior edge with a portion of the latissimus dorsi. Carefully free the xiphihumeralis and bisect it.

Part 2. The Superficial Muscles of the Neck and Shoulder
PROCEDURE

1. Remove additional skin from the left side of the neck up to the ear. Do not injure the external jugular vein, the large vein which lies on the ventral surface of the neck. (Refer to Figure V-7 and Photo 2 during this dissection.) You should be able to see the **platysma**, the dermal muscle of the neck and face.

2. Remove the platysma and connective tissue from the ventral
    and lateral surfaces of the left neck and jaw. Free the
    external jugular vein from the underlying muscles and
    leave it intact.
3. Examine the ventral surface of the neck. Locate the **ster-
    nomastoid,** (see Figure V-7) the band of muscle that ex-
    tends from the manubrium of the sternum diagonally towards
    the mastoid region of the skull. The muscle passes deep to
    the external jugular vein. The sternomastoid turns and
    bends the head. Free both borders of this muscle. Do not
    bisect.
4. The **sternohyoids,** a narrow pair of muscles which may be
    fused in the mid-line, lie along the mid-ventral line of
    the neck. The posterior ends are covered by the sternomas-
    toid. The sternohyoids extend from the first costal carti-
    lage and the sternum to the hyoid bone which they depress.
    (See Figure V-7.)

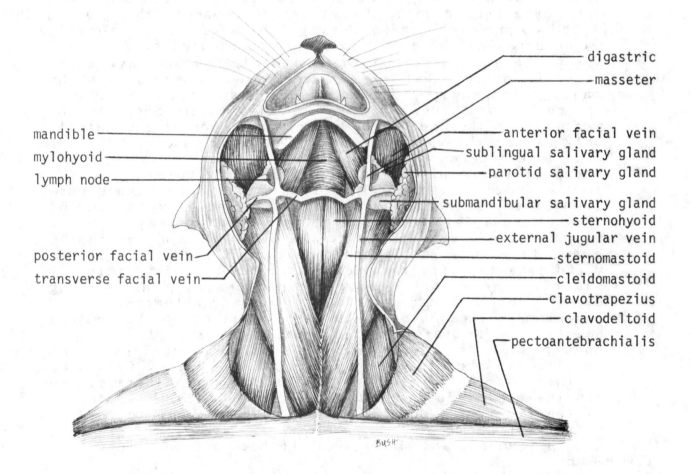

Figure V-7: Ventral View of the Neck Musculature

KEY TO PHOTO 2

1. mandible
2. digastric
3. mylohyoid
4. masseter
5. sublingual
   salivary gland
6. parotid
   salivary gland
7. submandibular
   salivary gland
8. sternohyoid
9. sternomastoid
10. external jugular
    vein
11. cleidomastoid
12. clavotrapezius

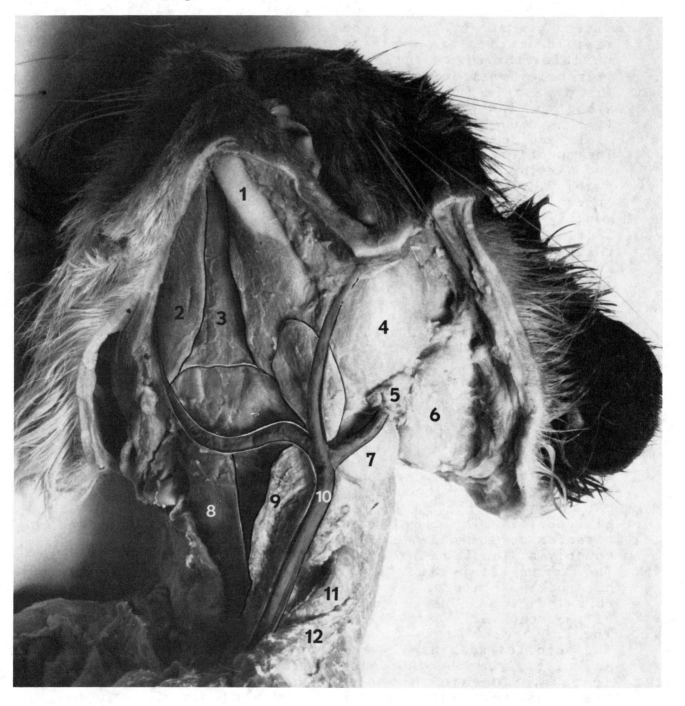

Photo 2: Ventrolateral View of Neck Muscles

5. In order to locate the next muscle, the **cleidomastoid**, again locate the sternomastoid. The cleidomastoid is a narrow deep band of muscle found between the clavotrapezius and the sternomastoid. It originates on the clavicle deep to the clavotrapezius and inserts on the mastoid region of the temporal bone. The anterior portion of the cleidomastoid passes deep to the sternomastoid. Much of the cleidomastoid is under the clavotrapezius (see step No. 9). Free the cleidomastoid along both borders. Do not bisect. In man the lower ends of the sterno- and cleidomastoid muscles are separate, but they are fused near the mastoid; therefore this compound muscle is known as the **sternocleidomastoid.**

6. The **digastric** muscle is the superficial muscle extending along the inner surface of the mandible (see Figure V-7). It runs from the occipital and temporal bones to the mandible and depresses the lower jaw.

7. The superficial muscle running transversely in the midline and passing deep to the digastric is the **mylohyoid.** It is a thin, sheetlike muscle, originating on the mandible and inserting on the median raphe. It raises the floor of the mouth (Figure V-7).

8. Locate the large **parotid salivary gland** ventral to the ear (Figure V-7). The large muscle mass anterior and ventral to the parotid at the angle of each jaw is the **masseter** muscle. It extends from the zygomatic arch to the mandible and elevates the mandible.

9. Clean off the connective tissue from the left shoulder and upper back. Do not remove the fascia in the midline between the scapulae since this is part of the origin of the trapezius. The **trapezius** group of muscles covers much of the dorsal surface of the scapula (refer to Figure V-8 and Photo 3 for steps 9-16 of the procedure). The **clavotrapezius** is the broad muscle located on the back and side of the neck dorsal to the cleidomastoid. It originates from the occipital bone and the first few cervical vertebrae and inserts on the clavicle. It elevates the clavicle. The **clavodeltoid** continues from the clavicle, the insertion of the clavotrapezius, to the ulna. Therefore the clavotrapezius can be located by determining the origin of the clavodeltoid. The clavotrapezius is the muscle dorsal and anterior to the clavodeltoid. Free these muscles from the underlying fascia. Do not bisect.

10. The **acromiotrapezius** (see Figure V-8) covers the upper part of the scapula. It arises from fascia along the mid-dorsal line and inserts on the spine and acromion process of the scapula.

11. The triangular sheet of muscle on the back, posterior to the acromiotrapezius, is the **spinotrapezius** (Figure V-8). It arises from the thoracic vertebrae and inserts on the scapula. Separate this muscle from underlying muscles. Free the anterior and posterior borders of both the acromiotrapezius and spinotrapezius muscles. Do not bisect these at this time. These muscles adduct the scapula. In man these three separate muscles are merged into one large

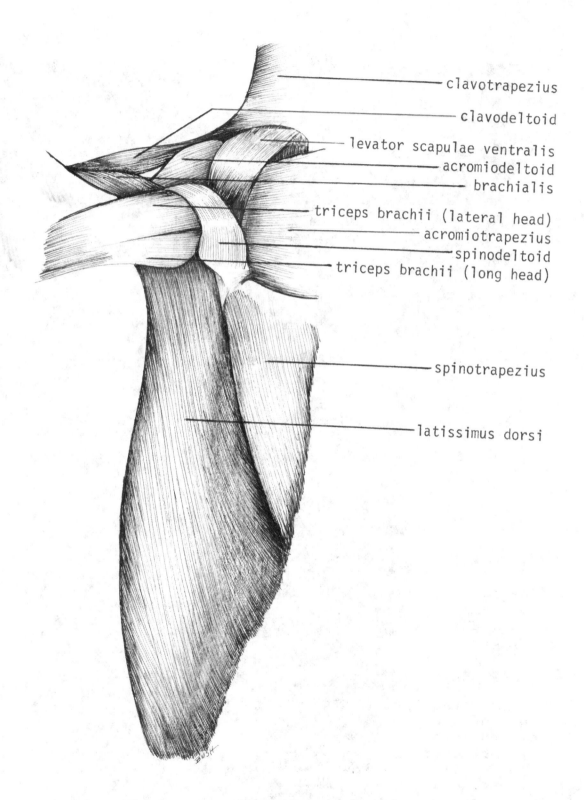

clavotrapezius

clavodeltoid

levator scapulae ventralis

acromiodeltoid

brachialis

triceps brachii (lateral head)

acromiotrapezius

spinodeltoid

triceps brachii (long head)

spinotrapezius

latissimus dorsi

Figure V-8: Superficial Muscles of the Back

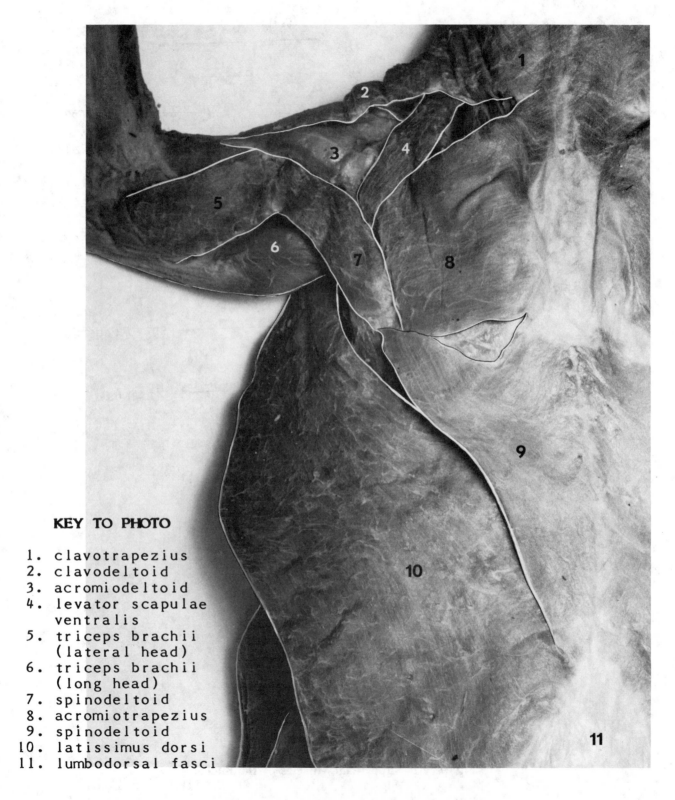

KEY TO PHOTO

1. clavotrapezius
2. clavodeltoid
3. acromiodeltoid
4. levator scapulae
   ventralis
5. triceps brachii
   (lateral head)
6. triceps brachii
   (long head)
7. spinodeltoid
8. acromiotrapezius
9. spinodeltoid
10. latissimus dorsi
11. lumbodorsal fasci

Photo 3: Superficial Muscles on the Back

trapezius muscle which adducts and elevates the scapula, and extends and rotates the head.

12. The **latissimus dorsi** is the large muscle posterior to the trapezius group. It arises from the spines of the thoracic vertebrae and a wide sheet of fascia covering the lumbar region of the back called the **lumbodorsal fascia** (Figure V-8). The latissimus dorsi runs anteriorly and ventrally to insert on the proximal end of the humerus with the xiphihumeralis. It extends the humerus. Clean the connective tissue from this muscle **but do not remove the lumbodorsal fascia.** Free the anterior and lateral edges of the latissimus dorsi. Part of the anterior border lies beneath the spinotrapezius.

13. The strap-like band of muscle in the cat that lies on the side of the shoulder between the clavotrapezius and the acromiotrapezius is the **levator scapulae ventralis.** It arises from the atlas and the occipital and passes posteriorly beneath the clavotrapezius to insert on the acromion process of the scapula. It pulls the scapula forward. (See Figure V-8.)

14. The **deltoid** muscle, which flexes, extends, rotates, and abducts the humerus, lies lateral to and below the insertion of the levator scapulae ventralis (Figure V-8). It is subdivided into three parts in the cat. The **clavodeltoid** (clavobrachialis), seen earlier, originates on the clavicle and inserts on the ulna flexing the forearm. This is the most anterior portion of the muscle.

15. The **spinodeltoid,** the most posterior portion, originates on the scapula ventral to the insertion of the acromiotrapezius. It runs almost parallel with the edge of the spine of the scapula. It inserts on the proximal humerus. Free the borders of the muscle.

16. Locate the **acromiodeltoid,** the middle muscle of this group, posterior to the clavodeltoid. It originates from the acromion process of the scapula deep to the levator scapulae ventralis and inserts on the proximal end of the humerus. It is not necessary to dissect out this muscle, which may appear double at its origin.

Part 3. The Deeper Muscles of the Back and Shoulder

PROCEDURE

1. In order to expose the deeper muscles of the shoulder and back, carefully bisect the acromiotrapezius and spinotrapezius muscles through muscle fibers halfway between their origins and insertions. Reflect the muscle fibers. Next bisect and reflect the latissimus dorsi. Refer to Figure V-9 and Photo 4 for steps 1-6 of the Procedure.

2. The **supraspinatus** muscle fills the supraspinous fossa of the scapula; the **infraspinatus** muscle fills the infraspinous fossa. Both muscles originate on the scapula and insert on the humerus. The supraspinatus extends the humerus and the infraspinatus rotates it laterally. Do not dissect or bisect these muscles.

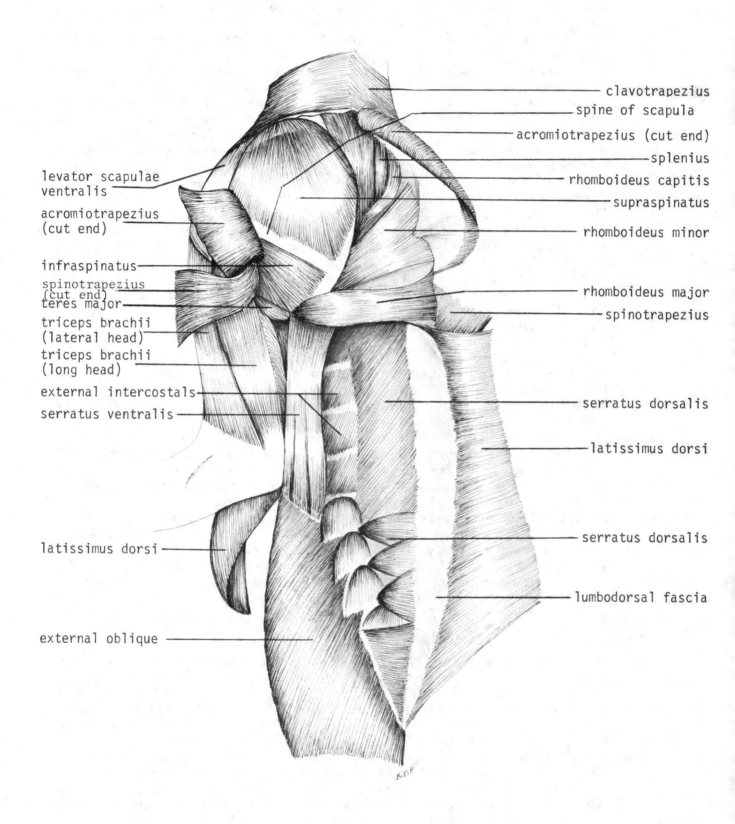

levator scapulae ventralis

acromiotrapezius (cut end)

infraspinatus

spinotrapezius (cut end)

teres major

triceps brachii (lateral head)

triceps brachii (long head)

external intercostals

serratus ventralis

latissimus dorsi

external oblique

clavotrapezius

spine of scapula

acromiotrapezius (cut end)

splenius

rhomboideus capitis

supraspinatus

rhomboideus minor

rhomboideus major

spinotrapezius

serratus dorsalis

latissimus dorsi

serratus dorsalis

lumbodorsal fascia

**Figure V-9: Deep Muscles of the Shoulder
(cat propped on left forearm)**

KEY TO PHOTO 4

1. supraspinatus
2. spinodeltoid
3. teres major
4. infraspinatus
5. serratus ventralis

7. brachialis
8. triceps brachii
   (medial head)
9. triceps brachii
10. latissimus dorsi
    (cut)

Photo 4: Deep Muscles of the Shoulder and Arm

3. The **teres major** muscle originates on the axillary border of the scapula posterior to the infraspinatus. It inserts on the proximal end of the humerus with the latissimus dorsi and extends and rotates the humerus. Separate the teres major from the infraspinatus. Do not bisect this muscle.

4. Gently pull the scapula away from the vertebral column. The large muscle that arises from the posterior cervical and anterior thoracic vertebrae and inserts along the vertebral border of the scapula is the **rhomboid minor.** The **rhomboid major** is immediately posterior to this, inserting on the dorsal posterior angle of the scapula. Some authors refer to these two muscles as one, the rhomboideus. In man, the rhomboid major is larger than the minor. These two muscles draw the scapula dorsally (adduct) and rotate it.

5. The **rhomboideus capitis** is the most anterior muscle of this group. It is a narrow, thin, ribbon-like muscle, extending from the occipital bone to the scapula on the side of the rhomboideus minor muscle. It elevates and rotates the scapula. In man, this muscle is united with the rhomboideus minor.

6. Deep to this muscle is a broad flat muscle, the **splenius.** It covers most of the dorsal and lateral surface of the neck; its action is to extend and turn the head.

7. Look posterior and ventral to the scapula. The large fan-shaped muscle originating by separate slips from the ribs, passing ventral to the scapula, and inserting on the vertebral border of the scapula is the **serratus ventralis** (see Figure V-10 and Photos 5 & 6). Observe that the broad flat muscle between the scapula and splenius is also part of the serratus ventralis. This muscle pulls the scapula forward and down. Clean the connective tissue from the origins so that the sawtooth (serrated) appearance is visible.

8. The subscapular fossa of the scapula is filled with the **subscapularis** muscle (see Figure V-11) which inserts on the humerus and rotates it medially. Do not dissect or bisect.

Part 4. The Muscles of the Brachium and Antebrachium

PROCEDURE

1. Clear away the fascia from the **brachium** (arm). Refer to Figures V-9, V-10, V-11, and Photos 5 and 6 for steps 2-9.

2. Locate the **epitrochlearis**, a flat muscle that arises from the surface of the latissimus dorsi, extends along the ventro medial surface of the arm, and inserts on the olecranon process of the ulna. This muscle is not present in man. Bisect this muscle and reflect. The long head of the triceps brachii lies posterior and deep to this muscle (see Figure V-11).

3. Now examine the lateral surface of the arm. The **triceps brachii** is the large muscle with three heads which lies posterior to the humerus. It extends the forearm. Separate

the subdivisions of the triceps. Refer to Figures V-9 and V-10. The **long head** is the most posterior head and the largest. Note that it arises from the scapula posterior to the glenoid cavity and inserts on the olecranon process. Free the anterior border of the long head; do not bisect.

4. Locate the **lateral head**, the large head that originates from the proximal end of the humerus and covers much of the lateral surface of the arm. Bisect and reflect the lateral head.

5. A long narrow **medial head** can be found beneath the lateral head. Do not bisect this muscle.

6. The triceps of the cat has a fourth head, the **anconeus**, a tiny muscle which lies deep to the distal end of the lateral head of the triceps. (See Figure V-10.)

7. The **brachialis** can be seen on the anterolateral surface of the humerus, anterior to the lateral head of the triceps. It arises from the humerus and inserts on the proximal end of the ulna. The brachialis flexes the forearm.

8. The **biceps brachii** lies on the ventromedial surface of the humerus. It originates on the scapula and inserts on the radius. Much of this muscle lies beneath the insertion of the pectoralis major and minor. (Reflect the pectoralis group to the humerus if this was not done previously.) Trace the biceps to its insertion. This muscle flexes the forearm. (See Figure V-11 for this step and step 9.)

9. Next locate the tiny **coracobrachialis** muscle beneath the pectoralis. This is a small muscle extending from the coracoid process of the scapula to the proximal end of the humerus. It adducts the arm.

10. Optional: locate the **teres minor** muscle, a small muscle between the infraspinatus and the triceps. Reflect the lateral head of the triceps and push the spinodeltoid dorsally. Look deep between the proximal end of the triceps and the infraspinatus. The teres minor appears to be the lateral edge of the infraspinatus. This muscle rotates the humerus.

11. Optional: note the tough layer of deep fascia which covers the forearm muscles. Observe the tendons of these muscles at the wrist. Separate, but do not bisect, the superficial muscles of the forearm. Compare your dissection with Figure V-12 and V-13. Identify each of the labeled muscles. The dorsal group of muscles, in general, extend and supinate. The ventral group of muscles are flexors and pronators.

12. Separate the **extensor digitorum lateralis** from the **extensor indicis proprius** muscle (see Figure V-14). The **extensor pollicis brevis** and **supinator** are now visible.

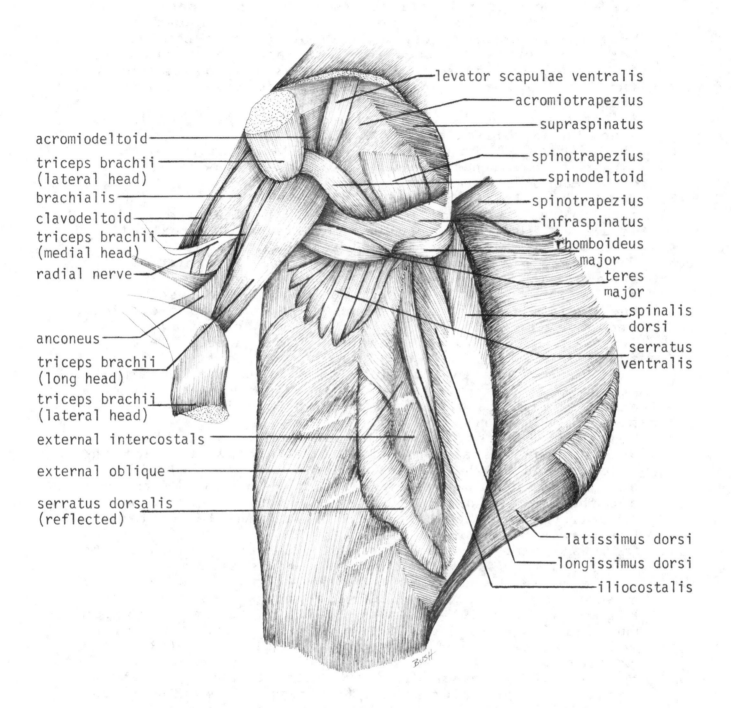

acromiodeltoid

triceps brachii
(lateral head)

brachialis

clavodeltoid

triceps brachii
(medial head)

radial nerve

anconeus

triceps brachii
(long head)

triceps brachii
(lateral head)

external intercostals

external oblique

serratus dorsalis
(reflected)

levator scapulae ventralis

acromiotrapezius

supraspinatus

spinotrapezius

spinodeltoid

spinotrapezius

infraspinatus

rhomboideus
major

teres
major

spinalis
dorsi

serratus
ventralis

latissimus dorsi

longissimus dorsi

iliocostalis

BUSH

Figure V-10: Deep Muscles of the Shoulder, Back, and Arm

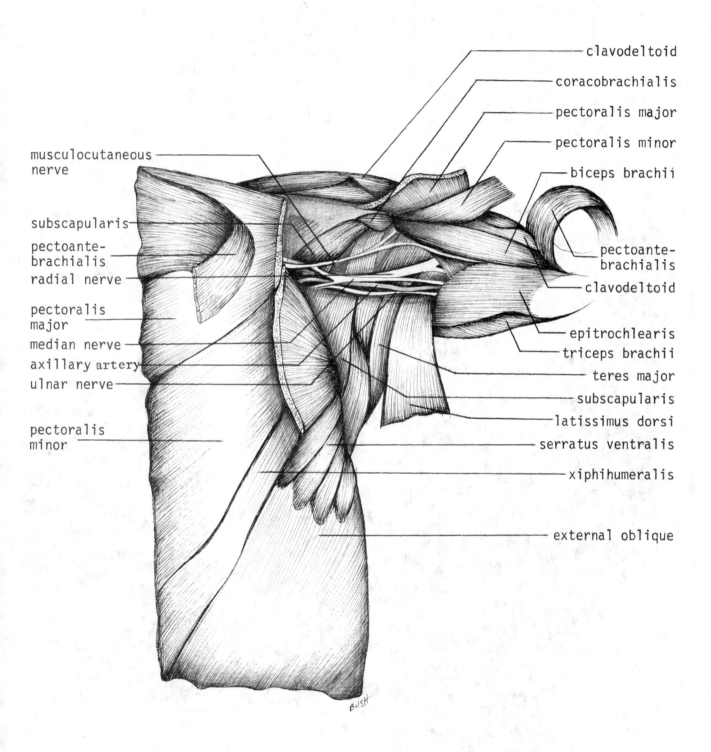

clavodeltoid

coracobrachialis

pectoralis major

pectoralis minor

biceps brachii

musculocutaneous
nerve

pectoante-
brachialis

clavodeltoid

subscapularis

pectoante-
brachialis

radial nerve

pectoralis
major

epitrochlearis

median nerve

triceps brachii

axillary artery

teres major

ulnar nerve

subscapularis

latissimus dorsi

pectoralis
minor

serratus ventralis

xiphihumeralis

external oblique

Figure V-11: Deep View of Muscles of the Chest and Brachium

KEY TO PHOTO 5

1. clavotrapezius
2. splenius
3. rhomboideus capitis
4. rhomboideus minor
5. rhomboideus major
6. serratus dorsalis
7. supraspinatus
8. infraspinatus
9. serratus ventralis
10. levator scapulae ventralis
11. clavodeltoid
12. acromiodeltoid
13. spinodeltoid
14. triceps brachii (lateral head)
15. triceps brachii (long head)

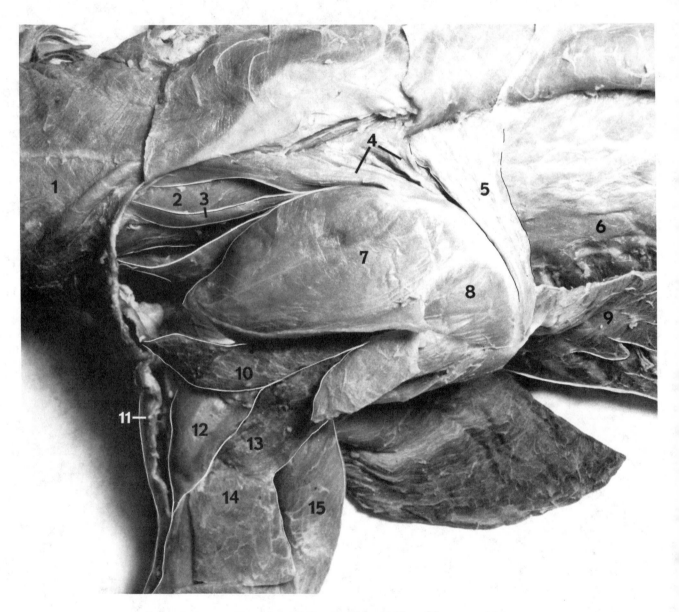

Photo 5: Deep Muscles of the Back and Shoulder

KEY TO PHOTO 6

1. spinalis dorsi
2. longissimus dorsi

3. iliocostalis
4. rhomboideus major

5. external intercostals
6. serratus ventralis
7. external oblique

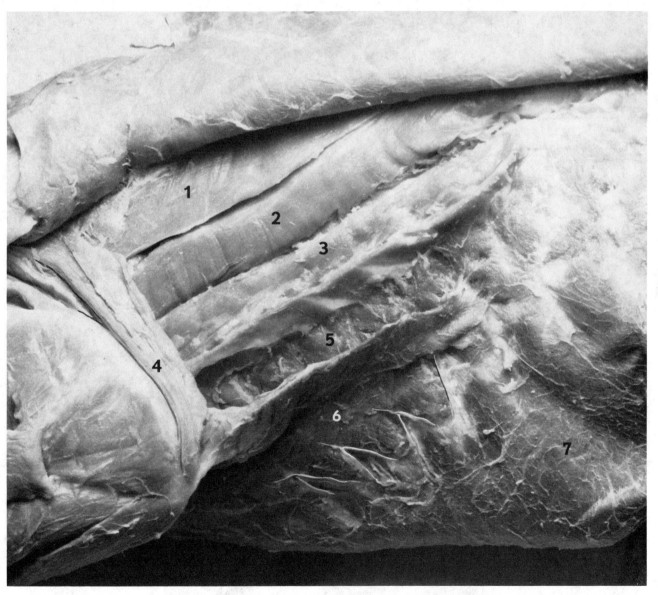

Photo 6: Very Deep Muscles of the Back

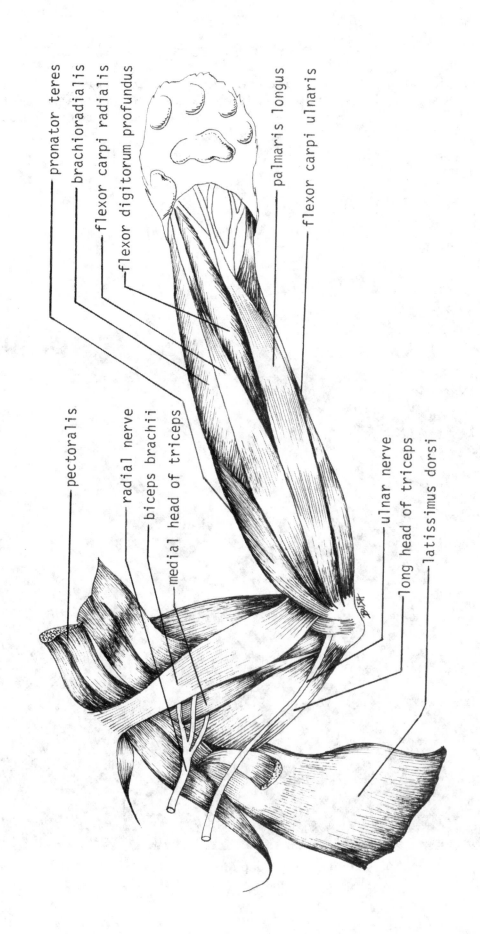

pronator teres
brachioradialis
flexor carpi radialis
flexor digitorum profundus
palmaris longus
flexor carpi ulnaris

pectoralis
radial nerve
biceps brachii
medial head of triceps
ulnar nerve
long head of triceps
latissimus dorsi

BUSH

Figure V-12: Ventral View of the Superficial Muscles of the Forearm

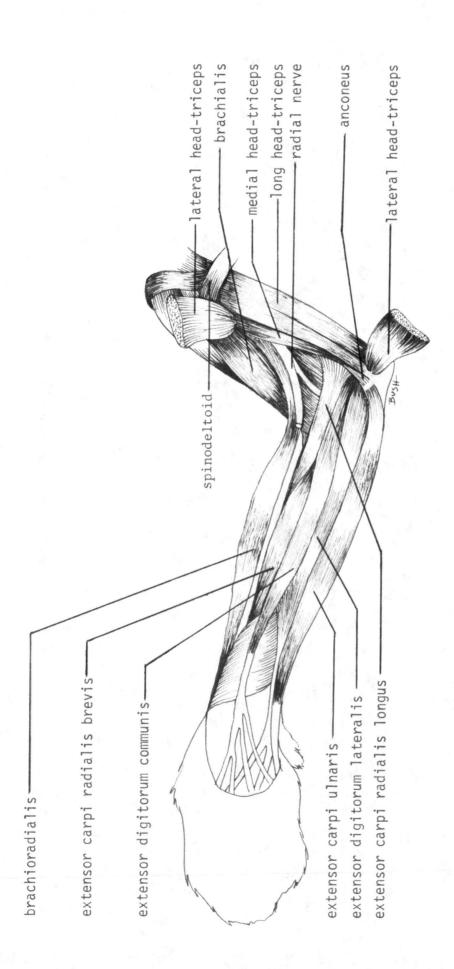

lateral head-triceps

brachialis

medial head-triceps

long head-triceps

radial nerve

anconeus

lateral head-triceps

spinodeltoid

BUSH

brachioradialis

extensor carpi radialis brevis

extensor digitorum communis

extensor carpi ulnaris

extensor digitorum lateralis

extensor carpi radialis longus

Figure V-13: Dorsal View of Muscles and Forearm

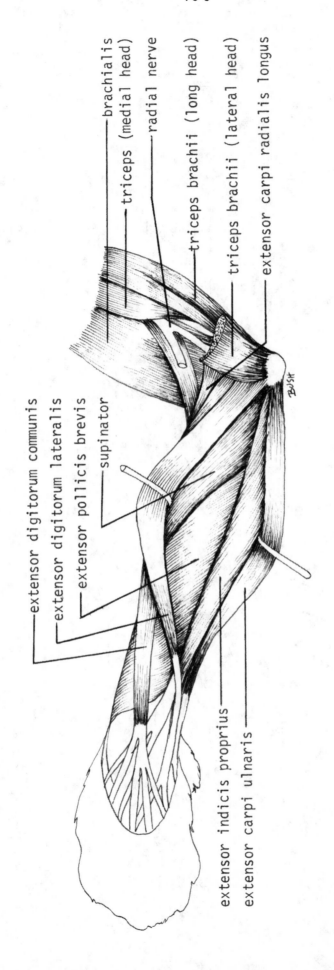

Figure V-14: Deep View of Muscles of Dorsal Forearm

extensor digitorum communis

extensor digitorum lateralis

extensor pollicis brevis

supinator

extensor indicis proprius

extensor carpi ulnaris

brachialis

triceps (medial head)

radial nerve

triceps brachii (long head)

triceps brachii (lateral head)

extensor carpi radialis longus

Part 5. The Abdominal Wall Muscles

PROCEDURE

1. Clean off the ventral and lateral surfaces of the left side of the trunk between the xiphihumeralis and the pelvic region.

2. As in man, the lateral abdominal wall of the cat is composed of three layers of muscle **(external oblique, internal oblique, transversus abdominis).** Since these muscles are very thin, be very careful to cut through only one layer at a time.

3. The lateral abdominal wall muscles serve to compress the abdomen. This action is important in forced expiration, defecation, urination, and childbirth. They are also important in flexion and lateral flexion of the trunk.

4. The **external oblique** forms the outermost layer of the lateral abdominal muscles. Note that part of its origin lies beneath the posterior edge of the latissimus dorsi muscle. It originates on the posterior ribs and lumbodorsal fascia. Its fibers run posterior and towards the midline. See Figure V-15 and Photo 7 for this step and for steps 5-12.

5. Make a **shallow** longitudinal incision (about five inches long) through the external oblique along the lateral surface of the abdomen. Extend this incision from the ribs to the pelvis. Do not cut deeply. As you cut, watch for a deep layer of muscles whose fibers run at approximately right angles to the fibers of the external oblique. When this deeper layer is reached, reflect the external oblique toward the midline and toward its origin.

6. Note the **aponeurosis** of the external oblique. Lift the muscle up and notice that the muscle fibers terminate at least an inch before the **linea alba,** the mid-ventral line formed by the union of the aponeuroses of the lateral abdominal wall muscles. The aponeurosis is superficial to the rectus abdominis muscle.

7. Observe the posterior border of the external oblique. In man this thickened border is called the **inguinal ligament.** This is not apparent in the cat.

8. The **internal oblique** lies beneath the external oblique and its fibers run in the opposite direction (anterior and toward the midline). It originates on the lumbodorsal fascia and inserts on the linea alba.

9. Make a four inch longitudinal incision through the muscle fibers of the internal oblique on the lateral side of the abdominal cavity. The internal oblique is even thinner than the external oblique and its fibers tend to adhere to the third layer of the lateral abdominal wall, the **transversus abdominis.** Watch closely for the transverse muscle fibers of the transversus abdominis, which extends from the vertebral column, the lumbodorsal fascia, and the sacrum to the linea alba. Reflect the internal oblique toward the midline until its aponeurosis becomes visible.

10. Carefully separate some of the fibers of the transversus abdominis. The shiny membrane visible beneath the muscle fibers is the parietal layer of the **peritoneum,** which should not be pierced.

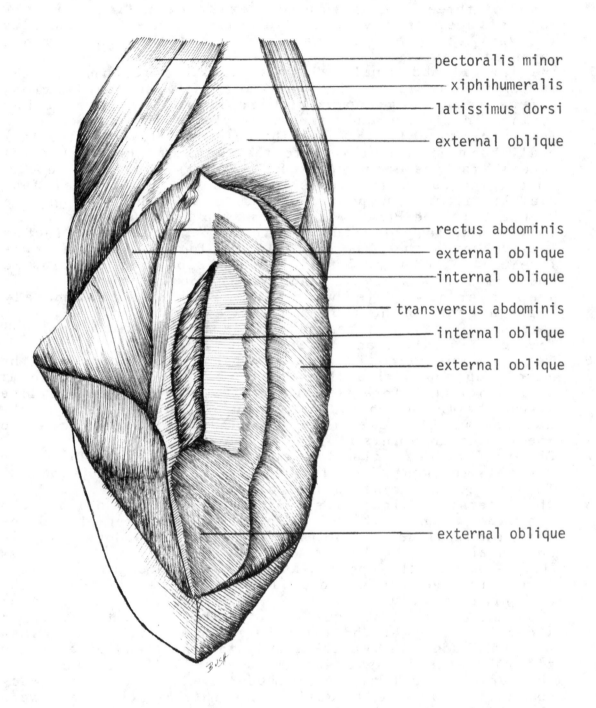

pectoralis minor
xiphihumeralis
latissimus dorsi
external oblique

rectus abdominis
external oblique
internal oblique
transversus abdominis
internal oblique
external oblique

external oblique

Figure V-15: Abdominal Wall Musculature (lateral view)

KEY TO PHOTO 7

1. rectus abdominis
2. transversus abdominis
3. internal oblique
4. external oblique

Photo 7: Muscles of the Abdominal Wall

11. In order to locate the **rectus abdominis,** the longitudinal band of muscle lying lateral to the linea alba, reflect the external oblique. The rectus abdominis, extending from the pubis to the sternum and costal cartilage, supports the abdominal wall, especially during pregnancy. Do not dissect out this muscle.

12. In mammals such as the pig, fat is deposited in the connective tissue layers between the muscles of the lateral abdominal wall so that the fat and muscle alternate. This part of the pig is sold commercially as bacon. The small pieces of cartilage often found in bacon are pieces of costal cartilage from the lower ends of the ribs.

Part 6. Superficial Muscles of the Thigh and Buttocks
PROCEDURE

1. Remove the fat and fascia from the surface of the lateral thigh and buttocks region. Be especially careful not to damage any muscles in the gluteal region as the fascia adheres tightly to the gluteal muscles. The tough white band of fascia that can be seen on the anterolateral thigh is the **iliotibial band.** This is the lateral thickening of the fascia lata. **Do not remove the iliotibial band.** Refer to Figures V-16, V-17 and Photos 8 and 9 for steps 2-11.

2. The broad muscle posterior to the iliotibial band covering the entire lateral surface of the thigh is the **biceps femoris.** This originates on the ischium and inserts on the tibia and fascia of the shank. It abducts the thigh and flexes the shank. Remove the large wad of fat in the popliteal fossa. Free both borders of this muscle. When freeing the anterior border of this muscle, begin with care near the knee and work upward looking for a small muscle, the caudofemoralis, at the proximal end of the muscle. (Figure V-17).

3. The **caudofemoralis** is a small muscle anterior to the origin of the biceps femoris, and inferior to the gluteus maximus. It is united with the gluteus maximus in man. It originates on the caudal vertebrae and inserts on the patella by way of a long, very narrow tendon visible on the inner surface of the biceps femoris. (Figure V-17 & V-18.)

4. The **gluteus maximus** (Figure V-17) is immediately anterior to the caudofemoralis. The fibers extend laterally from the sacrum and caudal vertebrae and insert on the proximal femur. It abducts the thigh.

5. The more diagonal fibers anterior to the gluteus maximus form the **gluteus medius,** which originates on the lateral ilium and the sacral and caudal vertebrae and inserts on the femur (Figure V-17). It abducts the thigh. It is a larger muscle than the gluteus maximus in the cat. Some of the fibers of the gluteus medius pass beneath the gluteus maximus. The two should be carefully separated.

6. Anterior and ventral to the gluteus medius is the **tensor fasciae latae.** In order to lift up this muscle, insert a scalpel along the anterior border of the iliotibial band and make a longitudinal incision. Insert your fingers under the iliotibial band to free it from the underlying tissue. Make another longitudinal incision along the posterior border by the biceps femoris. Bisect the iliotibial band. When the iliotibial band is raised up, the **tensor fasciae latae** can be seen inserting on the proximal end of the iliotibial band. This short, triangular muscle originates on the ilium and inserts on the fascia lata. It tenses the fascia lata and extends the shank. Locate the boundary between the tensor fasciae latae and the gluteus medius. (Figure V-17.)

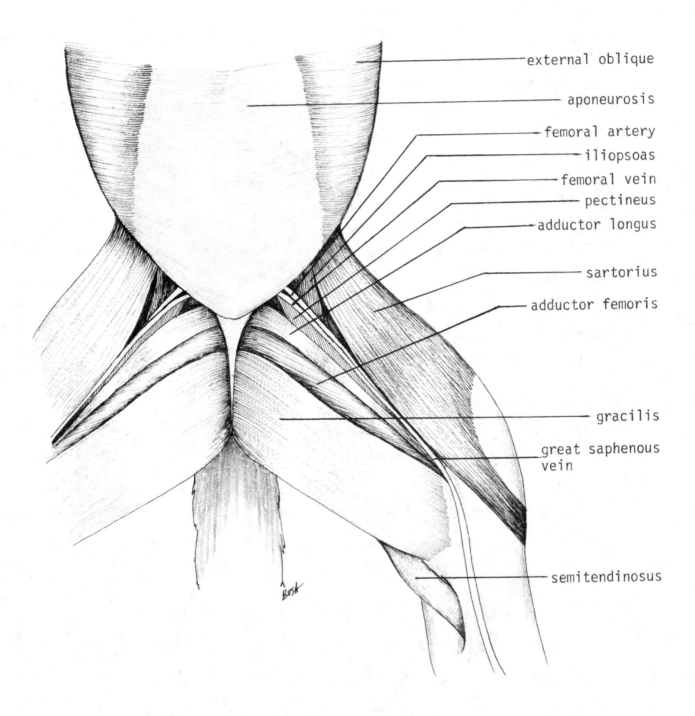

Figure V-16: Ventral View of Superficial Thigh Muscles

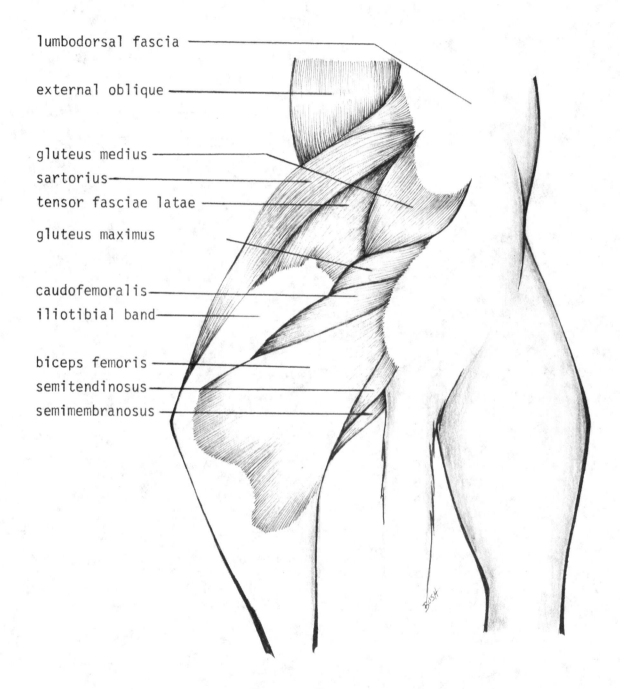

lumbodorsal fascia

external oblique

gluteus medius

sartorius

tensor fasciae latae

gluteus maximus

caudofemoralis

iliotibial band

biceps femoris

semitendinosus

semimembranosus

Figure V-17: Superficial Muscles of the Thigh and Buttocks (dorsal view)

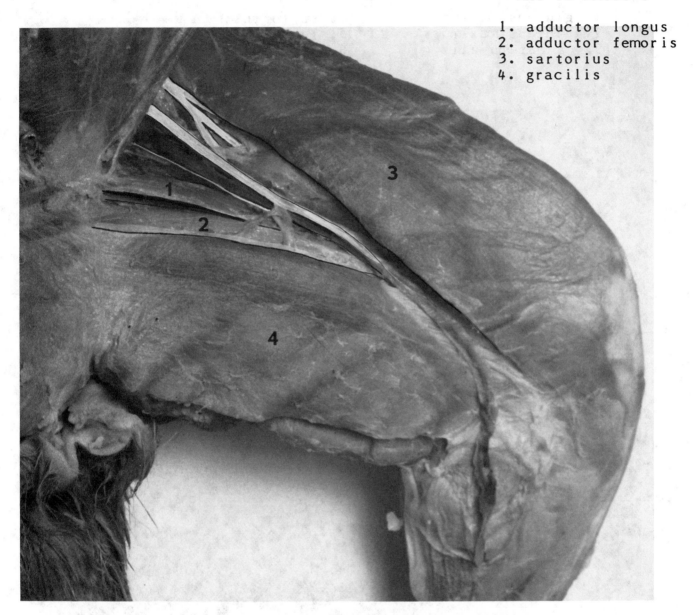

Photo 8: Superficial Muscles of the Ventral Thigh

7. Remove the fat and fascia from the ventromedial surface of the thigh being careful not to remove any blood vessels. Observe the two large superficial muscles; the **sartorius** is the more lateral of the two. It is about 1 1/2 inches wide and resembles a flattened band. Loosen the medial and lateral edges from the ilium to the tibia and bisect. The sartorius adducts and rotates the thigh. (Figure V-16.)
8. The **gracilis** (Figure V-16) is the large, wide, flat muscle covering the medial surface of the ventral thigh below the sartorius. Free both borders of this muscle. Bisect and reflect it, being careful not to completely reflect the insertion of the muscle. The gracilis originates on the os coxae bone and inserts on the tibia and fascia of the shank. It adducts the thigh.

KEY TO PHOTO 9

1. gluteus medius
2. gluteus maximus
3. caudofemoralis

4. sartorius
5. tensor fasciae latae
6. iliotibial band
7. biceps femoris

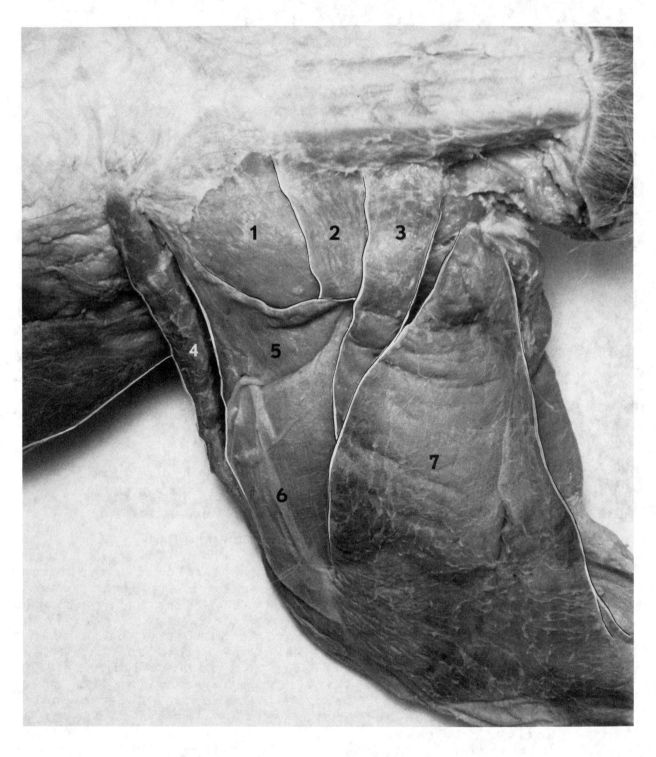

Photo 9: Superficial Muscles of the Dorsal Thigh and Buttocks

Part 7. Deeper Muscles of the Thigh
PROCEDURE

1. With the cut ends of the sartorius and gracilis reflected, the deeper muscles of the ventromedial thigh are visible. The most posterior is the **semitendinosus**, a strap-like muscle which is thicker than the sartorius but only about one-half as wide. It arises from the ischial tuberosity and inserts on the tibia posterior and medial to the biceps femoris forming the posteromedial border of the popliteal fossa. It flexes the shank. Free both borders. (See Figure V-18 and Photo 10.)

2. The large muscle anterior and medial to the semitendinosus beneath the gracilis is the **semimembranosus** (Figure V-18). This originates on the ischium, and inserts on the femur. The semimembranosus, the semitendinosus, and the biceps femoris form the hamstring group of muscles.

3. The large muscle anterior to the semimembranosus is the **adductor femoris** (equivalent to the adductor magnus in man). With the gracilis in place, a small anterior portion of the adductor femoris is visible. Do not separate this muscle into two portions. Immediately anterior to the adductor femoris is the small, narrow **adductor longus** muscle. The origin of the adductor muscles is the ischium and pubis; they insert on most of the length of the femur and adduct the thigh (Figures V-17 & V-18).

4. Clean the fat from around the blood vessels. The **pectineus** should then be visible just anterior to the adductor longus. This small, deep muscle is just posterior to the femoral artery and vein. The pectineus originates on the pubis and inserts on the femur; it adducts the thigh. (Figure V-18.)

5. Above the pectineus is the **iliopsoas** muscle, a compound muscle originating from the lumbar vertebrae and ilium and inserting on the femur. It rotates and flexes the thigh. Only a small portion of the iliopsoas is visible. It may be seen anterior and lateral to the femoral artery and vein; the blood vessels run at an angle across the muscle. (Figure V-18.)

6. In order to locate the **quadriceps femoris** muscle on the anterior thigh, reflect the cut ends of the sartorius muscle and the iliotibial band. Deep to the iliotibial band is the **vastus lateralis**, the largest head of the quadriceps. This and other vasti head arise from the proximal femur. (See Figures V-18, V-19 and Photos 10, 11 and 12 for steps 3-8.)

7. On the anteromedial thigh find the **vastus medialis**. Barely visible between the vastus lateralis and vastus medialis is a third head, the **rectus femoris**. The rectus femoris originates on the ilium. In order to expose the rectus femoris, free the borders of the vastus medialis and vastus lateralis next to the rectus femoris. Slide your fingers under the rectus femoris; bisect this head.

8. The deep head observed beneath the rectus femoris is the **vastus intermedius**. These four heads make up the quadriceps femoris which inserts on the tibial tuberosity. The patella develops in the tendon of this muscle; the portion

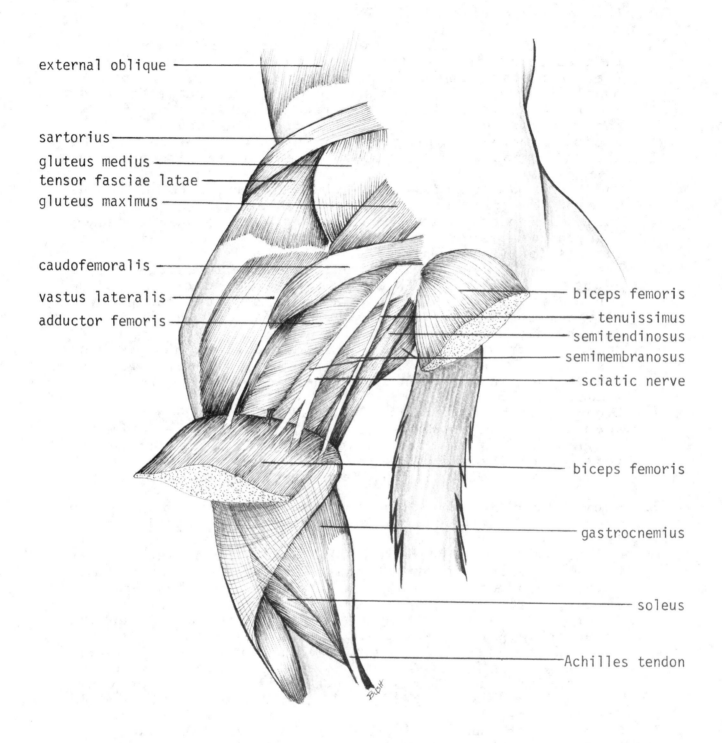

external oblique

sartorius
gluteus medius
tensor fasciae latae
gluteus maximus

caudofemoralis

vastus lateralis
adductor femoris

biceps femoris
tenuissimus
semitendinosus
semimembranosus
sciatic nerve

biceps femoris

gastrocnemius

soleus

Achilles tendon

Figure V-18: Deep Muscles of the Dorsal Thigh

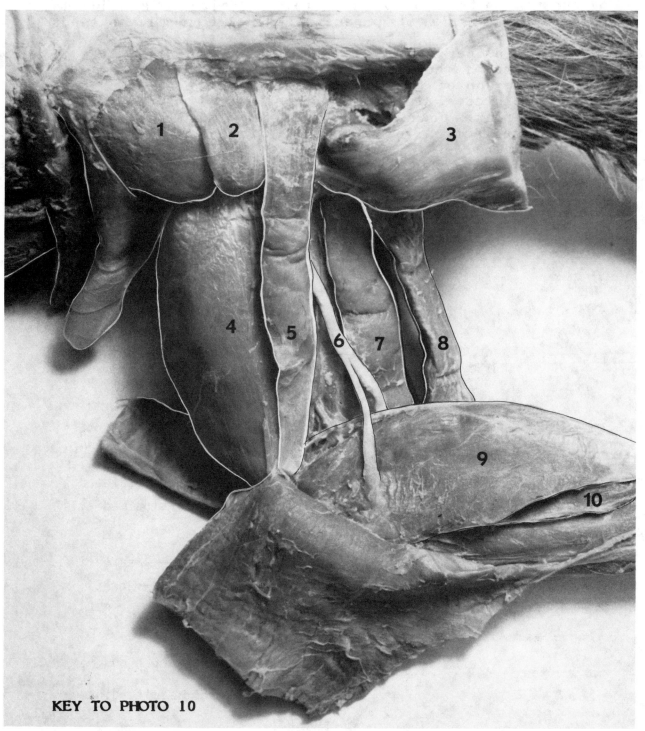

KEY TO PHOTO 10

1. gluteus medius
2. gluteus maximus
3. biceps femoris (cut)
4. vastus lateralis
5. caudofemoralis
6. sciatic nerve
7. semimembranosus
8. semitendinosus
9. gastrocnemius
10. soleus

Photo 10: Deep Muscles of the Dorsal Thigh

of the tendon from the patella to the tibial tuberosity is called the **patellar ligament.** The entire complex extends the shank.

9. To see the deeper structures of the lateral thigh, lift up both borders of the biceps femoris. Be careful not to detach the tendon of the caudofemoralis at the anterior border of the biceps. Gently free the biceps from the sciatic nerve and tenuissimus muscle lying beneath. Bisect the biceps and reflect, being careful not to bisect the sciatic nerve. (Figure V-19.)

10. A very thin long muscle can be seen lying beneath the biceps femoris, running parallel to the sciatic nerve. This muscle, the **tenuissimus,** extends from the second caudal vertebra to the fascia of the biceps femoris. It abducts the thigh and flexes the shank.

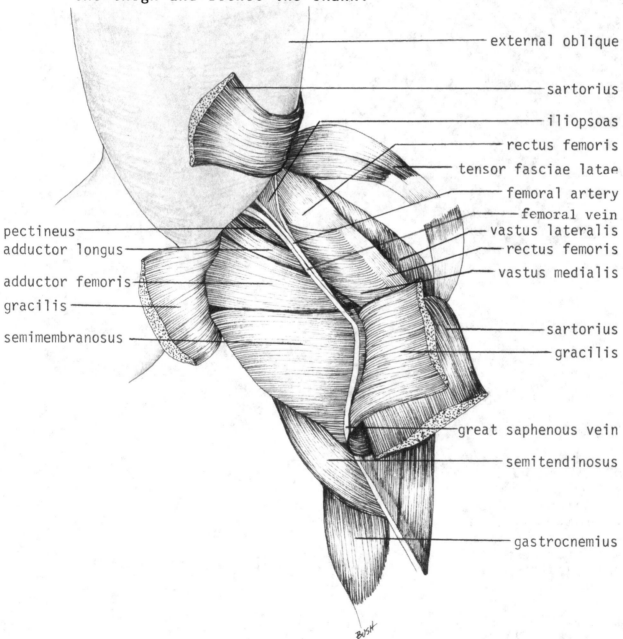

Figure V-19: Deep View of Ventral Thigh Musculature

Part 8. Posterior Leg Muscles
PROCEDURE
1. The large calf muscle, the **gastrocnemius** (see Figure V-19) is visible on the posterior leg (shank). Follow it up to its origin, primarily the distal femur, and down to its insertion, the **tendon of Achilles,** which then inserts on the calcaneus. The muscle plantar flexes the foot.
2. Examine the lateral surface of the calf, ventral to the gastrocnemius, in order to locate the **soleus** (Figure V-19). This originates on the fibula and then inserts by way of the Achilles on the calcaneus. It also plantar flexes the foot.

Part 9. Muscles of the Thorax and Deep Back
PROCEDURE
1. Refer to Figures V-9, V-10 and Photos 5 and 6 for steps 1-5. To study the intercostal muscles, raise the posterior border of the origin of the serratus ventralis muscle in order to expose the ribs.
2. The fibers of the external intercostals (Figures V-9 and V-10) can be seen between the ribs passing medially and inferiorly toward the sternum. The external intercostals lift the ribs in inspiration.
3. Bisect one external intercostal muscle in order to expose the **internal intercostals,** the fibers of which run at right angles to the external intercostals. These muscles depress the ribs in active expiration.
4. In order to study the deep back muscles, reflect the latissimus dorsi towards its origin. The **serratus dorsalis** (Figure V-9), which consists of a number of short muscle slips, arises from a mid-dorsal aponeurosis and inserts on the ribs. Reflect this muscle by separating it from its origin to expose the sacrospinalis.
5. The **sacrospinalis** (Figure V-10), the muscle which extends the spine and neck, consists of three longitudinal divisions in the thoracic region. Remove the fascia over this muscle if the subdivisions are not visible. Carefully separate the three divisions. The most lateral, the **iliocostalis,** lies beneath the serratus dorsalis. It inserts on the ribs. The middle division is called the **longissimus dorsi.** It fills the space between the spinous and the transverse processes of the thoracic and lumbar vertebrae. In the lumbar region it appears as three separate bundles. The most medial subdivision of the sacrospinalis, the **spinalis dorsi,** is found next to the spinous processes of the thoracic vertebrae.

114

KEY TO PHOTO 11

1. vastus lateralis
2. rectus femoris
3. vastus medialis

4. adductor longus
5. aductor femoris
6. semimembranosus

7. semitendinosus
8. gastrocnemius
9. Achilles tendon

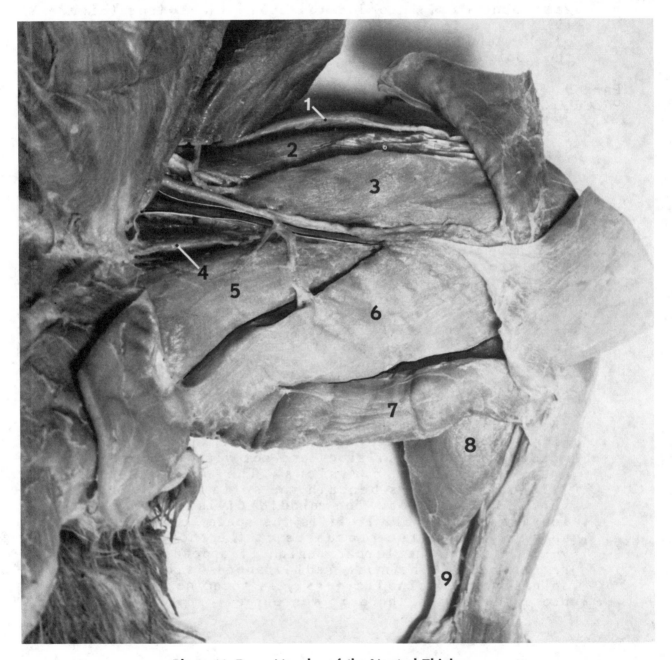

Photo 11: Deep Muscles of the Ventral Thigh

KEY TO PHOTO 12

1. iliopsoas
2. femoral nerve
3. sartorius
4. pectineus
5. adductor longus
6. femoral artery
7. femoral vein
8. adductor femoris
9. gracilis

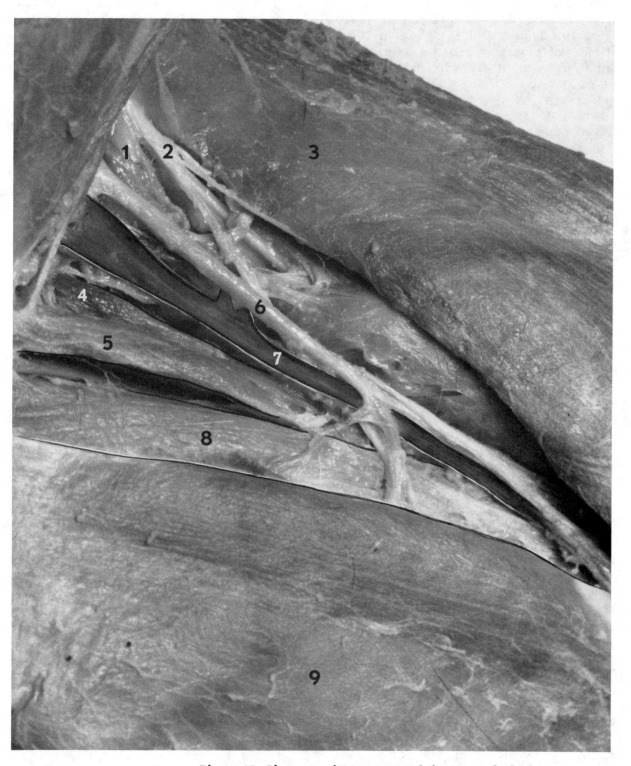

Photo 12: Close-up of Structures of the Ventral Thigh

SELF-TEST: MUSCULAR SYSTEM

DIRECTIONS: See Chapter 1, Self-Test, p. 12

1. **Striated** muscle contains branched fibers.
2. A skeletal muscle has its insertion on a relatively **immovable** part of the skeleton.
3. The "hamstring" muscles are found **in the shoulder.**
4. The muscle in the calf of the leg that is most prominent when taking a step is the **deltoid.**
5. The insertion of the biceps brachii is on the **ulna.**
6. Muscles of expression include the **orbicularis oculi and orbicularis oris.**
7. When you reach upward for an object, the principal muscle involved in elevating the arm is the **trapezius.**
8. The pectoral muscles bring the arms **across the chest.**
9. Flexion of the trunk is brought about by the contraction of the **vastus lateralis** muscles.
10. In walking, the heel is elevated by the contraction of both the **gastrocnemius and soleus.**
11. After a radical mastectomy which involves the removal of the pectoral muscles, a woman **should not** comb her hair with the affected hand for several months.
12. An indirect inguinal hernia refers to a loop of intestine which protrudes into the **inguinal canal.**
13. The "weak" areas of the abdominal wall are the **umbilicus, the inguinal ring and the femoral ring.**
14. Muscles that serve as valves are called **sphincters.**
15. **Myofibrils** are made up of thick and thin myofilaments.
16. Each skeletal muscle cell has **many** nuclei.
17. Paired muscles (e.g., right and left), acting together, **may cause a different type of movement** of the body or its part than when acting separately.
18. Extensor muscles, which support the body or its parts, act against gravity and hence are **called antigravity muscles.**
19. The visceral muscles play a role in increasing the pressure within the **abdominal cavity** and thus assist respiration, parturition, coughing, micturition, defecation, and vomiting.
20. The back muscles that extend the vertebral column are the **erector spinae** and the **semispinalis.**
21. The **triceps brachii** is a powerful extensor or antigravity muscle which aids in standing and in extending the leg in walking.
22. The pectoral muscles act in **adduction** of the arm.
23. Extension of the foot is bending the foot **upward.**
24. The membrane surrounding a single muscle cell is called the **sarcolemma.**
25. The cytoplasm of the skeletal muscle cell is called **myoplasm.**
26. An **aponeurosis** is a sheet of white fibrous tissue connecting a muscle to another muscle.
27. A **ligament** is a band or cord of white fibrous tissue connecting muscle to bone.

28. **Synergistic** muscles are muscles which work together smoothly.
29. The endings of axons of an **afferent** nerve fiber on the muscle fibers they innervate are called motor end plates or myoneural junctions.
30. A **motor unit** consists of a ventral horn cell in the spinal cord, its axon, and all the muscle fibers it innervates.
31. Women cannot run as fast as men because the thigh bone is attached to the pelvis **at a more oblique angle.**
32. Muscular dystrophy is a **communicable** disease.
33. The broadest muscle of the back is the **trapezius.**
34. The **superior rectus** muscles turn the eyes toward the nose.
35. The deltoid muscle originates on the **occipital.**
36. The muscle filling the ventral surface of the scapula is the **serratus anterior.**
37. The quadriceps femoris **extends** the leg.
38. The **zygomaticus** produces the expression of smiling.
39. The biceps brachii **extends** the forearm.
40. The iliopsoas **extends** the thigh.
41. The biceps femoris, semimembranosus, and semitendinosus form the **quadriceps femoris** group of muscles.
42. The muscle covering the top of the skull is the **epicranius.**
43. The latissimus dorsi **flexes** the arm.
44. The external intercostals **elevate** the ribs.
45. The rhomboids **adduct** the scapulae.
46. The sternocleidomastoid **extends** the head.

KEY

1. cardiac	21. quadriceps	34. medial rectus
2. movable	femoris	35. scapula and
3. on the	23. downward	clavicle
posterior thigh	25. sarcoplasm	36. subscapularis
4. gastrocnemius	27. tendon	39. flexes
5. radius	29. efferent	40. flexes
7. deltoid	32. hereditary	41. hamstring
9. rectus abdominis	33. latissimus	43. extends
11. should	dorsi	46. flexes
(good exercise)		

Chapter VI
THE DISGESTIVE SYSTEM

Ex. VI-A. Anatomy of the Human Digestive System

DISCUSSION

The digestive system is concerned with receiving, transporting, digesting, and absorbing food. The alimentary canal or digestive tract, a tube approximately thirty feet long, is subdivided into the following regions: **mouth, pharynx, esophagus, stomach, small intestine,** and **large intestine,** all of which are considered to be true digestive organs. In addition, other organs are connected to the alimentary canal and are considered to be part of the digestive system. These accessory digestive organs include the **tongue, teeth, salivary glands, liver, gall bladder,** and **pancreas.**

PROCEDURE

1. Use Figure VI-1 as a self-test. See Section J, p. 5 (illustrations as Self-Tests) for a suggested approach.
2. Locate the structures listed in the key to Figure VI-1 on the dissectable torso and determine at least one important function of each.
3. Learn the parts of a typical tooth and the various types of teeth by studying your text or other references.

Ex. VI-B. Dissection of the Digestive System of the Cat

DISCUSSION

The digestive system of the cat is quite similar to that of man. However, there are certain differences that should be noted, such as the absence of the vermiform appendix and uvula in the cat.

PROCEDURE

1. Locate the major **salivary glands** of the cat on the left side of the head. If the glands were destroyed during the dissection of the musculature of the head on the left, skin the right side of the head. These glands produce saliva which is carried to the mouth via ducts which pass through the musculature of the head and neck.
2. The largest salivary gland in the cat is the **parotid gland,** which is located ventral to the pinna (see Figure V-7, chapter V). This gland can be recognized by its lobular texture. The duct of the parotid crosses the masseter muscle and enters the oral cavity opposite the last upper premolar tooth. Two branches of the facial nerve also cross the masseter dorsal and ventral to the parotid duct.
3. The **submandibular gland,** which has a smoother texture than the parotid, lies posterior to the angle of the jaw and ventral to the parotid gland (Figure V-7). The posterior facial vein passes over this gland. Its duct opens into the floor of the mouth near the lower incisors.

KEY TO FIGURE VI-I

1. nasal chamber
2. oral cavity
3. pharynx
4. right lung
5. liver
6. gall bladder
7. duodenum
8. taenia coli
9. ascending colon
10. ileum
11. cecum
12. vermiform appendix
13. larynx
14. left bronchus
15. esophagus
16. diaphragm
17. stomach
18. spleen
19. pancreas
20. transverse colon
21. jejunum
22. descending colon
23. sigmoid colon
24. rectum

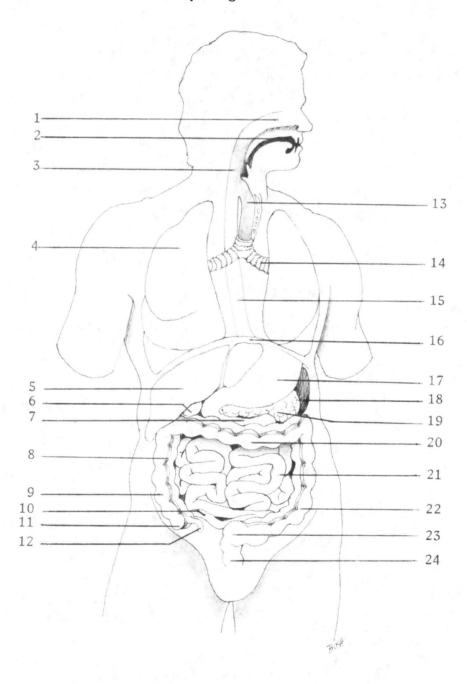

Figure VI-1: Digestive Organs

KEY TO FIGURE VI-2

1. crown
2. neck
3. root
4. enamel
5. dentin
6. pulp cavity
7. gingiva
8. cementum
9. root canal
10. periodontal membrane
11. bone

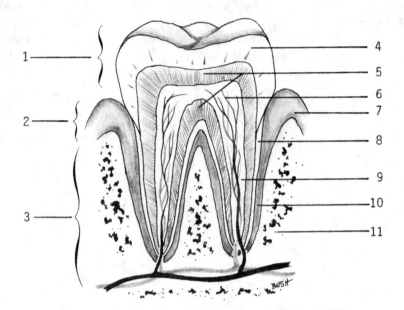

Figure VI-2: Longitudinal Section through a Molar

KEY TO FIGURE VI-3

1. second molar
2. first molar
3. cuspid
4. lateral incisor
5. central incisor

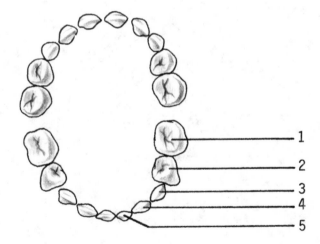

Figure VI-3: The Deciduous Teeth

KEY TO FIGURE VI-4

1. central incisor
2. lateral incisor
3. cuspid
4. first premolar

5. second premolar
6. first molar
7. second molar
8. third molar

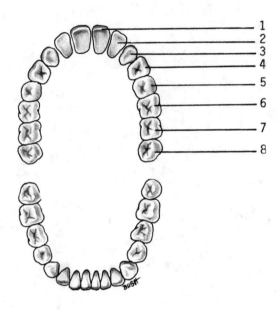

Figure VI-4: The Permanent Teeth

4. The smaller **sublingual gland** is located anterior to the submandibular gland. Do not confuse this gland with the small lymph node usually located deep to the anterior facial vein and ventral to the submandibular gland (Figure V-7).

5. The cat has two additional salivary glands which it is not necessary to locate: the **molar gland** which lies near the angle of the mouth, and the **infraorbital gland** on the floor of the orbit.

6. Open the oral cavity of the cat by cutting with bone shears through the angle of the jaw on each side. Locate the following structures in the **oral cavity** (see Figure VI-5): the **vestibule**, the area lying between the teeth and cheeks; the **hard palate**, the bony structure containing transverse ridges called the **palatine rugae**, making up the roof of the mouth; the **soft palate**, the posterior extension of the hard palate, the **fauces**, the opening between the oral cavity and the **oropharynx**; the two small **palatine tonsils**, masses of lymphatic tissue located on each lateral wall of the **pharynx** between the **glossopalatine arches**; the **lips**; and the **labial frenulum**, the mucous membrane attached to each lip in the midline.

7. The **tongue** makes up the floor of the oral cavity. Lift up the tongue in order to locate the **lingual frenulum**, the mucous membrane which connects the tongue to the floor of the mouth.

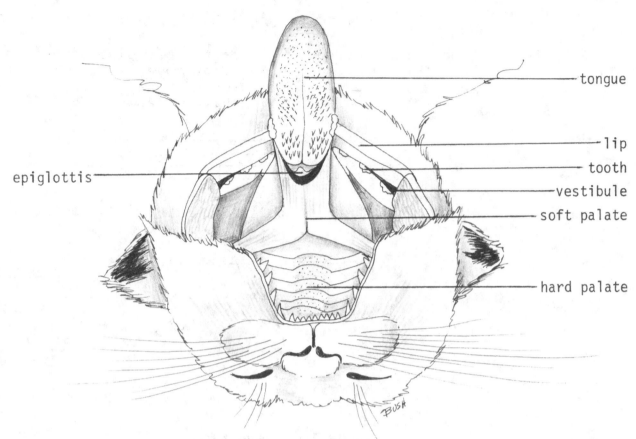

Figure VI-5: Oral Cavity of the Cat

8. Examine the **dorsum** of the tongue. This surface of the tongue is covered with papillae. The **filiform papillae** are the most numerous and are pointed; the anterior ones bear spines with which the cat grooms its fur. The filiform papillae are located primarily in the front and middle portion of the tongue. **Fungiform papillae**, which are small, mushroom shaped papillae, are located between and behind the filiform papillae. Four to six large **circumvallate (vallate) papillae** are located near the back of the tongue. Each of these is large and rounded, and surrounded by a circular groove. Microscopic taste buds are located in the depressions between papillae.

9. Examine the teeth of the cat. The following is the dental formula for the cat:

$$\frac{3 - 1 - 3 - 1}{3 - 1 - 2 - 1}$$

The numbers indicate, from left to right, the number of **incisors, canines, bicuspids** and **molars** on either side. Numbers in the upper row are for teeth in the upper jaw and numbers in the lower row are for the lower jaw.

10. Slit the soft palate in the midline in order to expose the **pharynx**. The part of the pharynx behind the nasal chamber and above the soft palate is the **nasopharynx**. In the dorsal wall of the nasopharynx locate two small slits, the nasal openings of the **auditory (Eustachian) tubes**. The **internal nares** also open into the nasopharynx.

11. The **oropharynx** is the part of the pharynx behind the oral cavity. Next locate the **laryngopharynx,** the part of the pharynx behind the **larynx.** This part of the pharynx opens into the larynx and esophagus.

12. Locate the **epiglottis,** the tongue-like white cartilage over the larynx near the root of the tongue. (See Figure VI-5.)

13. In order to study the remaining digestive organs it is necessary to open the body wall. Locate the **pubic symphysis.** Open the ventral body cavity by cutting through the body wall from the pubic symphysis to the base of the sternum along the linea alba, being careful not to cut through any internal organs. Lift up the origin of the pectoralis group of muscles (so that they will not be severed) and continue the incision along the left side of the sternum, cutting through the costal cartilages up to the clavicle. Do not sever the blood vessels supplying the ventral body wall. Immediately below the diaphragm make an incision to each side of the cat following the edge of the ribs. Just above the diaphragm make another incision to each side of the cat, cutting through the ribs and taking care not to damage the diaphragm.

14. Spread the chest wall gently so that the heart and lungs are visible. Separate the heart and left lung. The **esophagus** can be seen between the left lung and the diaphragm along the dorsal wall of the thoracic cavity. The esophagus is the muscular tube connecting the laryngopharynx to the stomach. Trace the esophagus down through the **diaphragm,** the muscle separating the thoracic cavity from the abdominal cavity.

15. Observe the **greater omentum,** the apron-like structure containing ribbons of adipose tissue which covers the abdominal organs ventrally. Free it carefully from the underlying organs. **Do not detach it from the stomach.** (Refer to Figures VI-6, VI-7, VI-8, VI-9 and Photos 13, 14, 15, 16, and 17 for steps 15-35.)

16. The **liver** is the largest organ in the abdominal cavity. It is the reddish brown structure located immediately below the diaphragm mostly on the right side. Pull down on the liver to observe the ligaments of peritoneum attaching the liver to the diaphragm and ventral body wall. The more ventral ligament is the **falciform ligament,** while the dorsal one is the **coronary ligament.** (See Figure VI-6. Compare to the human as seen in Figure VI-8.)

17. The **falciform ligament** divides the liver into two main lobes, the **right** and **left.** Each of these lobes is subdivided into two lobes (**lateral** and **medial**). The right lateral lobe, located on the extreme right side of the abdominal cavity behind the right medial lobe, is split into two lobules by a deep cleft. In addition there is a small **caudate** lobe beneath the left lateral lobe and deep to the lesser omentum (Figure VI-7).

18. Observe the **gall bladder** in a depression in the right medial lobe (Figures VI-6 and VI-8).

19. The **stomach** lies mainly on the left side of the abdominal cavity. Separate the stomach and liver to observe the esophagus. Locate the point at which the esophagus enters the stomach (see Figure VI-9). Identify the following regions of the stomach: the **cardiac region**, adjacent to the point of entrance of the esophagus; the **body**, the main part of the stomach; the **fundus**, the dome-shaped portion above the opening of the esophagus; the **pyloric region**, the most posterior portion of the stomach opening into the duodenum; the **greater curvature**, the left margin; and the **lesser curvature**, the right margin.

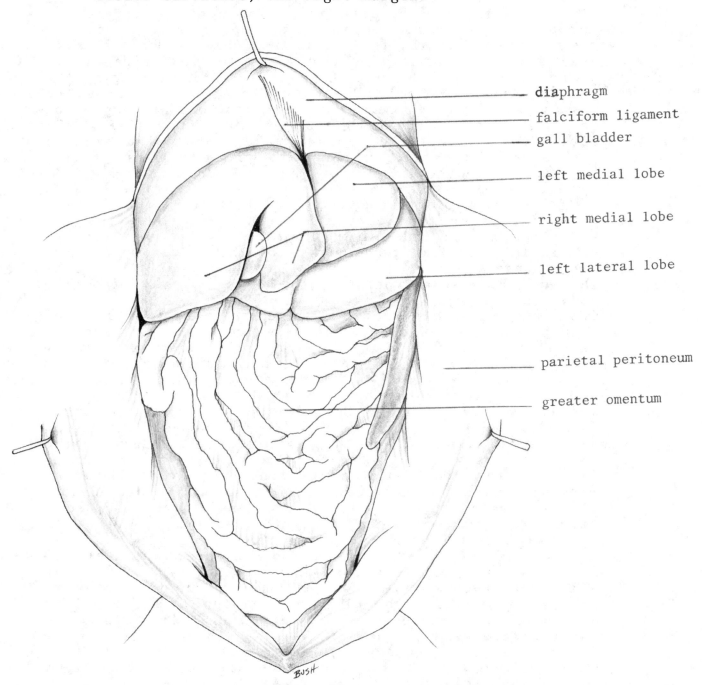

diaphragm

falciform ligament

gall bladder

left medial lobe

right medial lobe

left lateral lobe

parietal peritoneum

greater omentum

Figure VI-6: Superficial View of Abdominal Viscera

KEY TO PHOTO 13

1. gall bladder
2. right lobe of liver
3. left lobe of liver
4. pyloric region of stomach
5. body of stomach
6. greater omentum
7. spleen

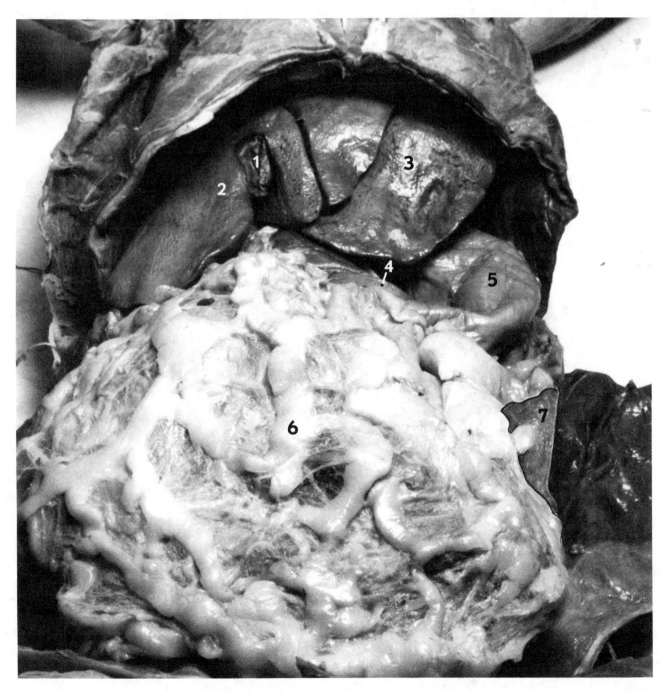

Photo 13: Superficial View of Abdominal Viscera

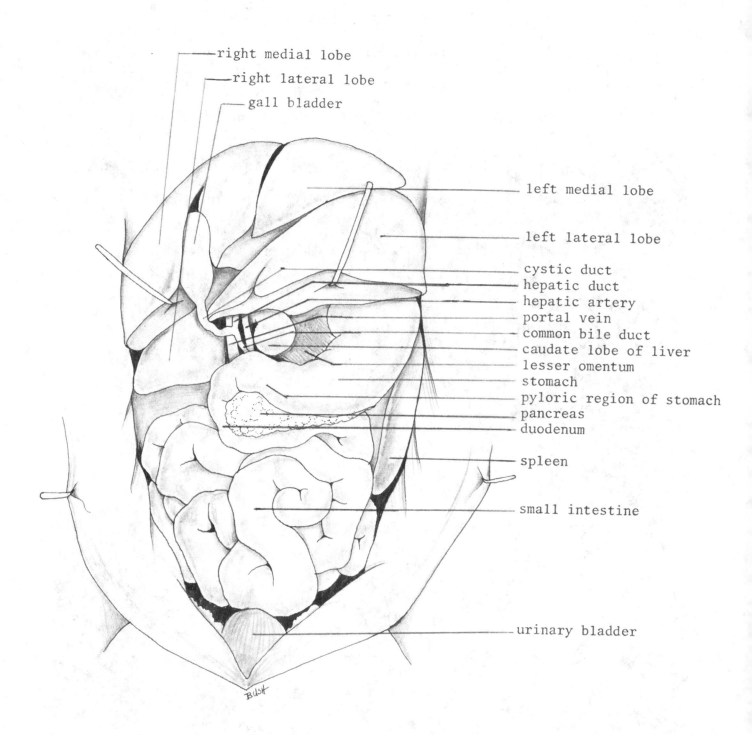

right medial lobe

right lateral lobe

gall bladder

left medial lobe

left lateral lobe

cystic duct
hepatic duct
hepatic artery
portal vein
common bile duct
caudate lobe of liver
lesser omentum
stomach
pyloric region of stomach
pancreas
duodenum

spleen

small intestine

urinary bladder

**Figure VI-7: Superficial View of Abdominal Viscera
(with greater omentum removed and liver raised)**

KEY TO PHOTO 14

1. gall bladder
2. right lobe of liver
3. left lobe of liver
4. stomach
5. greater omentum
6. spleen
7. small intestine
8. uterine horn

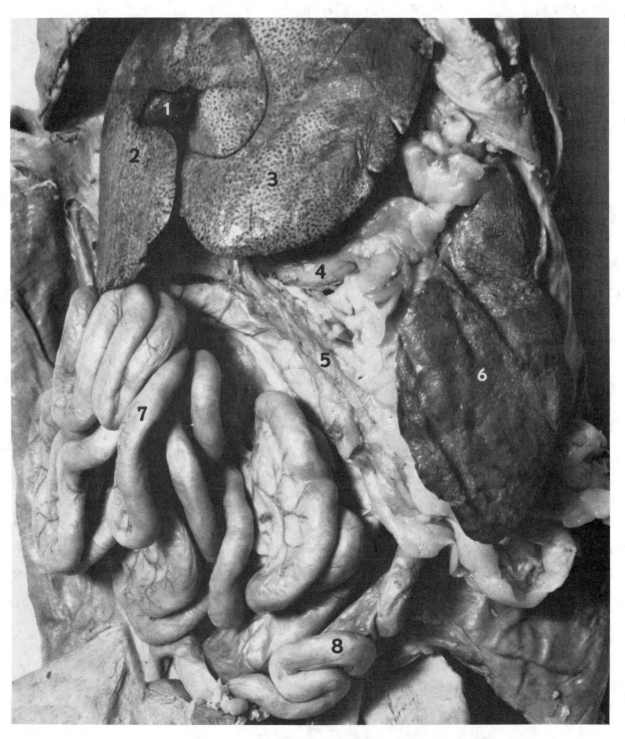

Photo 14: Superficial View of Abdominal Viscera
(with greater omentum pushed to the side)

KEY TO FIGURE VI-8

1. liver
2. gall bladder
3. hepatic duct
4. cystic duct
5. hepatic artery
6. portal vein
7. duodenum
8. common bile duct

9. accessory pancreatic duct
10. pancreatic duct
11. duodenal papilla
12. sup. mesenteric V.
13. R. hepatic duct
14. L. hepatic duct
15. gastric artery

16. celiac artery
17. adrenal gland
18. left kidney
19. splenic artery
20. spleen
21. aorta
22. pancreas
23. sup. mesenteric A.
24. ampulla of Vater

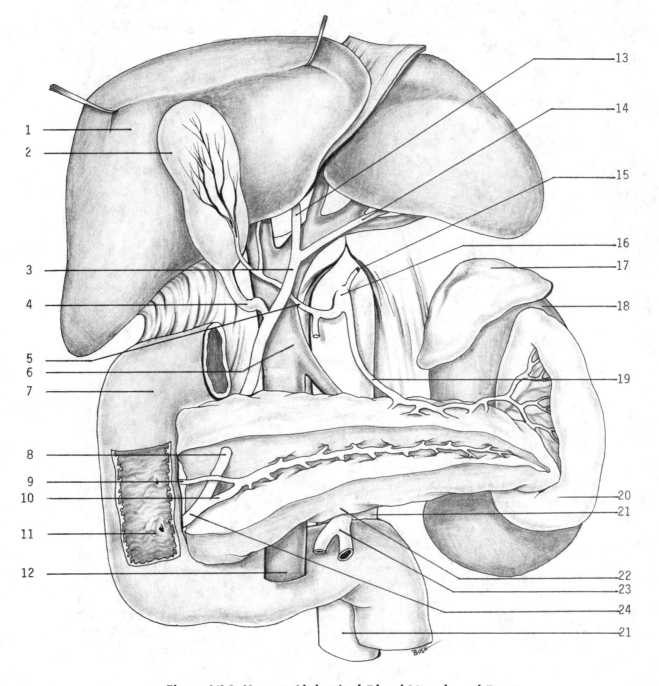

Figure VI-8: Human Abdominal Blood Vessels and Ducts

KEY TO PHOTO 15

1. cystic duct
2. hepatic duct
3. common bile duct
4. hepatic artery
5. lesser omentum
6. stomach
7. duodenum

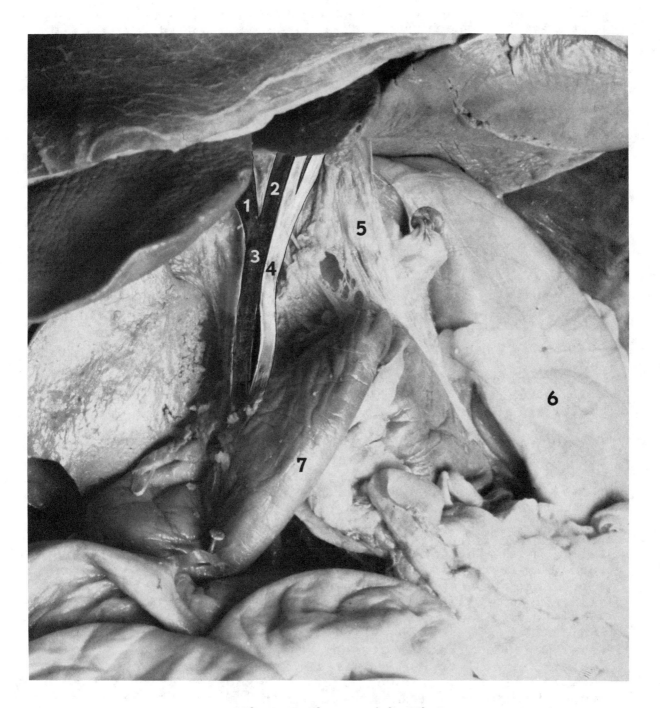

Photo 15: Close-up of the Bile Ducts

20. Make an incision through the stomach wall along the greater curvature beginning in the body and continuing into the duodenum. Wash out the stomach contents. From the interior observe the **cardiac sphincter** which guards the opening between the esophagus and stomach, and the **pyloric sphincter**, the sphincter between the stomach and duodenum. Note the longitudinal folds called **rugae** in the wall of the stomach.

21. Locate the **spleen**, the large reddish brown organ to the left of the stomach (Figure VI-9). This structure (part of the circulatory system) is larger and more elongated in the cat than in man. In the human the spleen is located closer to the diaphragm.

22. Lift up the **greater omentum**, the double layer of peritoneum attached along the greater curvature of the stomach and to the spleen. The **pancreas** (Figure VI-9 - compare also the human in Figure VI-8) lies between the duodenum and the spleen. It can be recognized by its lobular appearance (similar to that of the parotid salivary gland). Carefully tease apart some of the pancreas to locate the **pancreatic duct** (the **Duct of Wirsung**) in the interior of the gland. This white, thread-like duct carries pancreatic enzymes to the duodenum. It unites with common bile duct in the wall of the duodenum to form the **ampulla of Vater**. There is a small accessory pancreatic duct, but it is not necessary to find it.

23. Identify the three regions of the **small intestine** (Figure VI-9). The **duodenum** is the C-shaped (U-shaped in the cat) portion attached to the stomach. It is approximately four inches long in the cat. The common bile duct and the pancreatic duct open into the duodenum.

24. The **jejunum** is the next portion of the small intestine, and it makes up about half of the length of this organ. The **ileum** is the last half of the small intestine, opening into the large intestine. There is no external demarcation between the jejunum and the ileum. Open the jejunum or ileum. The velvety appearance in the interior is due to the presence of numerous microscopic **villi**, which are fingerlike projections that aid in the absorption of food. There may be parasitic roundworms or tape worms present in the small intestine.

25. Trace the small intestine to the point where it enters the **large intestine**. Observe that the small intestine enters the large intestine about 1/2 inch from the beginning of the large intestine. Locate the **ileocecal sphincter** between the small and large intestines by making a longitudinal incision through the wall of the colon in the region of the juncture of the two intestines. Wash out any fecal material that is present.

26. The portion of the large intestine posterior to the ileocecal valve is the **cecum**. Observe the posterior end of the cecum. Determine whether an appendix is present. Trace the **ascending**, **transverse**, and **descending** portions of the colon (Figure VI-9). Considerable variation exists in the cat and the ascending or transverse colon may be absent.

KEY TO PHOTO 16

1. greater omentum   2. pancreas   3. pancreatic duct

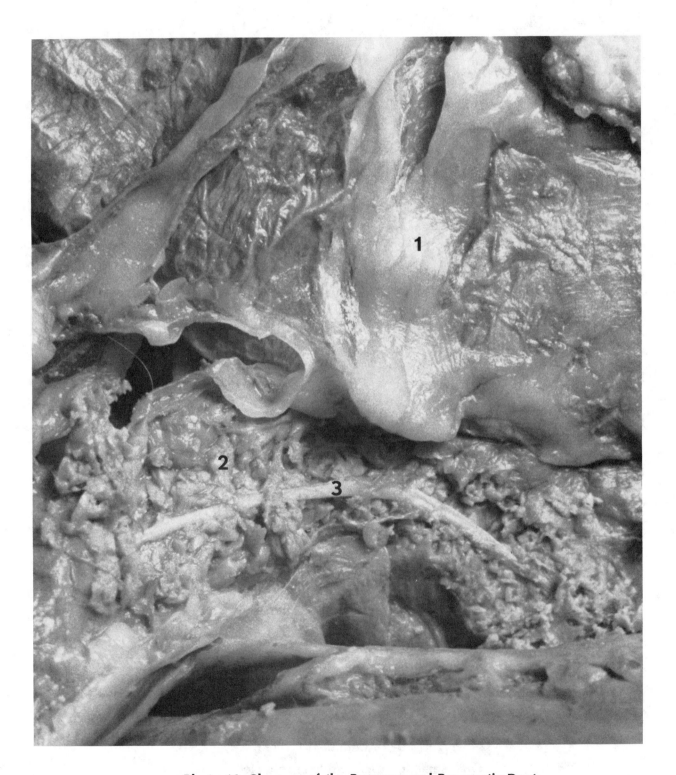

Photo 16: Close-up of the Pancreas and Pancreatic Duct

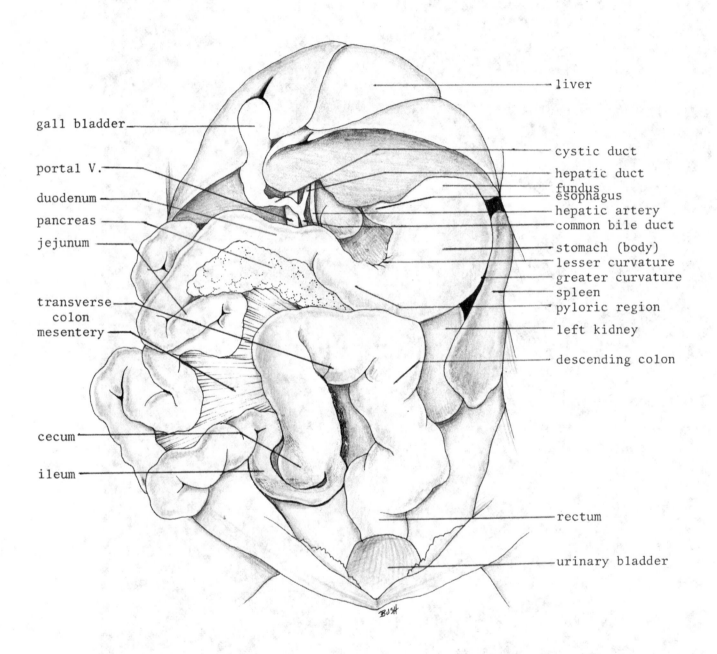

gall bladder

portal V.

duodenum

pancreas

jejunum

transverse
colon

mesentery

cecum

ileum

liver

cystic duct

hepatic duct

fundus

esophagus

hepatic artery

common bile duct

stomach (body)

lesser curvature

greater curvature

spleen

pyloric region

left kidney

descending colon

rectum

urinary bladder

BUSH

Figure VI-9: Abdominal Viscera
(with small intestine and liver reflected)

KEY TO PHOTO 17

1. duodenum
2. pancreas
3. common bile duct

4. hepatic artery
5. portal vein
6. gastrosplenic vein

7. superior mesenteric artery
8. superior mesenteric vein

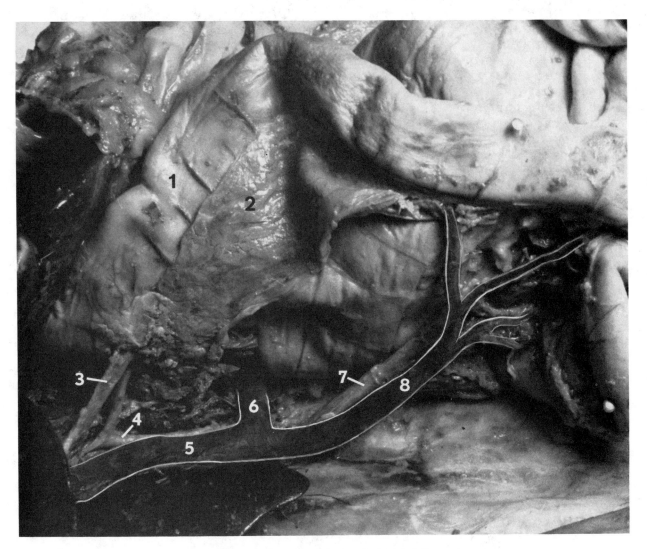

Photo 17: Hepatic Portal System

The ascending colon is on the right side of the abdominal cavity. It extends from the cecum anteriorly to the liver. The transverse colon extends across the abdominal cavity. The descending colon, on the left side of the abdominal cavity, extends in a posterior direction and towards the midline. The next structure, the **rectum**, then descends down into the pelvic cavity and opens to the outside. The external opening of the rectum is know as the **anus**.

27. Examine the interior of the abdominal wall. This wall is lined by **parietal peritoneum**. The **visceral peritoneum** covers the abdominal organs inside the abdominal cavity. Peel off a piece from the intestines. These two layers are connected by various modifications of the peritoneum.

28. The peritoneum also extends over and between some of the organs in the pelvic cavity. Identify the **urinary bladder,** the small ventral organ located in the pelvic cavity; the **uterus,** if your specimen is a female; and the **rectum** located dorsally in the pelvic cavity.

29. The portion of the abdominal cavity between the urinary bladder and the uterus is called the **vesicouterine pouch** or **excavation.** The **rectouterine pouch** extends between the uterus and rectum. In males the pouch between the large intestine and the urinary bladder is called the **rectovesical excavation.** These excavations are lined by peritoneum.

30. Identify the modifications of the peritoneum. Observe again the **greater omentum.** This structure extends from the greater curvature of the stomach and the spleen down over the intestines, folds on itself and ascends again. Due to its double-layered structure, there is a cavity present called the **omental bursa** between the ascending and descending layers. To verify this make a small shallow tear in the omentum. A finger can then be inserted between the two layers.

31. The **lesser omentum** (or **gastrohepatoduodenal ligament**) can be seen extending from the left lateral lobe of the liver to the lesser curvature of the stomach and duodenum. Three important vessels are located in the lesser omentum: the **common bile duct,** the **hepatic artery,** and the **portal vein.** Study the location of these ducts in the human (Figure VI-8), as well as in the cat (Figure VI-7). Locate the **cystic duct** coming from the gall bladder and the **hepatic duct** carrying bile from the liver. These two unite to form the **common bile duct.** If the ducts contain bile they will be green in color; otherwise, they are colorless and difficult to see. The common bile duct enters the duodenum about 3/4 inch below the pyloric sphincter.

32. Carefully tease away the lesser omentum and locate the **hepatic artery** dorsal and to the left of the common bile duct. This vessel is injected with red latex. In order to locate the **portal vein,** lift the duodenum and observe the dorsal surface of the lesser omentum and the duodenum. The portal vein is the large vessel entering the liver. It is not injected but has a dark color due to the presence of coagulated blood. As it is thin-walled, it may be damaged during the dissection. A beaded lymphatic vessel may also be seen in this area.

33. Lift up a loop of small intestine and notice that it is connected to the dorsal body wall by a fold of peritoneum called the **mesentery** (Figure VI-9). It contains arteries, veins, lymphatic vessels, adipose tissue, and lymph nodes. The lymphatic vessels are not injected and, therefore, are not easily seen. Feel the **mesentery** with your fingers to locate the lymph nodes embedded therein. The largest lymph node is called the **pancreas of Aselli.**

34. A dorsal mesentery called the **mesocolon** connects the large intestine to the dorsal body wall. Locate this structure.

35. Determine which of the organs in the abdominal cavity are retroperitoneal.

SELF-TEST: THE DIGESTIVE SYSTEM

DIRECTIONS: See Chapter 1, Self-Test, p. 12

1. The hardest substance in the body is **enamel**.
2. The **root** is the part of the tooth embedded in bone.
3. The **periodontal** membrane attaches the tooth to the bone.
4. The major nerves and blood vessels supplying a tooth are found in the **periodontal membrane**.
5. The enamel is formed by **odontoblasts**.
6. The **crown** is the exposed surface of the tooth.
7. When teeth fail to meet properly for eating, the condition is know as **gingivitis**.
8. The human adult set of teeth normally contains a total number of **32** teeth.
9. Dental **caries** are decayed areas in teeth.
10. **Deciduous** teeth come in after the primary teeth are shed.
11. The eight teeth in the front of the mouth are called **incisors**.
12. The dental formula for deciduous teeth is **2 - 1 - 0 - 2**.
13. Saliva is secreted by **three pairs** of salivary glands.
14. Swallowing is completed when the **pyloric** sphincter opens.
15. A portion of the roof of the mouth cavity is formed by the **hard palate**.
16. A baby with a **cleft palate** cannot take milk from a bottle because the mouth opens into the nasal cavities.
17. The esophagus is lined with **stratified squamous epithelium**.
18. The pyloric sphincter separates the **duodenum** from the stomach.
19. A lesion of the inner wall of the stomach or first part of the small intestine is called a **peptic ulcer**.
20. Lining the small intestine are many fine, velvetlike or fingerlike projections called **rugae**.
21. Enlarged veins in the **stomach** are referred to as hemorrhoids.
22. The appendix is a cul-de-sac attached to the **descending colon**.
23. A **hernia** is a protrusion of part of an organ through an abdominal opening.
24. A hernia occurring through the navel is called **an umbilical hernia**.
25. The membrane lining the abdominal cavity is called the **pleura**.
26. The scientific name for the throat is the **larynx**.
27. **Peritonitis** is an inflammation of the lining of the abdominal cavity.
28. Peristalsis occurs in the stomach and intestines, **but not** in the esophagus.
29. The two regions in which the liver is normally located are the **epigastrium and right hypochondrium**.
30. The common bile duct enters the small intestine at the **ampulla of Vater**.
31. The temporary folds in the mucosa of the stomach are called **papillae**.

32. Bile secreted by the liver is stored in the **gall bladder.**
33. The ileum empties its fluid contents into the **cecum.**
34. The tongue has nerve endings capable of detecting **hundreds of flavors.**
35. The mouth cavity opens posteriorly into the **nasopharynx.**
36. **Pyorrhea** is a condition of the gums and periodontal membrane which is characterized by inflammation and bleeding.
37. The liver receives blood (which it processes and refines) from the **hepatic vein.**
38. The cystic duct leads from the gall bladder and opens into the **common bile duct.**
39. The colon is divided into segments called **haustra.**
40. **Kupffer cells** located in the stomach are responsible for the secretion of hydrochloric acid.
41. The most important processes in digestion and absorption take place in the **small intestine.**
42. The first teeth of the permanent set to erupt are the **six-year molars.**
43. Gallstones are formed from substances in **bile.**
44. The first set of teeth **lacks** bicuspids.
45. The pancreas extends between the **spleen** and the portion of small intestine called the duodenum.
46. During an enema the patient should lie on his left side because the **descending colon** is on this side and the fluid will flow in easily.
47. Parotitis or "mumps" is an inflammation of the **parotid** gland.
48. A **gastroenterostomy** is the creation of an artificial passage between the stomach and the intestine.
49. **Sclerosis** is an excessive formation of the interstitial connective tissue that causes a hardening of an organ such as the liver.
50. Cholecystitis is an inflammation of the **urinary bladder.**
51. **Cholelithiasis** is the formation of stones in the gall bladder or ducts.
52. Lacteals are lymph vessels that absorb food from the **large intestine.**
53. The **longitudinal** layer of muscle in the large intestine forms the taenia coli.
54. The peritoneal cavity is the term to describe the space between the **parietal** and **visceral** layers of peritoneum.
55. A surgeon can readily distinguish between the large and small intestine, by sense of touch, due to the presence or absence of **haustra** and the **epiploic appendages.**
56. Succus entericus is secreted by the glands of the **small intestine.**
57. The **greater and lesser** omentums are folds of the visceral layer of the peritoneum.
58. The greater omentum hangs from the **lesser** curvature of the stomach.
59. The mesentery of the **small intestine** serves as a support and holds blood vessels, lymphatics, and nerves.

60. The gastric contents are reduced to a more or less homogenous creamy mass called the **bolus**.
61. The hepatic artery carries **oxygenated blood to the liver**.
62. The **palatine** tonsils are located between the glossopalatine arches.

KEY

4. root canal (pulp cavity)
5. ameloblasts
7. malocclusion
10. permanent
14. cardiac (lower esophageal)
20. villi
21. rectum
22. cecum
25. peritoneum
26. pharynx
28. as well as

31. rugae
34. four basic taste sensations
35. oropharynx
37. portal vein
40. parietal cells
49. cirrhosis
50. gall bladder
52. small intestine
58. greater
60. chyme

Chapter VII
THE RESPIRATORY SYSTEM

Ex. VII-A. Anatomy of the Human Respiratory System

PROCEDURE

1. Use Figures VII-1 and VII-2, two views of the larynx, as self-tests. See Section J, p. 5 (Illustrations as Self-Tests) for suggested approaches.
2. Locate the thyroid cartilage on your own larynx.
3. Hold the larynx down and try to swallow. Now release the larynx and swallow.
4. Use Figure VII-3 as a self-test. The structures indicated in the key for this figure should be located on the dissectable torso and the model of a sagittal section through the head.
5. Figure VII-4 includes three drawings illustrating the relationship of alveoli to the lungs. Note the anatomical and histological feature which provide the mechanical basis for gas exchange. This figure may be used as a self-test.

KEY TO FIGURE VII-1

1. epiglottis
2. hyoid bone
3. thyrohyoid membrane
4. thyroid notch
5. thyroid cartilage
6. laryngeal prominence
7. cricoid cartilage
8. trachea

KEY TO FIGURE VII-2

1. epiglottis
2. hyoid bone
3. thyrohyoid membrane
4. cricoid cartilage
5. trachea

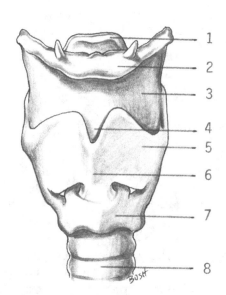

Figure VII-1: Larynx (anterior view)

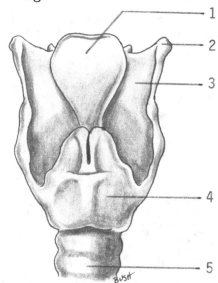

Figure VII-2: Larynx (posterior view)

Ex. VII-B. Dissection of the Cat Respiratory System

DISCUSSION

The respiratory systems of the cat and man are very similar. Be prepared to trace the path of air through the respiratory system.

PROCEDURE

1. The mouth and pharynx were examined earlier in the study of the digestive system. The air enters the **nasal chamber** through the **nostrils** or **external nares**, passes through the **internal nares** or **choanae** into the **nasopharynx**, through the **oropharynx**, and then the **laryngopharynx** into the **larynx**. Refer to Figures VII-1, VII-2, VII-3, VII-4, VII-5 and Photos 18 and 19 for steps 2-20.

2. Clean away the muscles from the ventral surface of the larynx and hyoid bone in the neck. The **hyoid** is immediately anterior to the larynx and serves for attachment of muscles of the tongue and larynx.

3. The larynx consists of a box of five cartilages. The **thyroid cartilage** is the large shield shaped cartilage on the ventral side of the larynx. It lies just posterior to the hyoid.

4. Next locate the **cricoid cartilage** posterior to the thyroid cartilage. This cartilage is shaped like a signet ring with the small band in front, the expanded portion in back. Remove any muscle remaining between the thyroid and cricoid cartilages.

5. The **epiglottis**, the most anterior cartilage of the larynx, has been observed earlier in the dissection of the mouth at the root of the tongue (see Figure VI-5 in Chapter VI). This tongue-like cartilage is attached ventrally to the thyroid cartilage.

6. To observe the other two cartilages of the larynx, make a longitudinal incision through the larynx and upper trachea. Do not sever the blood vessels or nerves located on either side of the trachea. Open the larynx and observe the two triangular cartilages, the **arytenoid cartilages**, on the inside dorsal wall. Feel them with your forceps to verify that they are cartilage. The **vocal cords** can be seen to the side of the arytenoid cartilages. These paired folds extend between the thyroid and arytenoid cartilages. The **glottis** is the space between the vocal cords (Figure VII-5).

7. The **trachea** leads from the caudal end of the larynx. Observe the large right and left **common carotid arteries** and the tiny **internal jugular veins** on each side of the trachea. The **vagus nerve** is the white flattened thread next to the common carotid artery. This nerve supplies many of the thoracic and abdominal organs.

8. Free the trachea laterally from the preceding blood vessels and nerves. Locate the **esophagus**, the muscular tube dorsal to the trachea.

9. Locate the two small, dark lobes of the **thyroid gland**, one on each side of the upper trachea near the larynx (Figure VII-5).

KEY TO FIGURE VII-3

1. frontal bone
2. frontal sinus
3. superior, middle, & inf. nasal conchae
4. external nares
5. hard palate
6. tongue
7. mandible

8. hyoid bone
9. thyroid cartilage
10. cricoid cartilage
11. sella turcica
12. sphenoidal sinus
13. adenoid
14. eustachian tube opening

15. soft palate
16. nasopharynx
17. uvula
18. oropharynx
19. laryngopharynx
20. epiglottis
21. cricoid cartilage
22. larynx
23. trachea

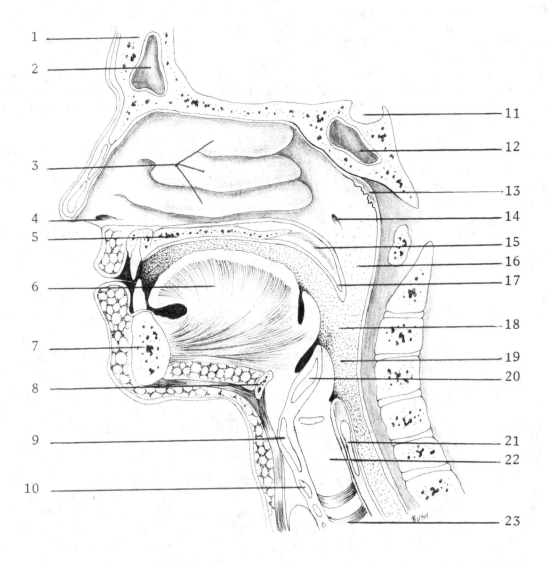

Figure VII-3: Sagittal Section through the Head

KEY TO FIGURE VII-4

1. thyroid cartilage
2. cricoid cartilage
3. trachea
4. right bronchus
5. secondary bronchi

6. apex (left lung)
7. rib
8. left bronchus
9. pulmonary artery
10. pulmonary vein

11. respiratory bronchiole
12. alveolar duct
13. alveoli
14. alveolar sac

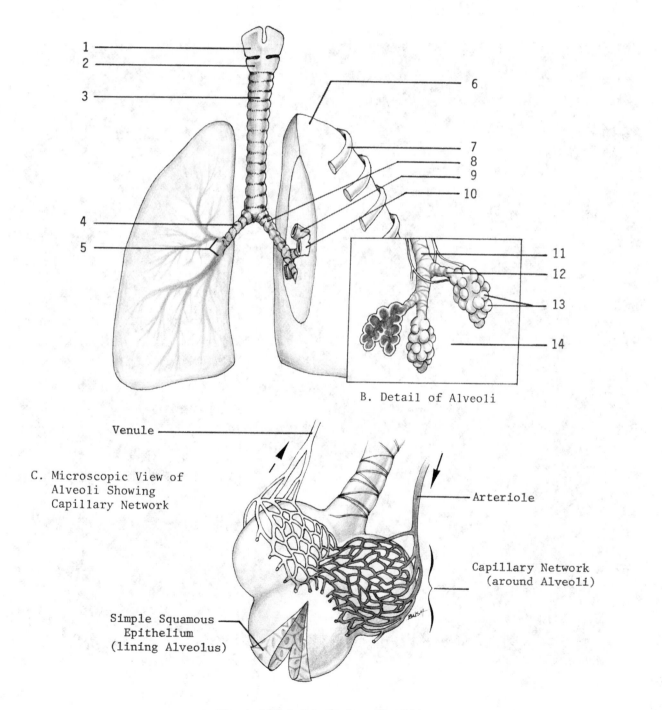

B. Detail of Alveoli

C. Microscopic View of Alveoli Showing Capillary Network

Venule

Arteriole

Capillary Network (around Alveoli)

Simple Squamous Epithelium (lining Alveolus)

Figure VII-4: Respiratory Tract

KEY TO PHOTO 18

1. trachea
2. right brachio-
   cephalic vein
3. left brachio-
   cephalic vein
4. superior
   vena cava
5. azygos vein

6. left lung
7. root of lung
8. right lung
9. right auricle
10. coronary sulcus
11. right ventricle
12. anterior longi-
    tudinal sulcus

13. left ventricle
14. inferior
    vena cava
15. right phrenic
    nerve
16. left phrenic
    nerve
17. diaphragm

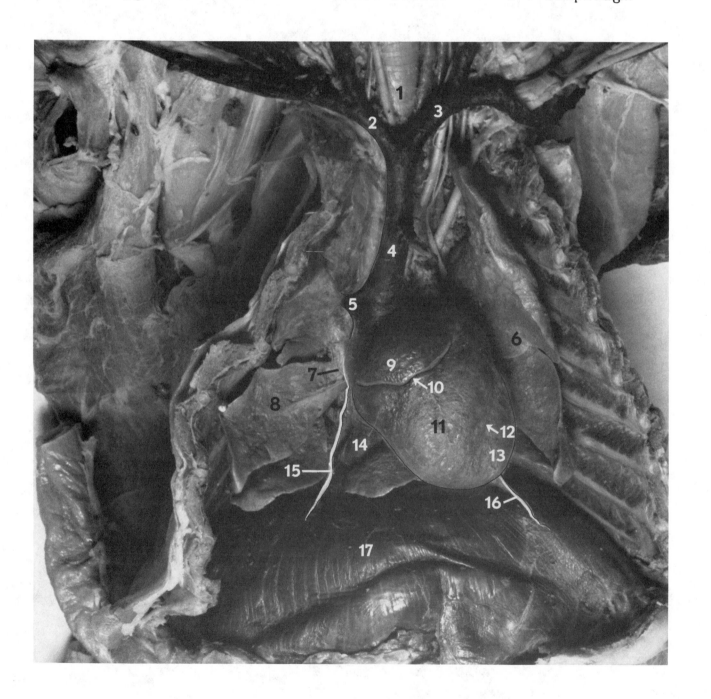

Photo 18: Organs of the Thoracic Cavity

KEY TO PHOTO 19

1. arytenoid
   cartilage
2. vocal fold
3. cricoid cartilage
4. trachea
   (cut open)

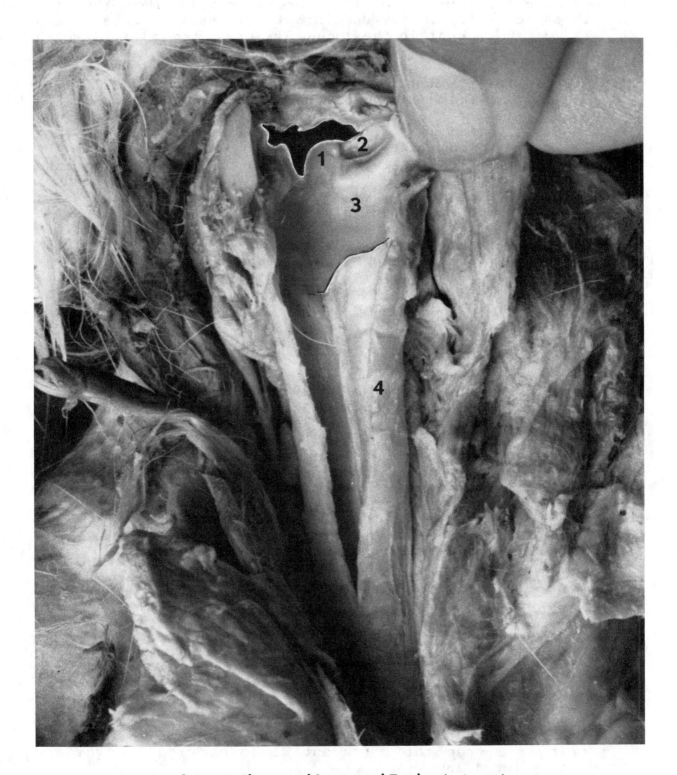

Photo 19: Close-up of Larynx and Trachea (cut open)

10. Trace the trachea into the thoracic cavity. Do not damage any blood vessels or nerves. Observe the C-shaped rings of cartilage in the wall of the trachea. The rings are completed dorsally by muscle and connective tissue.

11. Examine the interior of the thoracic cavity. Note that the thoracic cavity is divided into two lateral **pleural cavities,** which contain the lungs. The **pericardial sac,** which contains the heart, is located in the space between the lungs.

12. The **pleura** is a double-layered **serous membrane** which lines the thorax. That portion of the pleura lining the thoracic wall is called the **parietal pleura;** that which covers and adheres to the lungs is called the **visceral pleura.**

13. The **pericardium,** the membrane surrounding the heart, is also composed of two layers: the outer parietal layer and the inner visceral layer. Much of the **parietal pleura** forming the medial walls of the pleural cavities is tightly bound to the **parietal pericardium.**

14. Examine the lungs. Each lung is divided into lobes. In the cat, the right lung is divided into four lobes and the left lung into three lobes. Cut through a section of the lung in order to observe its internal structure. Many small blood vessels (branches of the pulmonary artery and vein) and tubes (branches of the bronchi) can be seen in the spongy interior.

15. Locate the **right** and **left pulmonary arteries** going to the lungs. These are usually injected with blue latex.

16. Note that the lung is attached to other structures in the thorax only by the root. The **root of the lung** is formed by the bronchus, pulmonary artery and vein, bronchial arteries and veins, nerves, lymphatic vessels, and bronchial lymph nodes, all encircled by pleura.

17. The trachea divides into two **bronchi** at its posterior end. Lift up the lungs and locate the right and left bronchi. These tubes can be identified by the cartilage in their walls. The bronchi branch repeatedly into **secondary bronchi** and **bronchioles** inside the lungs. Tease away the tissue of the left lung to see the organization of the **bronchial tree** blood vessels. Leave the vessels intact.

18. The mediastinum is the space between the lungs. This space is nearly filled with the heart and pericardium. Locate the **thymus gland** (Figure VII-5) in the mediastinum, anterior to and ventral to the heart. This gland, divided into lobules, is large in young cats, smaller in old.

19. Examine the interior of the wall of the thoracic cavity. Peel off some of the parietal pleura and locate the **intercostal vein, artery,** and **nerve** next to each rib.

20. The **diaphragm** makes up the floor of the thoracic cavity. Locate the paired **phrenic nerves,** white-threadlike structures directed posteriorly on each side of the pericardium to the surface of the diaphragm. The phrenic nerves originate from the fifth and sixth cervical nerves and supply the diaphragm.

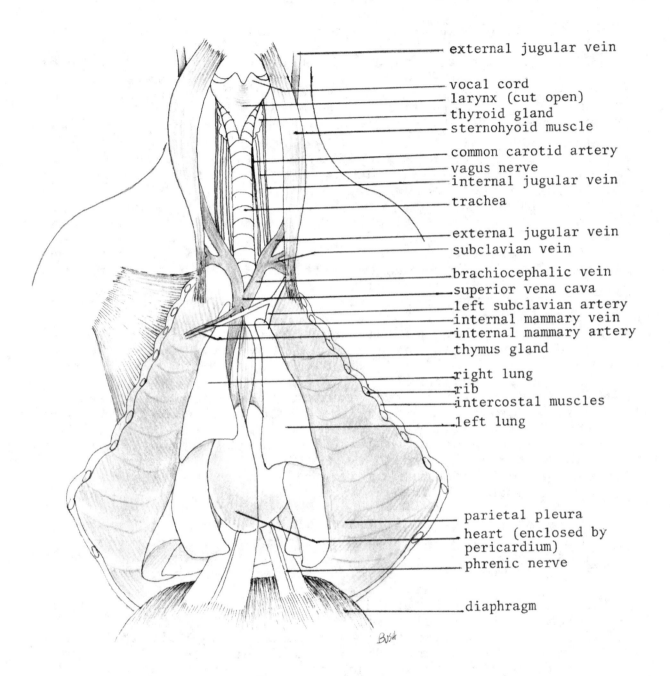

external jugular vein

vocal cord
larynx (cut open)
thyroid gland
sternohyoid muscle

common carotid artery
vagus nerve
internal jugular vein

trachea

external jugular vein
subclavian vein

brachiocephalic vein
superior vena cava
left subclavian artery
internal mammary vein
internal mammary artery
thymus gland

right lung
rib
intercostal muscles

left lung

parietal pleura
heart (enclosed by
pericardium)
phrenic nerve

diaphragm

Figure VII-5: Thoracic Viscera

SELF-TEST: THE RESPIRATORY SYSTEM

DIRECTIONS: See Chapter 1, Self-Test, p. 12

1. **Cilia** aid in the movement of dust particles along the breathing passages.
2. The structure which is common to both the digestive and respiratory systems is the **trachea.**
3. The structures in cytoplasm containing the enzymes of cellular respiration are called **mitochondria.**
4. The **glottis** prevents food from entering the larynx.
5. The opening between the two vocal folds is called the **laryngeal aperture or glottis.**
6. Inspiration is an **active process** involving primarily the contraction of the diaphragm and external intercostal muscles.
7. The gaseous exchange across the respiratory membrane from the alveoli of the lungs to the capillary circulation is called **internal** respiration.
8. **Sinus infection** is an extension of an infection from the nasal passages.
9. Bones making up the **lateral** wall of the nasal cavity include the inferior nasal concha, the maxilla, and the ethmoid.
10. The **pharyngeal** tonsils are also called the adenoids.
11. The tonsils are located within the **laryngeal aperture.**
12. Passive expiration is primarily due to the **contraction** of the muscles of inspiration.
13. The lungs expand during inspiration because the **two layers of the pleura adhere** to each other.
14. The **pulmonary veins** contain a greater concentration of oxygen than the **alveoli.**
15. Most of the oxygen carried in the body has combined with **hemoglobin** to form **oxyhemoglobin.**
16. The cartilaginous rings of the **trachea** are incomplete behind.
17. The **left** bronchus is shorter, larger in diameter, and more nearly vertical than the **right.**
18. The **thyroid** cartilage is the shield-shaped cartilage to which the vocal folds attach.
19. The **intrapleural** cavity is a true cavity only when accident or disease results in an opening between the potenial **intrapleural** space and the atmosphere.
20. The principal **afferent** nerve in respiration is the phrenic nerve.
21. The maxillary sinus drains into the **middle nasal meatus.**
22. The respiratory center is located in the **hypothalamus.**
23. Pleurisy is an inflammation of the **peritoneum.**
24. Bronchitis is an inflammation of the **lungs.**
25. A pneumonectomy is the removal of **one lung,** while a lobectomy is the removal of **a lobe of the lung.**
26. **Bronchoscopy** is visual examination of the bronchi with a special instrument.
27. A laryngectomy is the removal of the **vocal cords.**

28. Pulmonary emphysema is **overdistention** of the air spaces in the lungs.
29. The frontal, maxillary, ethmoidal, and sphenoidal sinuses constitute the **paranasal sinuses**.
30. The paranasal sinuses drain into the **pharynx**.
31. The **nasolacrimal ducts** receive lacrimal fluid ("tears") from the lacrimal ducts.
32. Both air and food must pass through the **larynx**.
33. The **larynx** is made up of three paired cartilages and three single cartilages.
34. The trachea is immediately **posterior** to the esophagus.
35. The smallest subdivisions of the bronchial tree are known as **bronchioles**.
36. Air sacs consist of grape-like bulges known as **alveoli**.
37. The right lung in humans has **two** lobes.
38. The bronchi enter the lungs at the **hilum**.
39. The **pulmonary artery** carries unoxygenated blood from the heart to the lungs.
40. The air sacs are made up of **stratified squamous epithelium**, which is, for the most part, only one cell thick.
41. The **mediastinum** is the interpleural space which contains the heart, large blood vessels, nerves and some other structures of the thoracic cavity.
42. The part of the pleura which lines the inner surface of the chest wall and covers the diaphragm is called the **pulmonary** pleura.
43. The pleura is a **serous** membrane.
44. The nerve endings for the sense of smell are found in olfactory epithelium which is part of the covering of the **superior concha**.

KEY

2.	pharynx	17.	right--left	30.	nasal cavity
4.	epiglottis	20.	efferent	32.	pharynx
7.	external	22.	medulla	34.	anterior
11.	pharynx		oblongata	37.	three
12.	relaxation	23.	pleura	40.	simple squamous
14.	alveoli--	24.	bronchi		epithelium
	pulmonary veins	27.	larynx	42.	parietal

Chapter VIII
THE CIRCULATORY SYSTEM

Ex. VIII-A. Structure of an Artery, Vein, and a Lymph Vessel Valve

DISCUSSION

An artery may be defined as any vessel carrying blood away from the heart; a vein as any vessel returning blood from the capillary network to the heart. The lymphatic vessels form a different route for the return of fluid to the veins.

The wall of an artery is composed of three layers: the innermost **tunica intima (tunica interna)**, a thin coat composed of one layer of endothelium, a small amount of connective tissue, and an internal elastic membrane; the thick **tunica media**, composed of smooth muscle arranged perpendicular to the length of the vessel and elastic connective tissue; and the outermost coat, the **tunica adventitia (tunica externa),** composed of loose connective tissue. This external layer contains the **vasa vasorum,** the nutrient blood vessels nourishing the wall of all arteries and veins larger than one mm. in diameter.

The veins contain the same three coats as arteries; the main difference is that the tunica media is thinner. The muscular and elastic tissue is much more poorly developed in the veins than in the arteries. Many veins (and lymphatic vessels) contain valves in their walls in order to assist the return of fluid against gravity. Each valve consists of two semilunar pouches which open to let blood return to the heart and close to prevent backward flow of the blood.

PROCEDURE

1. Examine the prepared slide of a cross section through an artery using the low power objective. Locate the three coats in the wall. Diagram the artery wall, showing the three layers in the correct proportions.
2. Draw one small section through the entire wall in detail. In order to see tissue in the tunica intima it will be necessary to use the high power objective of the microscope. The innermost layer of the tunica intima is the endothelium. Observe the internal elastic membrane, the wavy purple line which forms the boundary between the tunica intima and media.
3. Returning to low power, examine the tunica media. This layer contains both smooth muscle, which stains pink, and purple-staining elastic connective tissue. It is not necessary to draw cellular detail in the smooth muscle. Locate the external elastic membrane which separates the tunica media from the tunica adventitia.
4. Locate the vasa vasorum and adipose tissue in the tunica adventitia. Include these in your drawing.

5. Examine a prepared slide of a cross section through a vein. Diagram the same three layers through the wall of the vein, showing differences in thickness of the wall. It is not necessary to include cells on this diagram.
6. Examine a slide of a longitudinal section of a lymphatic vessel with a valve. Diagram a section of the vessel with a valve; include the shape of the valve.

Ex. VIII-B. Gross Anatomy of the Human Circulatory System

DISCUSSION

The circulatory system consists of the heart, blood vessels, and blood. Its primary function is to transport materials around the body. It transports nutrients and oxygen to the cells, wastes away from the cells, hormones, antibodies, enzymes, etc.

The heart is a double pump located in the thoracic cavity. The right side of the heart pumps blood to the lungs, the left to the rest of the body. Be prepared in your study of the heart and blood vessels to trace the path of blood around the body.

PROCEDURE

1. Use your text, charts, and references for orientation while studying the following figures.
2. Use Figures VIII-1, VIII-2, VIII-3, and VIII-4 as self-tests. See Section J, p. 5 (Illustrations as Self-Tests) for a suggested approach.

Ex. VIII-C. The Dissection of the Sheep Heart

DISCUSSION

The anatomy of the sheep heart is very similar to that of the human and the cat. Observe carefully in this exercise the remnants of structures important in fetal circulation. Directions for this exercise are given with the heart in anatomic position. Refer to Figures VIII-4, VIII-5, VIII-6 and Photos 20 and 21 for steps 1-29.

PROCEDURE

1. Locate the following structures on the models of the human heart:

   a. aorta
   b. aortic semilunar valve
   c. bicuspid (mitral) valve
   d. chordae tendineae
   e. inferior vena cava
   f. left atrium
   g. left auricle
   h. left ventricle
   i. papillary muscle
   j. pulmonary artery
   k. pulmonary semilunar valve
   l. pulmonary vein
   m. right atrium
   n. right auricle
   o. right ventricle
   p. superior vena cava
   q. tricuspid valve

2. The same structures listed under Step 1 should also be located on the sheep heart. Rinse the sheep heart in water to remove as much preservative as possible.

KEY TO FIGURE VIII-1
(ARTERIES)

1. R. common carotid
2. R. subclavian
3. brachiocephalic
4. axillary
5. aortic arch
6. brachial
7. superior mesenteric
8. radial
9. ulnar
10. middle sacral
11. palmar arch
12. digital
13. anterior tibial
14. dorsalis pedis
15. arcuate
16. L. common carotid
17. L. subclavian
18. celiac
19. renal
20. spermatic
21. inferior mesenteric
22. common iliac
23. internal iliac
24. external iliac
25. femoral
26. popliteal
27. posterior tibial

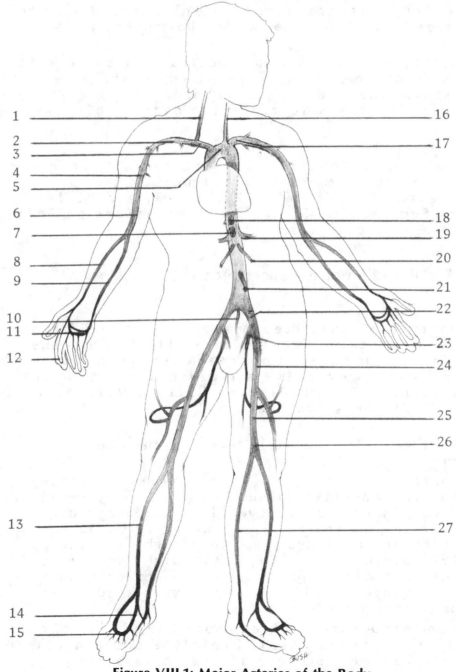

Figure VIII-1: Major Arteries of the Body

KEY TO FIGURE VIII-2
(VEINS)

1. external jugular
2. internal jugular
3. subclavian
4. axillary
5. brachial
6. cephalic
7. basilic
8. internal iliac
9. external iliac
10. great saphenous
11. brachiocephalic
12. superior vena cava
13. inferior vena cava
14. hepatic
15. renal
16. common iliac
17. middle sacral

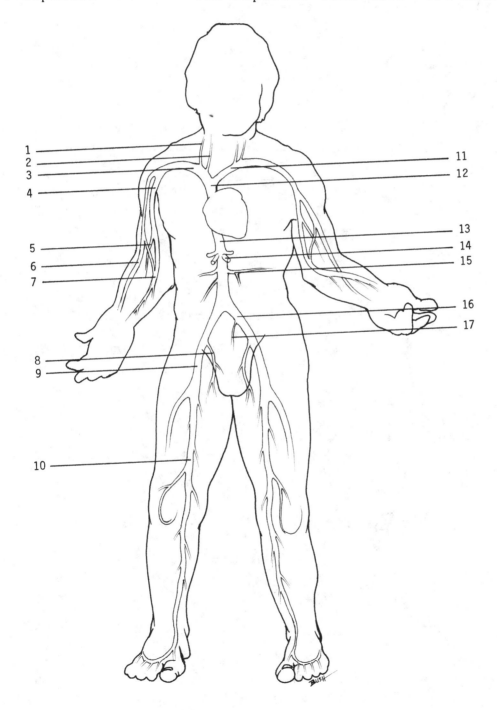

Figure VIII-2: Major Veins of the Body

KEY TO FIGURE VIII-3

1. gall bladder
2. cystic duct
3. hepatic duct
4. liver
5. common bile duct
6. duodenum
7. superior
   mesenteric vein

8. ascending colon
9. vermiform appendix
10. ileum
11. left hepatic duct
12. portal vein
13. coronary vein
14. stomach
15. splenic vein

16. spleen
17. pancreas
18. inferior mes-
    enteric V.
19. descending
    colon
20. rectum

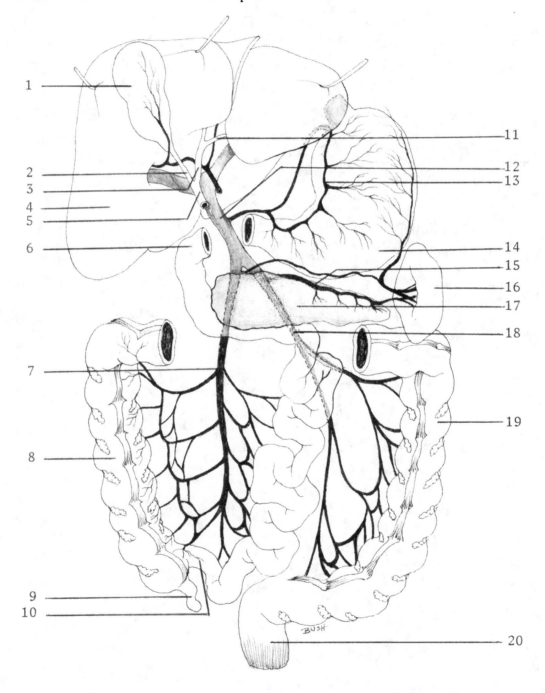

Figure VIII-3: Digestive Organs and Portal Circulation (Diagrammatic)

KEY TO FIGURE VIII-4

1. external jugular vein
2. internal jugular vein
3. common carotid artery
4. brachiocephalic artery
5. right pulmonary artery
6. right pulmonary veins
7. superior vena cava
8. aortic semilunar valve
9. right atrium

10. tricuspid valve
11. right ventricle
12. inferior vena cava
13. axillary vein
14. subclavian vein
15. brachiocephalic vein
16. aortic arch
17. L. pulmonary artery
18. pulmonary artery
19. L. pulmonary veins

20. pulmonary semilunar valve
21. left atrium
22. bicuspid (mitral) valve
23. chordae tendineae
24. left ventricle
25. papillary muscle
26. interventricular septum

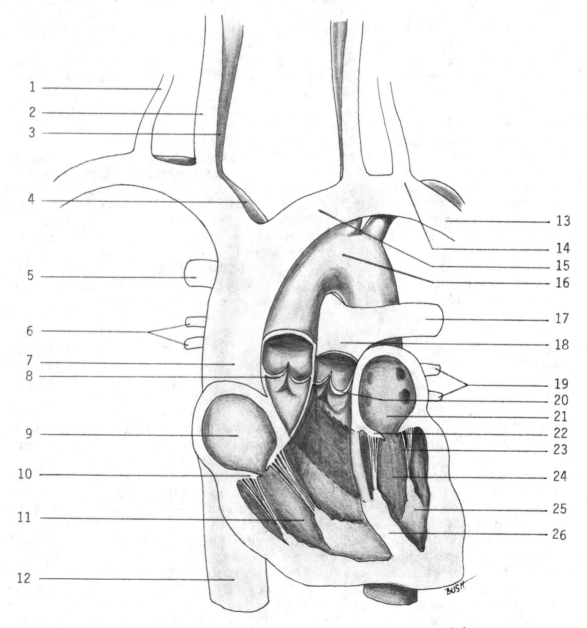

Figure VIII-4: Blood Vessels of the Neck and Interior of the Heart

3. The **pericardium** (the fibro-serous membrane surrounding the heart) may have been largely removed in preparing the sheep heart. If so, observe the remnants of this membrane attached to the large blood vessels above the heart. If the pericardium is present, slit it open and remove most of it; leave just a small amount attached to the large blood vessels above the heart.

4. Separate a small portion of the **epicardium** (the visceral layer of the pericardium) from the **myocardium** by careful dissection with a scalpel. The third layer of the heart, the **endocardium,** will be visible when the heart is opened.

5. Locate the **pulmonary artery** on the ventral surface of the heart. This artery emerges from the anterior ventral surface of the heart, medial to the **left auricle.** (To determine which is the ventral surface of the heart, compare the sheep heart with Figure VIII-5.)

6. Note the **anterior longitudinal sulcus** separating the right ventricle from the left ventricle. The **coronary blood vessels** can be seen in this sulcus.

7. Compare the thickness of the wall of the **right ventricle** with the **left ventricle** by pressing the wall of each ventricle between your thumb and forefinger.

8. If there is a demonstration dissected sheep heart on display, observe the incisions before proceeding. Using great care, make an incision through the ventral wall of the pulmonary artery and the right ventricle **parallel to, and 3/4 of an inch to the right of,** the anterior longitudinal sulcus. Do not dissect so deeply that you cut into the dorsal surface of either the pulmonary artery or right ventricle. Continue the incision forward anteriorly to the point where the pulmonary artery branches into the **right** and **left pulmonary arteries.** Remove as much adipose tissue as necessary to expose the branches of the pulmonary artery.

9. Open the pulmonary artery and note the **pulmonary semilunar valve.** Observe the number of pouches in this valve. Remove any coagulated blood present in the blood vessels or heart.

10. Continue the original incision through the right ventricle wall **(keeping parallel to the anterior longitudinal sulcus)** around and through the dorsal wall of the right ventricle until reaching the **interventricular septum.**

11. Examine the dorsal surface of the heart. The thin-walled **superior vena cava** can be seen above the right auricle, extending straight down into the right atrium. Make a longitudinal incision through the dorsal wall of the superior vena cava, continuing down through the right atrium (immediately to the left of the right auricle). Be careful not to cut through the inferior vena cava. Continue this incision down the dorsal right ventricle wall to the point of juncture with the first incision.

12. If the incisions were properly made, it should now be possible to spread open the superior vena cava, right atrium, and right ventricle. Compare your dissection with Figure VIII-6.

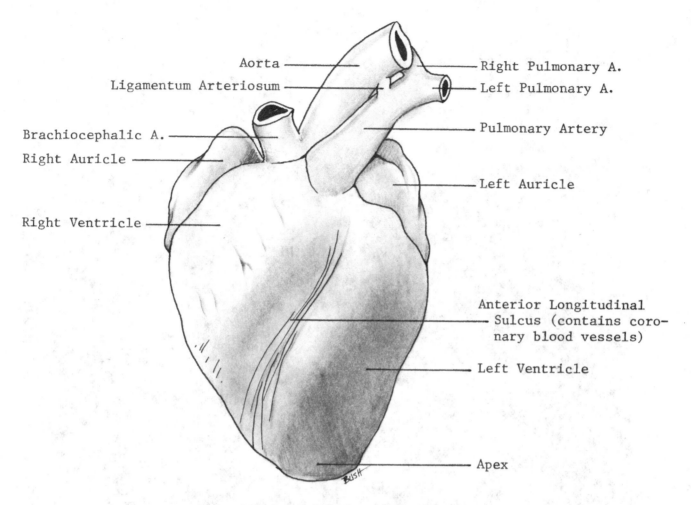

Aorta ——————

Ligamentum Arteriosum ——————

Brachiocephalic A. ——————

Right Auricle ——————

Right Ventricle ——————

—————— Right Pulmonary A.

—————— Left Pulmonary A.

—————— Pulmonary Artery

—————— Left Auricle

—————— Anterior Longitudinal Sulcus (contains coronary blood vessels)

—————— Left Ventricle

—————— Apex

BUSH

Figure VIII-5: Ventral View of the Sheep Heart

13. Determine whether there is a valve present at the entrance of the superior vena cava into the right atrium.

14. Observe the internal structure of the right auricle. The muscle visible in the interior of the auricle is called the **pectinate muscle,** since it resembles a comb (pecten).

15. Locate the large opening of the **inferior vena cava** on the left side of the interior of the right atrium. Insert a finger or probe through the mouth of this vein in order to locate the external opening on the dorsal surface of the heart. Compare the location of this vein with the corresponding vein in humans.

16. Locate the orifice of the **coronary sinus** just below the opening of the inferior vena cava. Locate this vessel on the dorsal surface of the heart.

17. Locate the **interatrial septum,** the wall that separates the two atria. Examine this septum from the interior of the right atrium. Feel the septum to locate the **fossa ovalis,** the oval-shaped depression ventral to the entrance of the inferior vena cava.

18. Examine the **tricuspid valve** between the right atrium and the right ventricle. Determine the number of cusps that form this valve.

KEY TO PHOTO 20

1. superior vena cava (cut)
2. opening of inferior vena cava
3. right atrium
4. tricuspid valve
5. chordae tendineae
6. myocardium of right ventricle

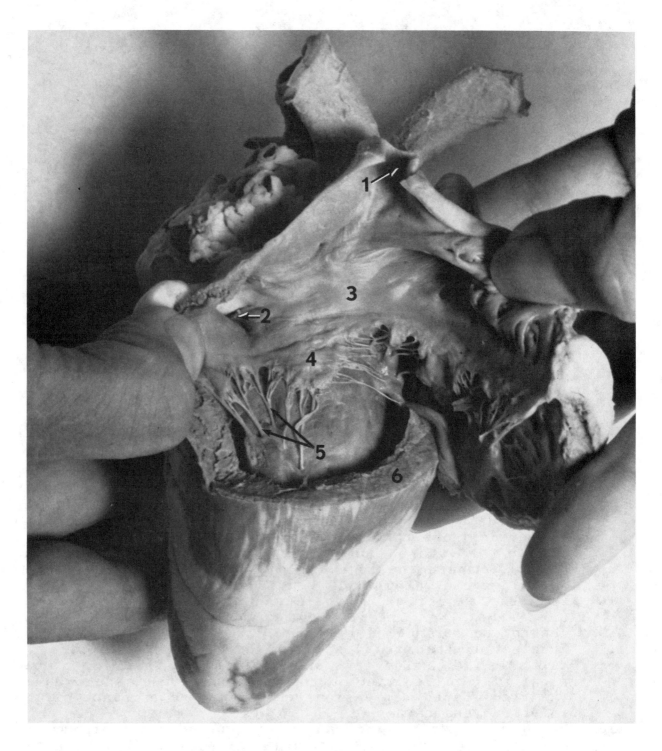

Photo 20: Right Side of the Sheep Heart

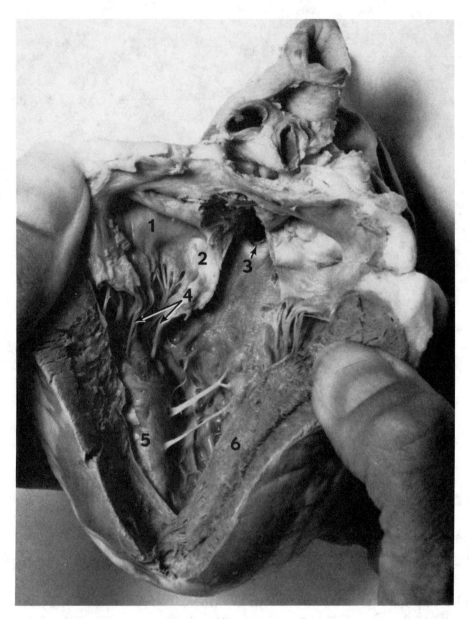

KEY TO PHOTO 21

1. left atrium
2. bicuspid (mitral) valve
3. aortic semilunar valve
4. chordae tendineae
5. papillary muscle
6. myocardium of left ventricle

Photo 21: Left Side of the Sheep Heart

19. Locate the **papillary muscles** and **chordae tendineae** in the wall of the right ventricle. Determine the number of papillary muscles.
20. Locate the **moderator band** crossing the lumen of the right ventricle. It received this name because it was once believed that it prevented overdistention of the ventricle. It is now known that it contains some fibers of the conduction system.
21. Try to locate the **four pulmonary veins** entering the **left atrium.** These vessels are visible on the dorsal surface of the left atrium. Whether all four vessels can be located depends on how they were cut when the heart was removed from the sheep.

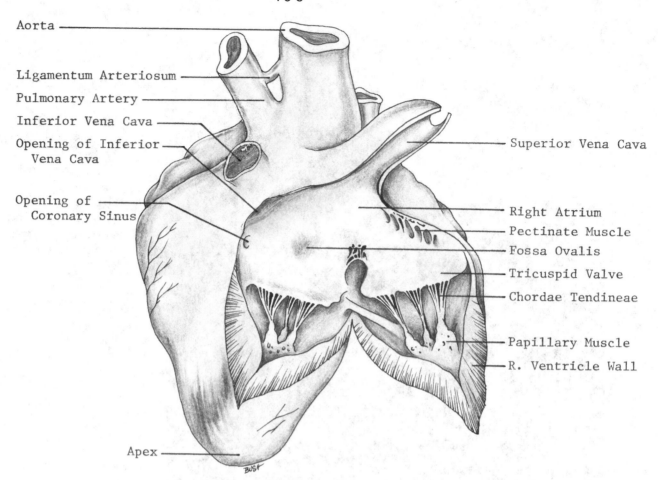

Aorta

Ligamentum Arteriosum

Pulmonary Artery

Inferior Vena Cava

Opening of Inferior Vena Cava

Opening of Coronary Sinus

Superior Vena Cava

Right Atrium

Pectinate Muscle

Fossa Ovalis

Tricuspid Valve

Chordae Tendineae

Papillary Muscle

R. Ventricle Wall

Apex

Figure VIII-6: Right Side of the Sheep Heart

22. Make a longitudinal incision through the most lateral of the pulmonary veins. Continue this incision down through the wall of the left atrium and the left ventricle to the **apex** of the heart.

23. Spread open the left side of the heart. Compare the wall thickness of the left ventricle with that of the right.

24. Observe the **bicuspid valve.** Determine how many major cusps comprise this valve. Determine which of the following are present in the left ventricle: moderator band, chordae tendineae, or papillary muscles.

25. Insert a finger up along the midline of the left ventricle into the **aorta.** Cut along this line until the **aortic semi-lunar valve** is visible. Count the number of pouches in this valve.

26. Returning to the external surface of the heart, locate the thick-walled aorta above the heart, arching to the left. Locate the **brachiocephalic artery** which branches from the aortic arch. This vessel later branches into the subclavian and common carotid arteries, which supply the arms and head. In humans, three large blood vessels branch from the aortic arch.

27. Open the aorta as it emerges from the network of blood vessels anterior to the heart. Observe the smooth lining of this vessel.

28. If the pulmonary artery was not severed too close to the heart when the heart was removed from the sheep, you will be able to locate the **ligamentum arteriosum,** the remnant of the **ductus arteriosus.** Carefully dissect away the adipose tissue between the pulmonary artery and the aorta anterior to the heart. Be careful not to sever the ligamentum arteriosum.

29. Locate all the preceding structures on the preserved horse and human hearts.

Ex. VIII-D. The Dissection of the Circulatory System of the Cat

DISCUSSION

The general plan of the circulatory system is much the same in all mammals. However, in the cat observe the differences in the branches of the aortic arch and in the terminal branches of the aorta. Use the diagrams of the cat circulatory system as a guide in your dissection. (Note: there is some variation among cats in the location of the vessels.)

The arteries of the cat have been injected with red latex; the veins with blue. In dissecting the blood vessels, each vein and artery must be gently freed from adjacent tissues so that it is clearly visible. A probe is most effectively used in freeing the blood vessels from the connective tissues.

In addition to Figures VIII-7 and VIII-8, refer to Photos 22 to 26 for the following procedures.

Part 1. Dissection of the Veins of the Cat (see Figure VIII-7)
PROCEDURE

1. Observe the **pericardium** surrounding the heart. After determining the structures to which it is attached, remove the parietal layer and the thymus gland. Do not damage the phrenic nerves to each side of the pericardium. The visceral layer pericardium forms the **epicardium** of the heart.

2. Note that the **apex** of the heart is directed towards the left. The heart is tilted so that the greater part of the **right ventricle** lies directly in front, along the ventral surface of the heart. The **left ventricle** forms the apex of the heart.

3. The **atria** lie anterior to the ventricles. Each atrium has a conspicuous ear-like appendage called the **auricle** on the ventral surface.

4. A groove, the **coronary sulcus,** separates the right atrium from the right ventricle. The **anterior longitudinal sulcus** is the groove that separates the right ventricle from the left ventricle. Dorsal to this sulcus is the **interventricular septum.** The coronary blood vessels are located in these grooves (the **right coronary artery** in the coronary sulcus, a branch of the **left** in the anterior longitudinal sulcus). The heart will not be dissected since it is very similar to the sheep heart.

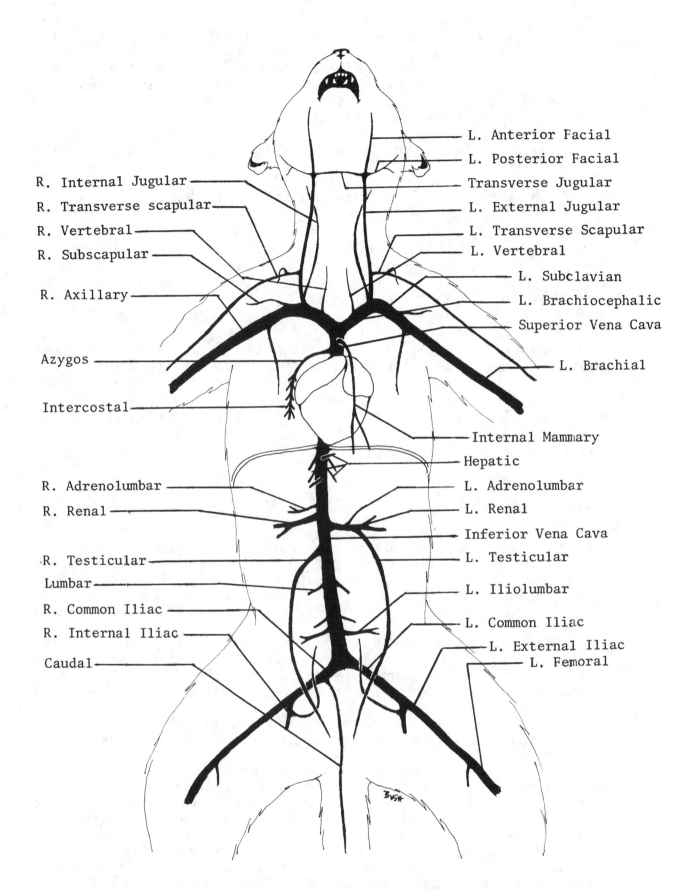

Figure VIII-7: Venous System of the Cat

5. Observe the **superior vena cava (precaval vein)**, the large vessel entering the anterior part of the right atrium. This vein drains the head, neck, and arms.

6. Trace this vessel forward and note that it is formed by the union of the two **brachiocephalic veins** (see Figure VIII-7 and Figure VII-5 in Chapter VII).

7. Lift up the heart, the superior vena cava, and the right lung; push these organs over to the left side of the thoracic cavity. Carefully dissect away tissue beneath the superior vena cava and right lung. The large azygos vein can be seen entering the dorsal surface of the superior vena cava immediately anterior to the heart. Under the right lung, the azygos vein is visible against the right side of the vertebral column. The tributaries of the azygos vein are the **intercostal veins** from the body wall, the **esophageal veins**, and the **bronchial veins**. Clean away connective tissue so that you can see the intercostal veins emptying into the azygos. It is not necessary to locate the esophageal and bronchial veins.

8. The superior vena cava also receives the **internal mammary vein** from the ventral chest wall (see Figure VII-5 in Chapter VII). The two internal mammary veins unite shortly before they empty into the superior vena cava. The **right vertebral vein** from the brain also enters the dorsal surface of the superior vena cava.

9. Trace the **left brachiocephalic vein** forward. This vein receives the **left vertebral vein**. The brachiocephalic vein is formed by the union of the large superficial **left external jugular vein** which drains the head and the very short **left subclavian vein**, which drains the arm.

10. Trace the external jugular vein towards the head. It receives the small **internal jugular vein** immediately above the point of union of the external jugular with the subclavian. The internal jugular vein, which drains the brain, lies next to the **left common carotid artery** near the trachea. In man the internal jugular vein is larger than the external jugular vein. The **thoracic duct**, a large lymphatic vessel, also empties into the left external jugular at the point of union of the external jugular with the subclavian vein. This duct may appear blue if latex was forced into it, or brown and beaded (due to the presence of valves) if it is empty. Continue tracing the external jugular vein towards the head. The large **transverse scapular (suprascapular) vein** empties into the external jugular.

11. The **external jugular vein** is formed by the union of the **anterior** and **posterior facial veins** under the lower jaw (see Figure V-7 in Chapter V). The **transverse jugular vein** can be seen connecting the two external jugular veins at this point.

12. Trace the left subclavian vein through the chest wall. It receives the **subscapular vein** from the shoulder just before it unites with the external jugular. Be careful not to damage any nerves in this region. In the axillary region the subclavian is known as the **axillary vein**. On the arm it becomes the **brachial vein**.

KEY TO PHOTO 22

1. transverse jugular
2. common carotid
   artery
3. internal jugular
   vein
4. external jugular
   vein
5. transverse
   scapular vein
6. subscapular vein
7. right brachio-
   cephalic vein
8. left brachio-
   cephalic vein
9. subclavian vein
10. axillary vein
11. brachial vein
12. superior
    vena cava
13. azygos vein

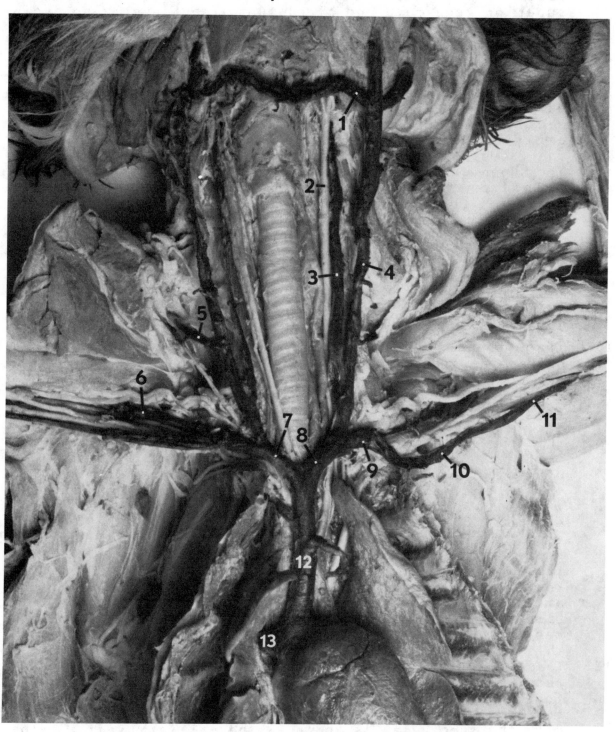

Photo 22: Veins Above the Diaphragm

13. Leave the lungs in position and lift up the heart. Locate the **inferior vena cava (postcaval vein)** posterior to the heart and trace it forward to the point where it drains into the right atrium. This large vein drains the lower part of the body.

14. Trace the inferior vena cava caudally through the diaphragm into the abdominal cavity where it lies to the right of the aorta. In order to see the vein and its tributaries it will be necessary to dissect away the peritoneum, since the inferior vena cava as well as the aorta is retroperitoneal. The tributaries usually accompany the arteries of the same name.

15. The **hepatic veins** drain blood from the liver into the inferior vena cava. To locate these veins, first press down on the liver to see where the IVC passes through the liver on the right of the falciform ligament and then gently scrape away liver tissue in this region. Several large hepatic veins may be located in this manner.

16. The **adrenolumbar veins** drain the adrenal glands and body wall. The right adrenolumbar vein drains into the inferior vena cava, the left drains into the renal vein. These veins may be located by examining the dorsal body wall anterior to the kidneys and by finding the adrenal glands. The adrenal glands resemble lymph nodes and are located anterior but close to the kidneys. The right adrenal gland is anterior to the left.

17. Locate the **renal veins**, which carry blood from the kidneys into the inferior vena cava. The right renal vein may be multiple. Note that the right renal vein is higher than the left.

18. Below the renals are the long, very thin, paired **ovarian** or **testicular veins.** They are most easily located by tracing the vessels from the gonads back towards the inferior vena cava. If the cat is a female, locate the **ovaries,** small oval bodies near the anterior ends of the **uterus,** below the kidneys. The ovarian artery and vein should now be visible. If the cat is a male, the **internal spermatic (testicular vein), artery,** and **vas deferens** can be seen passing through the **inguinal canal** (the opening in the posterior abdominal wall). Trace these blood vessels cranially towards the aorta and the inferior vena cava. The **left testicular (ovarian) vein** enters the renal vein in the cat; the right enters the inferior vena cava.

19. Several pairs of **lumbar veins** enter the dorsal surface of the inferior vena cava at intervals in the abdominal cavity. Gently push the inferior vena cava to one side to see these veins. The larger right and left **iliolumbar veins** enter the inferior vena cava from each side approximately one inch above where the inferior vena cava begins. These vessels drain the abdominal wall muscles.

20. Observe the **great saphenous vein** on the lower thigh and leg if it was not removed in skinning the cat. Trace it forward to where it drains into the **femoral vein,** the vein on the ventral surface of the thigh between the gracilis and sartorius muscles. Trace the femoral vein anteriorly

until it passes beneath the posterior border of the external oblique muscle. If your cat is a male, be careful not to damage the inguinal canal and vas deferens.

21. As the femoral vein disappears beneath the external oblique muscle, it becomes the **external iliac vein**. The **external iliac** is approximately one half inch long and it joins with the **internal iliac vein**, the vessel which drains the rectum, bladder, and internal reproductive organs to become the **common iliac vein**. Trace the right and left common iliac veins anteriorly until they unite to form the inferior vena cava. Close to their junction locate the **median sacral vein**. It drains blood from the sacrum and tail.

22. The portal system is usually not injected in cats, so it will not be necessary to dissect the smaller veins. The **portal vein (hepatic portal vein)** has been dissected earlier with the digestive system (see Figure VI-7 in Chapter VI). The portal vein and its tributaries drain the digestive organs and carry the blood to the liver. Follow the portal vein caudally. It is formed by the union of the **gastrosplenic vein** coming in on the left from the stomach and spleen, and the larger **superior mesenteric vein** coming in posteriorly from the intestines and the pancreas.

Part 2.   Dissection of the Arteries of the Cat (see Figure VIII-8)

1. Locate the **pulmonary artery** on the ventral surface of the heart. Trace it down to its origin in the right ventricle; then follow it toward the lungs, noting that it branches into a **right** and **left pulmonary artery**. Remove any remaining pericardium so that these vessels can be clearly seen. Note: the pulmonary artery contains blue latex.

2. Push the right auricle to the right. The large white vessel that can be seen emerging from the left ventricle and passing beneath the pulmonary artery is the **aorta (dorsal aorta)**. This is injected with red latex, but due to the thickness of the wall of the aorta the color often can not be seen. (Do not remove the wall of the aorta in your dissection.)

3. Dissect around the base of the ascending aorta until the **right** and **left coronary arteries** are visible. These arise just anterior to the **aortic semilunar valve**. The right coronary artery can then be seen in the coronary sulcus on the surface of the heart; a branch of the left coronary artery in the anterior longitudinal sulcus.

4. The dorsal aorta passes anteriorly for a short distance and then turns to the left. This region of the aorta is called the **aortic arch**. Two large arteries originate from the aortic arch in the cat. The first branch is the **brachiocephalic artery**. Trace this vessel forward. The brachiocephalic gives off first the **left common carotid artery** and then branches into the **right subclavian** and the **right common carotid arteries**. The left subclavian artery leaves the arch separately. In the human the left common carotid comes directly off the aortic arch.

KEY TO PHOTO 23

1. thyroid cartilage
2. cricoid cartilage
3. transverse scapular artery
4. right brachial artery
5. subscapular artery
6. right axillary artery
7. right common carotid artery
8. left common carotid artery
9. left vagus nerve
10. left axillary artery
11. left brachial artery
12. right internal mammary artery
13. right subclavian artery
14. brachiocephalic artery
15. left subclavian artery
16. aortic arch

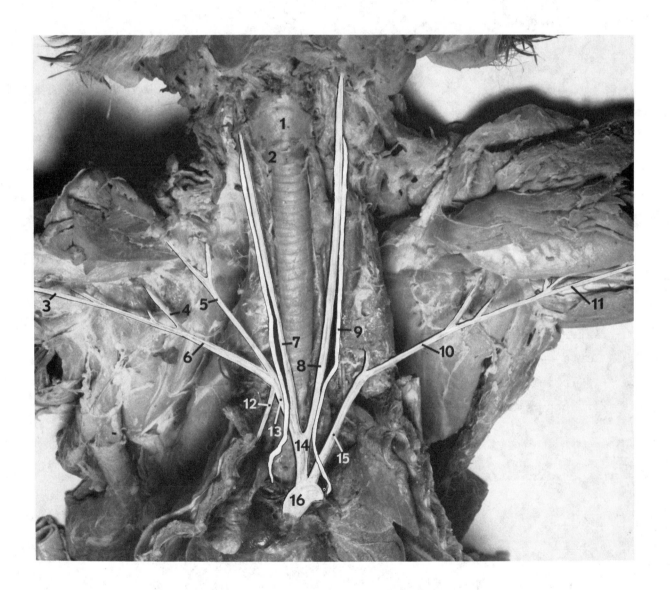

Photo 23: Arteries Above the Diaphragm

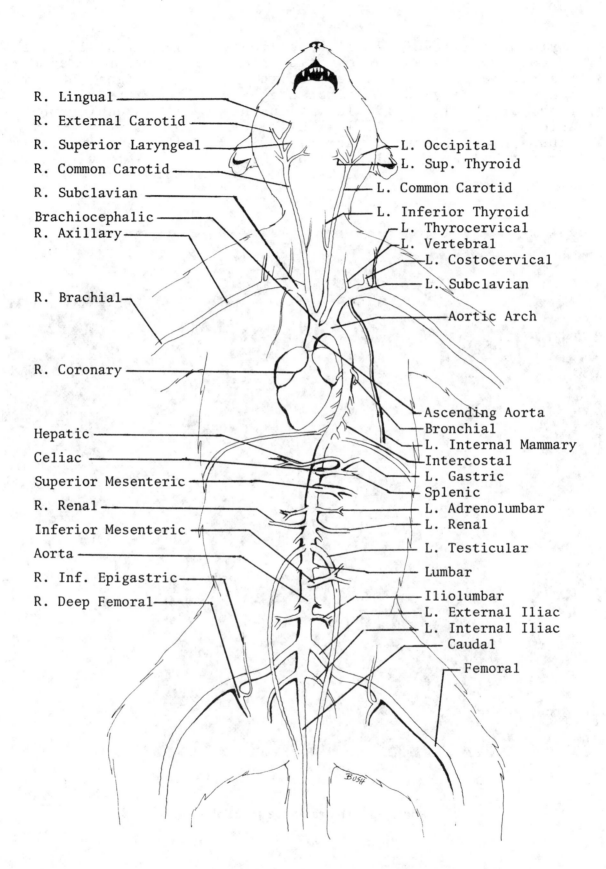

R. Lingual
R. External Carotid
R. Superior Laryngeal
R. Common Carotid
R. Subclavian
Brachiocephalic
R. Axillary

R. Brachial

R. Coronary

Hepatic
Celiac
Superior Mesenteric
R. Renal
Inferior Mesenteric
Aorta
R. Inf. Epigastric
R. Deep Femoral

L. Occipital
L. Sup. Thyroid
L. Common Carotid
L. Inferior Thyroid
L. Thyrocervical
L. Vertebral
L. Costocervical
L. Subclavian
Aortic Arch

Ascending Aorta
Bronchial
L. Internal Mammary
Intercostal
L. Gastric
Splenic
L. Adrenolumbar
L. Renal
L. Testicular
Lumbar
Iliolumbar
L. External Iliac
L. Internal Iliac
Caudal
Femoral

Figure VIII-8: Arterial System of the Cat

5. Trace the **left common carotid artery**. It ascends in the neck, lying between the tiny internal jugular vein and trachea. The first branch of the left common carotid artery is the **inferior thyroid artery**. This runs anteriorly along the trachea. The **superior thyroid artery** originates at the level of the thyroid cartilage. It supplies the thyroid gland and some of the neck musculature. Anterior to this is the **occipital artery**, which supplies the back of the neck.

6. The left common carotid branches to form the **external** and **internal carotid arteries** at the anterior border of the larynx. The internal carotid is very small in the cat and need not be located. It passes dorsally to enter the skull. The larger external carotid artery continues on to supply the external structures of the head.

7. Returning to the aortic arch, locate the **left subclavian artery**, which supplies the left side of the chest and eventually the left arm. Trace along the left subclavian artery. The **internal mammary artery** branches from the ventral surface of the subclavian and passes to the ventral thoracic wall where it accompanies the corresponding vein.

8. The **vertebral artery** arises from the dorsal surface of the subclavian artery nearly opposite the internal mammary artery. This passes cranially and supplies the brain. The next branch of the subclavian artery is the **costocervical trunk**. This supplies some of the neck, back, and intercostal muscles. Locate next the **thyrocervical trunk**, which ascends for a short distance and then branches. It also supplies some of the neck and shoulder muscles.

9. The subclavian artery becomes the **axillary artery** as it emerges from the chest cavity and crosses the axillary space. It then continues into the arm where it is known as the **brachial artery**. Follow the brachial artery until it branches to form the **radial** and **ulnar arteries** which supply the forearm.

10. Returning to the aortic arch, trace the aorta caudally. Push the viscera in the thorax to the right to expose the aorta in the thoracic cavity. As this vessel passes through the thorax it is called the **thoracic aorta**. Remove the pleura to expose this vessel in the thorax.

11. Note the **intercostal arteries** emerging from the thoracic aorta. These supply the intercostal muscles. There are also, branching from the thoracic aorta, several **bronchial arteries** which supply the lungs and **esophageal arteries** which supply the esophagus.

12. Trace the descending aorta through the diaphragm. The first major branch from the abdominal aorta is the short **celiac artery**. In order to locate this artery it is necessary to remove the peritoneum covering the anterior end of the abdominal aorta immediately beneath the diaphragm. The celiac artery divides into three branches: **hepatic, left gastric,** and **splenic.** The hepatic artery is usually the first branch off the celiac. Trace the hepatic artery from the celiac artery under the stomach to the liver. The hepatic artery was located earlier in the lesser omentum to

KEY TO PHOTO 24

1. urinary bladder
2. common iliac vein
3. internal iliac artery
4. external iliac artery
5. inferior mesenteric artery

6. aorta
7. inferior vena cava
8. renal vein
9. superior mesenteric artery
10. celiac artery
11. iliolumbar artery

12. uterine horns
13. ovary
14. ureter
15. ovarian artery
16. ovarian vein
17. renal artery
18. left kidney

Photo 24: Arteries and Other Structures Below Diaphragm

KEY TO PHOTO 25

1. spleen
2. superior mesenteric artery
3. splenic artery
4. left gastric artery
5. hepatic artery
6. inferior vena cava
7. renal vein
8. left adrenal gland
9. aorta
10. renal artery
11. ureter
12. left kidney

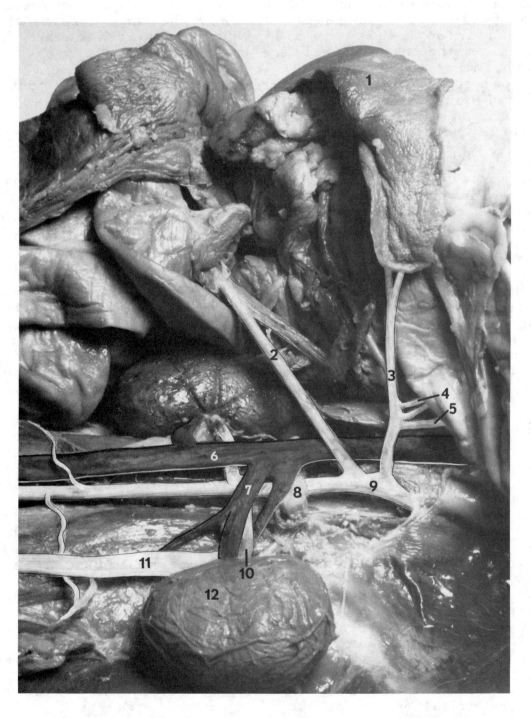

Photo 25: Close-up of Blood Vessels of Anterior Abdominal Cavity

the left of the portal vein during the dissection of the digestive system (See Figure VI-7, Chapter VI). Locate the **cystic artery**, a branch of the hepatic artery, which supplies the gall bladder. The left gastric artery, the smallest and second branch, runs directly to the lesser curvature of the stomach and then branches to supply the stomach. The remaining artery, the splenic, is the largest branch of the celiac. Trace this to the spleen. Note that the aorta lies to the left of the inferior vena cava.

13. Locate the **superior mesenteric artery**, the unpaired vessel just posterior to and approximately the same size as the celiac artery. This vessel is also retroperitoneal. It supplies the small intestine and the first half of the large intestine.

14. The paired **adrenolumbar arteries** run from the aorta to the dorsal body wall. They supply the adrenal glands, diaphragm and muscles of the body wall.

15. Observe the **renal arteries** posterior to the superior mesentric artery. These arteries supply the kidney.

16. The right and left genital arteries are small thread-like vessels that emerge from the ventral surface of the aorta posterior to the renals. If your specimen is a male, follow the **testicular (internal spermatic) arteries** from the inguinal canal to the aorta. The testicular artery supplies the testis. If your specimen is a female, trace the **ovarian artery** to the ovary. In the cat, this vessel supplies the uterus as well as the ovary.

17. Push the descending colon to one side to see the unpaired **inferior mesenteric artery**. This vessel is much smaller than the superior mesenteric artery. It arises from the aorta posterior to the ovarian or testicular arteries. It is approximately one inch long and soon divides, with one branch (the **left colic artery**) proceeding anteriorly, and one branch (the **superior hemorrhoidal**) posteriorly along the dorsal surface of the colon.

18. The cat has approximately seven pairs of **lumbar arteries** emerging at intervals along the abdominal aorta. These are paired with the lumbar veins and the arteries supply the abdominal wall. A large pair of arteries, the **iliolumbars**, may be seen just above the termination of the aorta running laterally to the body wall.

19. Observe carefully the base of the aorta (see Figure XIII-19, Chapter XIII). There is no common iliac artery in the cat. Instead, the paired **external iliac arteries** arise from the aorta, and then the paired **internal iliac arteries** arise independently from the aorta. The branches of the internal iliac supply the gluteal muscles, rectum, and uterus. These arteries go deep into the pelvic cavity where they can be seen beside the internal iliac vein. As the external iliac artery passes through the body wall, it becomes the **femoral artery**. Trace this vessel down the ventral surface of the thigh.

20. After giving off the iliac arteries, the aorta continues as the **caudal** or **median sacral artery**. It travels down the median ventral surface of the sacrum and enters the tail.

KEY TO PHOTO 26

1. descending colon
2. left kidney (pushed to right side)
3. left uterine horn (pushed to right)
4. urinary bladder
5. left ureter
6. right ureter
7. superior mesenteric artery
8. inferior vena cava
9. aorta
10. iliolumbar artery
11. internal iliac artery
12. median sacral artery
13. common iliac vein
14. external iliac artery
15. internal iliac artery
16. internal iliac vein
17. external iliac vein
18. femoral vein
19. femoral artery

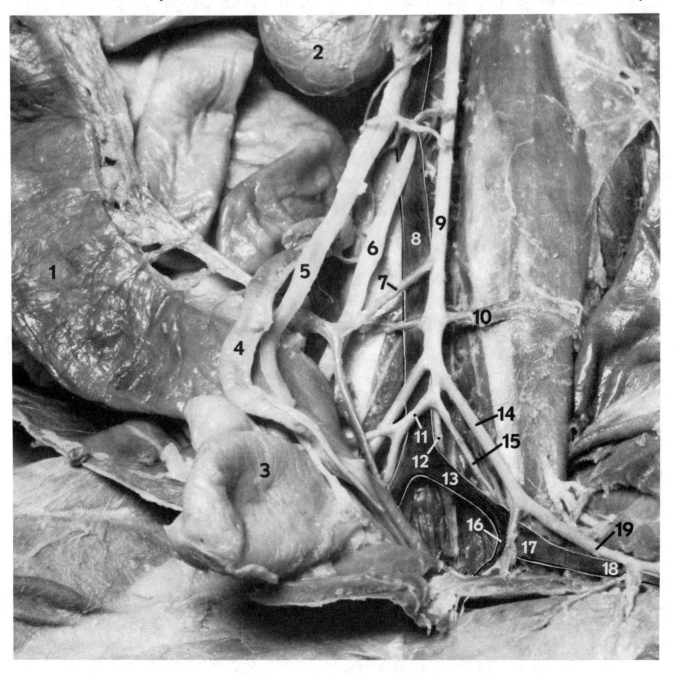

Photo 26: Close-up of Blood Vessels of Posterior Abdominal Cavity

21. Demonstration: observe the **ductus arteriosus, umbilical arteries, umbilical vein,** and **foramen ovale** in a dissected fetal pig. If this is unavailable, locate the following on models of human fetal circulation:

a. aorta
b. ductus arteriosus
c. ductus venosus
d. foramen ovale
e. inferior vena cava
f. internal iliac artery
g. pulmonary artery
h. superior vena cava
i. umbilical artery
j. umbilical cord
k. umbilical vein

Vessels carrying oxygenated blood are usually colored red, venous blood blue, and those with mixed blood purple.

SELF-TEST: THE CIRCULATORY SYSTEM

DIRECTIONS: See Chapter 1, Self-Test, p. 12

1. The right and left common iliac veins unite to form the **superior vena cava.**
2. The pulse is usually taken at the **radial** artery.
3. The blood vessel that carries blood from the fetus to the placenta is the **umbilical artery.**
4. Two fetal structures which allow blood to bypass the lungs are the **foramen ovale** and the **ductus arteriosus.**
5. The **aorta** has the highest blood pressure of any blood vessel.
6. The vagus nerve **accelerates** the heart.
7. The vasomotor center, located in the **cerebellum,** regulates blood pressure.
8. Lymph from the thoracic duct drains into the **left subclavian vein.**
9. An artery is a vessel which leads **from** the heart while veins lead **toward** it.
10. Small arteries are called **arterioles.**
11. The **endocardium** is a sac surrounding the heart.
12. The left atrium receives **deoxygenated** blood.
13. Contraction of the heart is called **systole,** and relaxation is called **diastole.**
14. The **atrioventricular** node is the pacemaker of the heart.
15. Constriction of a valve of the heart, making it difficult for blood to get through, is called **cardiac thrombosis.**
16. The internal carotid artery, the vertebral artery, and the Circle of Willis are involved in supplying blood to **the brain.**
17. The **internal jugular** veins drain the brain.
18. The common iliac veins drain the **legs and pelvis.**
19. The brachial artery supplies the **leg.**
20. The **great saphenous** vein drains the legs.
21. The **celiac** artery supplies the stomach, liver, spleen, and pancreas.
22. The hepatic **vein** carries oxygen to the liver.
23. The portal vein carries the end **products of digestion** to the sinusoids of the liver.
24. The principal function of an erythrocyte is to **carry oxygen,** while that of a leukocyte is to **fight infection.**
25. Red bone marrow is the source of **erythrocytes, leukocytes,** and **thrombocytes.**
26. **Neutrophils** are the most abundant type of leukocyte.
27. The lingual artery supplies the **tongue.**
28. The **popliteal** artery passes behind the knee.
29. Veins contain valves - arteries **do not.**
30. Arteries **always** carry oxygenated blood.
31. **Hypertension** is the term designating hardening of the arteries.
32. Blood is pumped to the lungs by the **left ventricle.**
33. **Endocarditis** is an inflammation of the lining and valves of the heart.
34. Congenital heart disease **appears during old age.**

35. The **mitral (bicuspid) valve** is located between the right atrium and the right ventricle.
36. Rheumatic fever frequently affects the **heart**.
37. A blue baby may result from the **Tetralogy of Fallot**.
38. A slow, strong heart rate would result from nerve impulses arising mainly from the **thoracolumbar (sympathetic)** portion of the nervous system.
39. The erythrocyte, in the mature stage, is **nucleated**.
40. Hemopoiesis **in the embryo** occurs in the liver, spleen, red bone marrow, and lymph nodes.
41. The **hepatic veins** drain the liver.
42. An important function of the spleen is to produce **erythrocytes** in the adult.
43. The heart muscle is called the **endocardium**.
44. Cardiac muscle has **striated** myofibrils.
45. The heart and portions of the great vessels fill the **pericardial cavity**.
46. The membrane surrounding the heart is a **serous** membrane.
47. The blood in the pulmonary **artery** is fully oxygenated.
48. The heart beat is initiated by the **Bundle of His**.
49. Blood entering the left atrium of the heart comes directly from the **inferior and superior venae cavae**.
50. Venous sinuses are found in the **skull and heart**.
51. The inner layer of tissue in the arterial wall is called the **endocardium**.
52. An **anastomosis** is a passageway or connection between two vessels.
53. The aorta arches to the **right**.
54. The coronary arteries are the **only** branches from the ascending aorta.
55. The **right and left common carotid arteries** divide into the internal and external carotid arteries.
56. There are **more** veins than arteries in the body.
57. The myofibrils in the walls of arteries are **striated**.
58. There are **two** umbilical arteries and **one** umbilical vein which provide for blood circulation between the placenta and the embryo.
59. A unique feature of the portal system is that blood from the digestive tract is detoured through the **kidney** instead of being returned directly to the inferior vena cava.
60. The umbilical vein carries **oxygenated** blood.
61. The prominent superficial vein in the neck is the **external carotid**.
62. The thoracic duct contains **lymph**.
63. The azygos vein drains blood from the intercostal veins into the **superior vena cava**.
64. Systolic blood pressure is **higher** than diastolic blood pressure.
65. Hemorrhage from an artery results in a **steady** flow of blood.
66. Blood flows least rapidly through **veins**.
67. Blood pressure is usually taken at the **radial** artery.
68. The formation of a clot in a branch of the coronary arteries is called a **cerebral vascular accident**.

69. Dilated veins of the rectum produce a condition known as **hemorrhoids.**
70. Studies show that vigorous exercise **enlarges** the heart.
71. The basilic vein drains the **brain.**
72. Fluid which is located between the cells is called **intra-cellular** fluid.
73. In making a complete circuit through the human body, blood passes through the heart **once.**
74. Leukocytes pass into the tissues through the walls of the **venules.**
75. During the beating of the heart, sounds are produced by the closing of the **semilunar valves.**
76. Muscle cells are present in the layer of an artery wall know as the **intima.**
77. Capillaries may be present in the walls of the **larger arteries.**
78. The spleen is concerned with the destruction of **lymphocytes.**
79. The coronary sinus opens into the **right atrium.**
80. The nutrient artery of the lungs is the **bronchial artery.**
81. The artery which brings oxygen to the liver is the **portal artery.**
82. Apoplexy is a term used for a **heart attack.**
83. A thrombus is a **moving** blood clot.
84. Localized death of cardiac tissue due to obstruction of a coronary artery is known as **myocardial infarction.**
85. The thoracic duct receives **blood** from the digestive tract.
86. Lymph flow is aided by **valves** in lymphatic vessels.
87. Lymph glands produce large numbers of **lymphocytes.**

KEY

1. inferior vena cava	35. tricuspid	66. capillaries
6. slows down	38. cranio-sacral (parasympathetic)	67. brachial
7. medulla oblongata	39. non-nucleated (anucleate)	68. coronary thrombosis
11. pericardium	42. leukocytes (lymphocytes)	71. arm
12. oxygenated	43. myocardium	72. intercellular (tissue or interstitial)
14. sino-atrial	47. vein	73. twice
15. stenosis	48. sino-atrial node	74. capillaries
19. arm	49. pulmonary veins	76. media
22. artery	51. endothelium	78. erythrocytes
30. do not always	53. left	81. hepatic artery
31. arteriosclerosis	57. nonstriated	82. stroke (cerebral vascular accident)
32. right ventricle	59. liver	83. stationary
34. appears at birth	61. external jugular	85. lymph
	65. pulsating	

Chapter IX

THE NERVOUS SYSTEM

Ex. IX-A. Anatomy of the Nervous System

DISCUSSION

For convenience of study, the nervous system may be divided into the **central nervous system (CNS),** the **peripheral nervous system (PNS),** and the **autonomic nervous system (ANS),** a special subdivision of the peripheral nervous system. The ANS is usually subdivided into the **sympathetic** and the **parasympathetic** divisions. The central nervous system is composed of the brain and the spinal cord; the peripheral nervous system of the spinal and cranial nerves. The structural and functional unit of the nervous system is the neuron. (The structure of the neuron and a medullated nerve fiber has been described in Ex. III-F, Chapter III.)

PROCEDURE

Part 1.   Structure of a Nerve
  1.   Obtain a slide of a cross section through a nerve. Examine the slide with the low power objective.
  2.   Observe the connective tissue sheath called the **epineurium** surrounding the entire nerve. This sheath contains connective tissue cells, collagenic fibers, adipose tissue, and nutrient blood vessels called the **vasa nervorum.**
  3.   Note that the nerve fibers comprising the nerve are arranged in bundles; each bundle (**funiculus**) is surrounded by connective tissue called the **perineurium.**
  4.   Locate the **endoneurium,** the connective tissue that surrounds each individual nerve fiber.
  5.   Make a diagram of the entire cross section of the nerve showing the preceding structures. Label the epineurium, endoneurium, nerve fibers, vasa nervorum, and adipose tissue. It is not necessary to draw any cells in this diagram.
  6.   Now, examine the slide with the high power objective. Locate a nerve fiber that contains a nucleus in the neurilemma. Draw this fiber below the diagram of the nerve. Include on this drawing the **axis cylinder,** located in the center of the fiber; the thick **myelin sheath;** the thin **neurilemma** surrounding the fiber; and the nucleus of the neurilemma. (Compare this with Figure III-21 in Chapter III.)

Part 2.   The Spinal Cord
  1.   Obtain a slide of a cross section through the spinal cord. First, study this slide with the naked eye to observe the shape and size of the cord. Since the cord was mounted upside down on the slide (so that it will appear right side up when using the microscope), be certain to hold the slide so that the printing at the bottom of the slide is upside down while examining it with the eye.

2. Diagram the shape of the entire cord and adjacent roots of the spinal nerve on a full sheet of paper. This drawing should include the shape of the central gray matter.

3. Now study the slide under the low power objective. (Return the slide to the usual position for microscope viewing.)

4. Observe the shape of the **central canal**, the **dorsal median septum**, and the **ventral median fissure**. Determine whether the latter two touch the central gray matter. Include these on the diagram. Use your text and/or other references to aid you in this study.

5. Locate nerve cell bodies in the **dorsal root ganglion** and in the **ventral horn** of the gray matter.

6. Include the following labels on your diagram: dorsal root, dorsal root ganglion, ventral root, dorsal horn, dorsal, lateral and ventral funiculi, dorsal median septum, ventral median fissure, central canal, white matter, and gray matter.

Part 3. The Gross Structure of the Brain

1. Figures IX-1 and IX-2 of the human brain may be studied as self-tests. See Section J, p. 5 (Illustrations as Self-Tests) for suggested approach.

2. Identify the structures indicated on Figures IX-1 and IX-2 on models of the human brain, preserved human brain, sheep brain (see Ex. IX-B), and with similar illustrations on charts and in reference material.

Ex. IX-B. The Dissection of the Sheep Brain

DISCUSSION

The structure of the sheep brain is very similar to that of the human and cat brains. Note any differences as you study the brains. The brain is surrounded by three layers of **meninges**. The outermost, the **dura mater**, is usually removed in preparing the sheep brains. This layer may be seen surrounding the brain of the cat if the surrounding bones are carefully cut away with scissors.

PROCEDURE

1. Obtain a sagittal section of the sheep brain and an entire sheep brain and rinse both with tap water. Use the entire brain for steps 2-15. Refer to Figures IX-1 to IX-5 and Photos 27-29 for steps 2-29.

2. The inner two layers of the meninges can be seen covering the brain. The **arachnoid**, the middle layer, lies between the **dura mater** and the **pia mater**, the innermost, vascular layer of the meninges. The arachnoid is most easily distinguished from the pia mater in the region overlying the grooves on the brain surface, since the pia mater dips into the grooves and the arachnoid does not. Peel off some of the arachnoid with your forceps.

3. Observe the anterior paired **cerebral hemispheres** and the posterior **cerebellum** on the dorsal surface of the brain. The cerebral hemispheres are separated from each other by the **longitudinal fissure**; the cerebellum is separated from the cerebral hemispheres by the **transverse fissure** (see Figure IX-3).

KEY TO FIGURE IX-1

1. corpus callosum
2. septum pellucidum
3. thalamus
4. mammillary body
5. hypothalamus
6. infundibulum
7. hypophysis
   (pituitary)

8. pons (pons
   Varolii)
9. medulla oblongata
10. fornix
11. splenium
12. pineal body
13. corpora
    quadrigemina

14. superior colliculus
15. inferior colliculus
16. cerebral aqueduct
17. cerebral peduncles
18. cerebellum
19. fourth ventricle

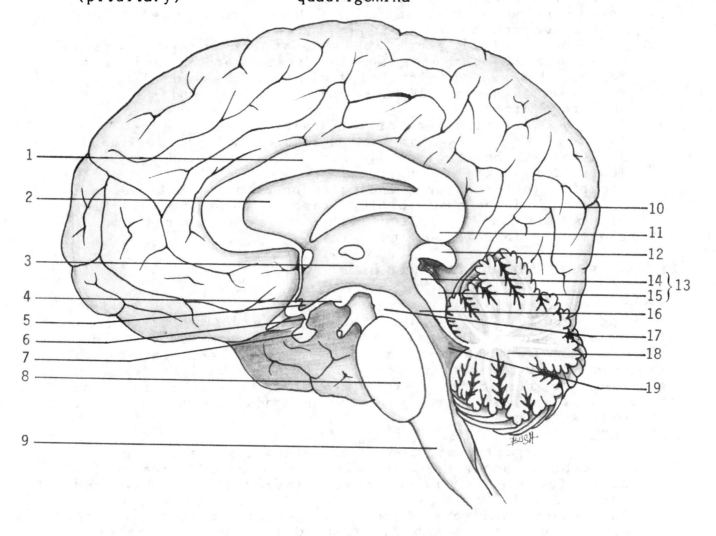

Figure IX-1: Sagittal Section of the Brain

4. Carefully spread the cerebral hemispheres apart and observe the thick transverse band of white matter, the **corpus callosum**, deep in the longitudinal fissure. These commissural fibers connect the cerebral hemispheres.

5. The surface of each hemisphere is composed of numerous folds. Each upfold is called a **gyrus (convolution)** and each shallow depression a **sulcus**.

KEY TO FIGURE IX-2

1. optic chiasma
2. hypothalamus
3. pons (pons Varolii)
4. medulla oblongata
5. olfactory bulb
6. olfactory tract

7. optic nerve
8. infundibulum
9. optic tract
10. mammillary body
11. oculomotor nerve
12. motor root

13. sensory root
14. trigeminal nerve
15. abducens nerve
16. vagus nerve
17. cerebellum

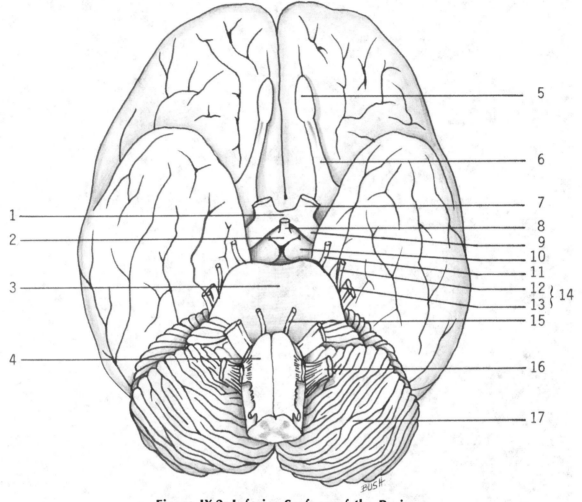

Figure IX-2: Inferior Surface of the Brain

6. The roof of the **midbrain (mesencephalon)** can be seen by spreading the cerebral hemispheres and cerebellum apart (see Figure IX-3). Four prominent round swellings, the **corpora quadrigemina,** form the roof of the midbrain. The larger, anterior pair is called the **superior colliculi;** the smaller posterior pair the **inferior colliculi.** The **pineal body** can be seen between the superior colliculi. The right and left **trochlear nerves** appear as thin, white strands, directed ventrally, slightly posterior to the inferior colliculi.

7. Posterior to the cerebral hemispheres is the **cerebellum.** The cerebellum is connected with the brain stem by three prominent fiber tracts or **peduncles.** Lift up the lateral edge of the cerebellum. The **middle cerebellar peduncle** can be seen connecting the cerebellum with the pons.

KEY TO PHOTO 27

1. spinal cord
2. cerebellum
3. transverse fissure

4. gyrus
5. sulcus
6. longitudinal fissure

7. left cerebral
   hemisphere

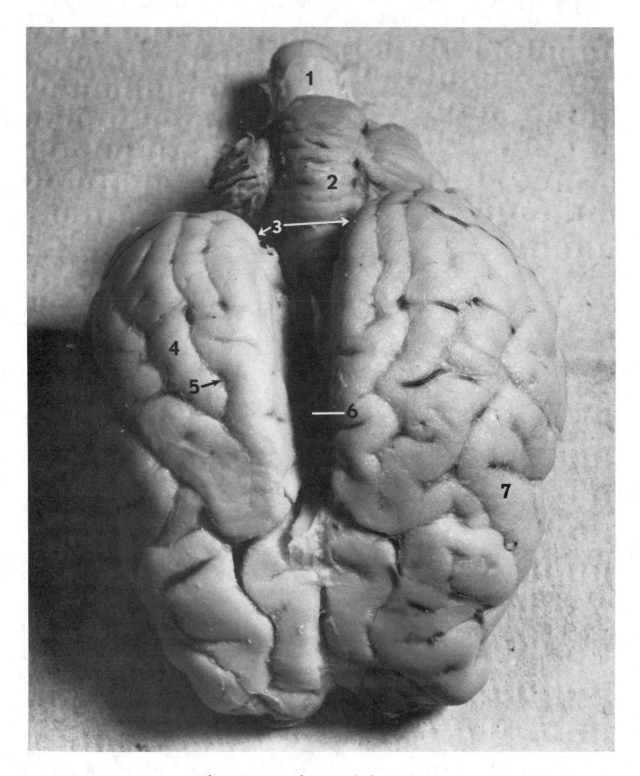

Photo 27: Dorsal View of Sheep Brain

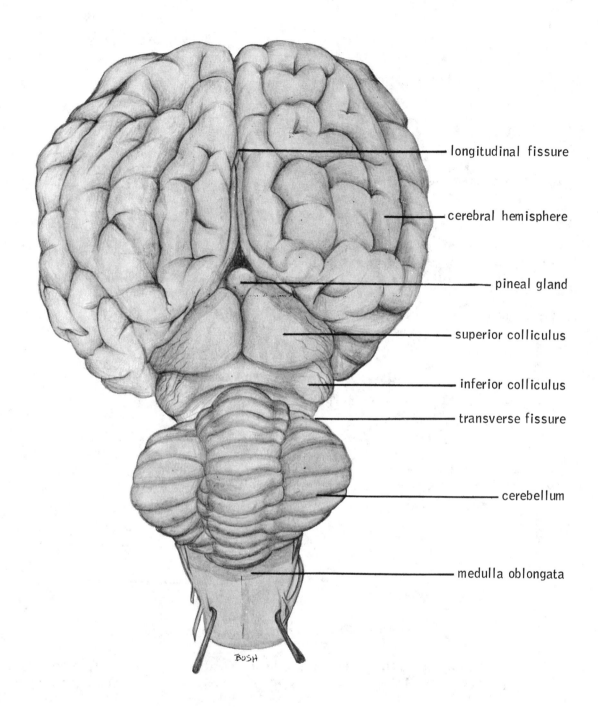

longitudinal fissure

cerebral hemisphere

pineal gland

superior colliculus

inferior colliculus

transverse fissure

cerebellum

medulla oblongata

BUSH

Figure IX-3: Dorsal View of Sheep Brain
(with cerebellum separated from cerebral hemispheres)

8. Observe the ventral surface of the sheep brain (see Figure
    IX-4). A pair of **olfactory bulbs** can be seen beneath the
    cerebral hemispheres. These bulbs lie over the cribriform
    plate of the ethmoid bone and receive the olfactory neu-
    rons from the nasal chamber.
9. A white band, the **olfactory tract** extends from each bulb
    along the ventral surface of the cerebral hemispheres.

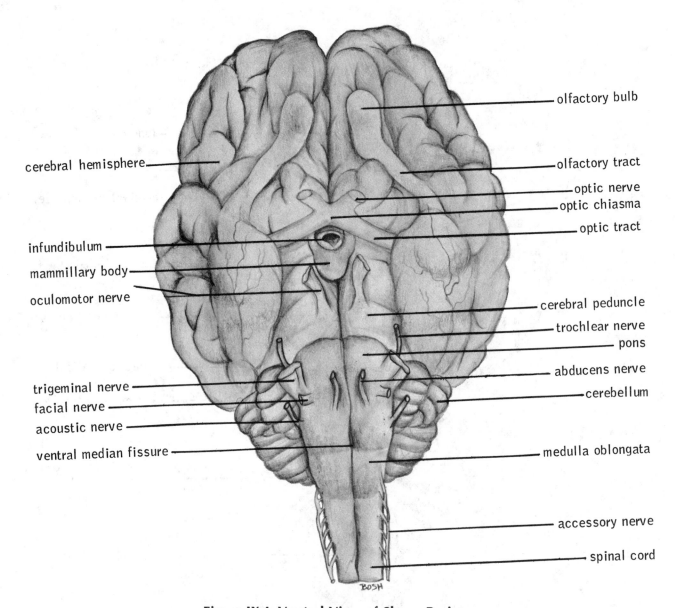

olfactory bulb

cerebral hemisphere

olfactory tract

optic nerve

optic chiasma

optic tract

infundibulum

mammillary body

oculomotor nerve

cerebral peduncle

trochlear nerve

pons

abducens nerve

cerebellum

trigeminal nerve

facial nerve

acoustic nerve

ventral median fissure

medulla oblongata

accessory nerve

spinal cord

BOSH

Figure IX-4: Ventral View of Sheep Brain

10. The ventral surface of the **diencephalon**, the **hypothalamus**, is posterior to the olfactory tracts. The optic nerves undergo a partial crossing over (decussation) at the anterior border of the hypothalamus, forming the cross known as the **optic chiasma.**

11. The remainder of the hypothalamus is the oval area lying posterior to the optic chiasma, covered by the **pituitary gland (hypophysis).** Do not remove the gland. A small stalk called the **infundibulum** can be seen connecting the pituitary to the hypothalamus.

12. Posterior to the infundibulum is the rounded **mammillary body** (there are two in humans).

13. Observe the **cerebral peduncles** on the ventral surface of the midbrain. The large **oculomotor nerves,** covered by the pituitary gland, arise from the cerebral peduncles posterior to the mammillary body.

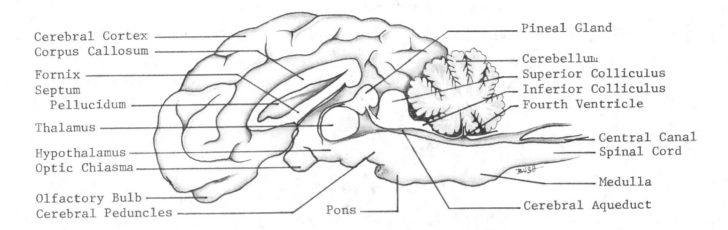

Cerebral Cortex
Corpus Callosum

Fornix
Septum
  Pellucidum

Thalamus

Hypothalamus
Optic Chiasma

Olfactory Bulb
Cerebral Peduncles

Pons

Pineal Gland

Cerebellum
Superior Colliculus
Inferior Colliculus
Fourth Ventricle

Central Canal
Spinal Cord

Medulla

Cerebral Aqueduct

Figure IX-5: Sagittal Section through Sheep Brain

14. Posterior to the midbrain is the **pons (pons Varolii)**. This is composed primarily of white fibers, many of which run transversely across the pons out to the cerebellum.

15. The **medulla oblongata** is posterior to the pons. The longitudinal bands of tissue at each side of the **ventral median fissure** on the ventral surface of the medulla are known as the **pyramids**. The **basilar artery** can be seen in the ventral median fissure of the medulla and midline of the pons.

16. To see the remaining parts of the brain, use the sagittal section of the sheep brain. (Compare the specimen with Figure IX-5, sagittal section of the sheep brain). Relocate the **corpus callosum**, which consists of the white fibers connecting the two cerebral hemispheres.

17. A thin, vertical partition of tissue, the **septum pellucidum**, lies ventral to the corpus callosum. The **lateral ventricle** lies behind this septum and may be seen by breaking the septum.

18. The **fornix**, a band of white fibers, lies ventral to the septum.

19. The **third ventricle** and the **thalamus** lie ventral to the fornix. The narrow third ventricle, the walls of which are covered by a shiny layer of epithelium, is in the midline. The thalamus forms the lateral walls of the third ventricle.

20. The **massa intermedia** extends across the third ventricle, connecting the two sides of the thalamus. This structure appears as a large dull circular area not covered by epithelium.

21. The **foramen of Monro**, the opening through which each lateral ventricle communicates with the third ventricle, lies in the depression anterior to the massa intermedia. Find this connection by passing a dull probe through it.

22. Relocate the **hypothalamus**. This lies ventral to the third ventricle.

23. Note the **pineal body** dorsal to the midbrain, near the **superior colliculus**.

KEY TO PHOTO 28

1. cerebral cortex
2. cerebellum
3. transverse fissure
4. spinal cord
5. pyramid

6. medulla oblongata
7. pons
8. cerebral peduncles

9. olfactory nerve
10. optic chiasma
11. olfactory tract
12. olfactory bulb

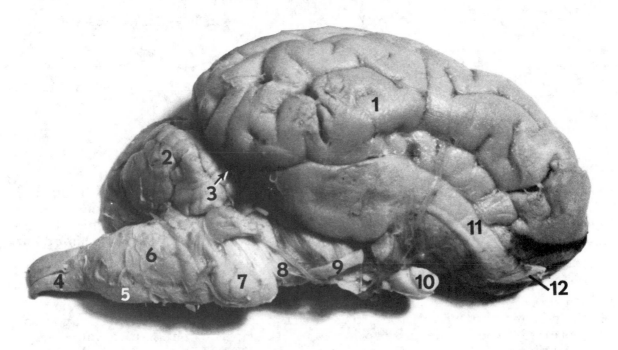

Photo 28: Lateral View of Sheep Brain

24. Observe the narrow **cerebral aqueduct** leading through the midbrain, connecting the third and fourth ventricles.
25. The **fourth ventricle** lies in the hindbrain, above the pons and medulla and below the cerebellum.
26. The beginning of the spinal cord may be seen connected to the medulla. A canal known as the **central canal**, which is connected to the fourth ventricle, is present in the center of the cord.
27. Note the treelike arrangement of white matter in the cerebellum. This arrangement is known as the **arbor vitae** (tree of life). The gray matter of the cerebellum is on the outside, the white is toward the center.
28. The outer layer of the cerebral hemispheres, the **cerebral cortex**, is also composed of gray matter. With a scalpel cut a wedge from the cerebral hemispheres in order to see the contrast of color between the cortex and the white matter located underneath.
29. Examine the human brain and locate as many of the preceding structures as possible. Note the paired mammillary bodies, the larger size of the cerebral hemispheres, the smaller midbrain and olfactory bulbs, and the deeper convolutions.

KEY TO PHOTO 29

1. cerebral cortex
2. lateral ventricle
3. fornix
4. corpus callosum
5. septum pellucidum
6. pineal gland
7. superior colliculi

8. cerebral aqueduct
9. cerebellum
10. arbor vitae (tree)
11. central canal
12. spinal cord
13. fourth ventricle
14. medulla oblongata

15. pons
16. cerebral peduncles
17. thalamus
18. hypothalamus
19. optic chiasma
20. pituitary gland
21. olfactory bulb

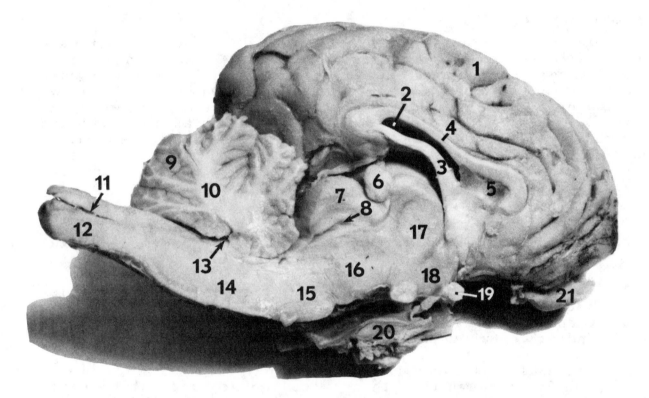

Photo 29: Sagittal Section Through Sheep Brain

Ex. IX-C. The Dissection of the Cat CNS (optional)

1. The cat brain is very similar in structure to the sheep brain. Remove the muscles from the top and sides of the skull.
2. Using either bone shears or a bone saw, make an opening in the parietal bones. Carefully chip away bone from the sides of this opening until the brain is completely exposed.
3. Remove the transverse bony septum that extends between the cerebellum and the cerebral hemispheres.
4. Remove the muscles dorsal to the vertebral column, exposing the entire vertebral column. Remove the spinous processes and vertebral arches from the vertebral column, exposing the spinal cord and dorsal roots of the spinal nerves.

5. Locate the cervical and lumbar enlargements, the dorsal root ganglia, and the cauda equina.
6. Make an incision separating the spinal cord from the brain at the foramen magnum.
7. Lift the brain carefully out of the cranial cavity, severing each cranial nerve as far from the brain as possible.
8. Remove the dura mater then follow steps 2-28 of the procedure for Ex. IX-B (The Dissection of the Sheep Brain).

Ex. IX-D. The Dissection of the Cat Peripheral Nervous System

DISCUSSION

There are 38 pairs of spinal nerves in the cat. There are usually 8 **cervical**, 13 **thoracic**, 7 **lumbar**, 3 **sacral** and 7 **caudal** nerves. Each spinal nerve emerges from the spinal cord through the **intervertebral foramen** and divides to form two rami, dorsal and ventral. The **ventral rami** form the major plexuses which supply the arms and legs as well as the skin and musculature of the ventral trunk. The **dorsal rami** are smaller and supply only the skin and musculature of the back. Only a few of the major nerves will be identified. Many of these have been located previously in the dissection of the cat muscular and respiratory systems.

PROCEDURE

1. The first four cervical nerves form the **cervical plexus** and supply the lateral neck musculature. It is not necessary to locate these nerves.
2. The **phrenic nerve** has been identified earlier in the dissection of the respiratory system (see Figure VII-5 in Chapter VII). The two phrenic nerves are formed by the 5th and 6th cervical nerves; they pass lateral to the heart on their way to the diaphragm. In man the phrenic nerve originates from the cervical plexus.
3. The 5th through the 8th cervical nerves and 1st thoracic nerve form the **brachial plexus** which supplies the muscles of the arm. This plexus has been exposed during the dissection of the chest and arm muscles (see Figure V-11 in Chapter V). If the plexus was severed on the left side during the dissection of the muscles, cut carefully through the pectoralis group on the right side of the chest until it is reached. (Refer also to Photo 30.)
   a. The most anterior nerve of the brachial plexus is the **musculocutaneous nerve**. This small nerve may be identified as it passes along the lower edge of the biceps brachii muscle. This nerve supplies the biceps, coracobrachialis, and brachialis muscles.
   b. The large flat nerve dorsal and anterior to the brachial artery, passing between the triceps and the humerus, is the **radial nerve,** the largest nerve of the plexus. Follow this nerve to the dorsal surface of the upper arm and trace it to the forearm. This splits in two near the elbow.

c. Raise the anterior portion of the plexus. A Y-shaped formation can be observed anterior to the teres major muscle at the lateral border of the scapula. This is the **median nerve.** It passes with the brachial artery (anterior to the artery) to the elbow region, through the supracondyloid foramen in the humerus, to the forearm. This foramen is not present in humans.

d. The **ulnar nerve** is the most posterior nerve of the important arm nerves. It emerges from the medial fork of the Y, runs posterior to the brachial artery down to the wrist. It passes between the medial epicondyle of the humerus and the olecranon process of the ulna at the elbow.

4. The next twelve thoracic nerves pass between the ribs with an artery and vein. They are known here as the **intercostal nerves, arteries** and **veins.** The nerves supply the intercostal muscles.

5. The **sciatic nerve** is the major nerve emerging from the **lumbosacral plexus.** This plexus is made up of the last four lumbar nerves and the three sacral nerves. Locate the sciatic nerve beneath the biceps femoris muscle (see Figure V-18 in Chapter V). Trace it to the popliteal fossa where it divides into two branches which supply the leg.

6. The **femoral nerve** also emerges from the lumbosacral plexus. This nerve is located on the ventral surface of the thigh with the femoral artery between the gracilis and sartorius muscles.

7. The larger cranial nerves have been identified in the dissection of the cat and sheep brain (see Ex. IX-B in Chapter IX).

8. The autonomic nervous system of the cat will not be dissected. It is possible to observe (in the thoracic cavity) without dissection the two **sympathetic trunks,** located one on each side of the vertebral column. Push the left lung to the right and locate the left trunk on the dorsal wall of the thoracic cavity. The trunks are beneath the parietal pleura parallel to the vertebral column. They resemble white threads.

KEY TO PHOTO 30

1. coracobrachialis
2. biceps brachii
3. radial nerve

4. musculocutaneous nerve
5. median nerve

6. ulnar nerve
7. brachial plexus
8. subscapularis

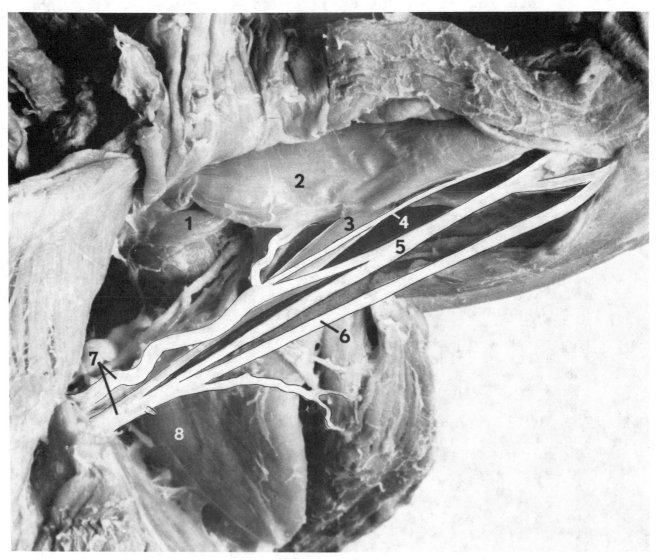

Photo 30: Ventral View of Nerves to the Arm

SELF-TEST: THE NERVOUS SYSTEM

DIRECTIONS: See Chapter 1, Self-Test, p. 12

1. Cell bodies of sensory neurons are located in the **dorsal root ganglia.**
2. The **autonomic nervous system** consists of the brain and spinal cord.
3. At the synapse impulses pass from the axon of one neuron to the **axon** of the next neuron.
4. **White matter** of the spinal cord contains the long ascending or descending motor and sensory pathways.
5. The radial nerve is a branch of the **cervical plexus.**
6. The **phrenic** nerve is a branch of the plexus that is formed by the first four cervical nerves.
7. The **reflex arc** is the functional unit of the nervous system.
8. In a reflex arc impulses pass from an internuncial neuron to an **afferent** neuron.
9. The motor area of the cerebral cortex lies in the **post-central** gyrus.
10. The spinal cord extends to the base of the **first sacral** vertebra.
11. The **hypothalamus** is an important relay station for sensory pathways between the brain stem and cerebral cortex.
12. Cerebrospinal fluid has a composition resembling **lymph.**
13. Temperature regulation is under the control of the **thalamus.**
14. The aggregations of nerve cell bodies located deep in the brain and spinal cord may be called **nuclei.**
15. A **synapse** is the small gap between a nerve and muscle.
16. The surface of the brain contains raised parts called convolutions or **sulci.**
17. The cortex of the brain consists of **white** matter.
18. Inflammation of a membrane of the brain or spinal cord is called **meningitis.**
19. Injury to a speech center affecting speech and word understanding is called **aphasia.**
20. The respiratory center is located in the **medulla oblongata.**
21. The lateral spinothalamic tract carries messages of **pain and temperature.**
22. Motor nerves to one side of the body originate in the **same** side of the brain.
23. The major control mechanisms for balance and posture are located in the **cerebellum.**
24. The cranial nerve conveying impulses concerned with equilibrium is the **acoustic.**
25. The cranial nerve conveying impulses to most of the viscera of the body is the **oculomotor** nerve.
26. The nerve carrying impulses causing us to shrug our shoulders and turn our head is the **accessory.**
27. The cranial nerve that would carry impulses warning you that the coffee was hot is the **trigeminal.**
28. The cranial nerve that carries impulses giving you informataions about decaying substances is the **acoustic.**
29. A lumbar puncture is done between **L5-S1** to avoid hitting the spinal cord.

30. In a lumbar puncture cerebrospinal fluid may be removed from the **subarachnoid space.**
31. When giving intramuscular injections, they should be given in the **upper, outer quadrant** of the buttocks.
32. It is important to give injections in the correct quadrant to avoid the **blood vessel** which courses through the buttucks.
33. A tic douloureux is a spasmodic neuralgia of the **glossopharyngeal** nerve.
34. It takes just a few seconds for the body to mobilize, because there are extensive synaptic connections and diffuse distribution of the **sympathetic** fibers.
35. A reflex is **a voluntary** response to a stimulus.
36. Axons carry nerve impulses **toward** the nerve cell body.
37. **Gray matter** of the brain and spinal cord is predominantly made up of unmyelinated nerve cell processes.
38. The **myelin sheath** functions to regenerate injured peripheral nerve tissues.
39. The **central nervous system** is composed of the brain and spinal cord, both of which may be involved in reflex actions.
40. The connective tissue cells of the CNS are called **neuroglia cells.**
41. The myelin sheaths of spinal and cranial nerves are broken into segments at sites known as **nodes of Ranvier.**
42. **Proprioceptors** are receptors located in muscles, tendons, and joints.
43. The chemical that transmits messages across a synapse is **sympathin.**
44. **White** matter of the brain consists of masses of nerve cell bodies.
45. The localization area for voluntary motion is found in the **frontal lobe** of the cerebrum.
46. The **longitudinal fissure** divides the cerebrum into right and left hemispheres.
47. The **thalamus** is responsible for conscious motor activity and conscious sensations.
48. The normal control of vital mechanisms of the viscera is mediated by the **ANS.**
49. An increase in respiratory and heart rate, as well as an elevation of blood pressure would result from stimulation of the **parasympathetic** division of the ANS.
50. Normal digestion and elimination is under control of the **craniosacral (parasympathetic)** division of the autonomic nervous system.
51. The pupil of the eye dilates due to stimulation of the **craniosacral** division of the autonomic nervous system.
52. The **dura mater** is the inner layer of the meninges at the surface of the spinal cord and brain.
53. Cell bodies of preganglionic neurons in the sympathetic division of the ANS are located in the **lateral horn** of the cord.
54. The **posterior** horn of the spinal cord contains cell bodies of motor neurons.
55. The vagus nerve emerges from the **medulla oblongata.**

56. The control of the rate of the heart beat is a function of the **pons Varolii.**
57. Selected disorders of the nervous system can be detected by means of an **electroencephalogram.**
58. The **arachnoid** forms the floor of the subarachnoid space.
59. The rate of respiration is controlled by a center in the **cerebellum.**
60. The cerebellum has a cortex composed of **white matter.**
61. The nerve that carries impulses resulting in the action of chewing is the **trigeminal.**
62. The **femoral** nerve supplies the quadriceps femoris muscle.
63. The nerve carrying impulses causing us to frown is the **glossopharyngeal.**
64. The nerve supplying the triceps muscle is the **radial.**
65. The **femoral** nerve supplies the gastrocnemius muscle.
66. The **musculocutaneous** nerve supplies the biceps brachii.
67. The femoral nerve emerges from the **lumbosacral** plexus.
68. Cranial nerves III, VII, IX, X form part of the **sympathetic division** of the autonomic nervous system.
69. The lateral chains of ganglia are part of the **sympathetic** division of the autonomic nervous system.
70. The **white** ramus contains postganglionic sympathetic neurons.

KEY

2. central nervous system	28. olfactory	54. anterior (ventral)
3. dendrite	29. L3-L4	56. medulla oblongata
5. brachial plexus	32. sciatic nerve	58. pia mater
8. efferent	33. trigeminal	59. medulla oblongata
9. precentral	35. involuntary	60. gray matter
10. first lumbar	36. away from	63. facial
11. thalamus	38. neurilemma	65. sciatic or tibial
13. hypothalamus	43. acetylcholine	68. parasympathetic
15. myoneural junction	44. gray	70. gray
16. gyri	47. cerebrum (or cortex)	
17. gray	49. sympathetic	
22. opposite	51. thoracolumbar	
25. vagus	52. pia mater	

Chapter X
SENSE ORGANS

Stimuli from both the external and internal environment are received by a variety of receptors. Specific stimuli are received by specific receptors which usually are modified histologically for their particular function. Receptors may be classified functionally (depending upon the particular kind of stimulus they respond to) as photoreceptors, mechanoreceptors, chemoreceptors, pressoreceptoros, or osmoreceptors. The following classification of receptors also includes the type of stimulus received:

A. EXTEROCEPTORS

These are receptors which are sensitive to stimuli arising at the surface of the body as well as those coming from the external environment. Included are the following:

1. Rods and cones in the retina of the eye (photoreceptors).
2. Hair cells of the Organ of Corti in the inner ear.
3. Nasal membrane receptors in the superior nasal concha (chemoreceptors).
4. The following are skin receptors:
   a. Meissner's corpuscles - touch (mechanoreceptors).
   b. Krause's end bulbs - cold (mechanoreceptors).
   c. Organ of Ruffini - warmth (mechanoreceptors).
   d. Pacinian corpuscle - deep pressure (mechanoreceptors).
   e. Bare (unencapsulated) nerve endings - pain (respond to a variety of stimuli).

B. INTEROCEPTORS

Interoceptors are receptor end organs which are located in and transmit impulses from the viscera. Stimulation of these receptors may give rise to sensations of discomfort or internal pain that may be the result of hunger, thirst, cramping pains accompanying disorders of the gastrointestinal tract, the sharp pain of acute appendicitis, etc. Other interoceptors, based on their functions, may be classified as follows:

1. **Pressoreceptors** (baroreceptors) are sensitive to changes in blood pressure. When stimulated, the following responses result:
   a. **Right heart reflex** - Pressoreceptors in the superior and inferior vena cavae are located at the entrances of these blood vessels into the right atrium. When stimulated by increased pressure, they convey impulses to the cardiac center in the medulla along vagus nerve fibers. This results in an accelerated heart beat.
   b. **Aortic reflex** - Pressoreceptors in the aortic sinus (located in the aortic arch) are sensitive to changes in pressure. Increased pressure slows the heart rate (impulses to cardiac center via vagus nerve).

c. **Carotid sinus reflex** - Pressoreceptors in the carotid sinus, which is a slightly dilated area of the internal artery at the point where the common carotid artery divides (bifurcates) into the internal and external carotid arteries, respond to fluctuations in pressure. Impulses are cardiac to the carotid center of the medulla by the glossopharyngeal nerve. Increased pressure slows the heart rate.

2. **Osmoreceptors** are sensitive to changes in osmotic concentrations in the blood (extracellular fluid), especially as infuenced by sodium and chloride ions. They are found in the hypothalamus and are important in regulating fluid balance within the body.

C. PROPRIOCEPTORS

These are receptors which give information concerning movements and position of the body. They are located primarily in muscles, tendons, joints, and the nonauditory portion of the ear.

Ex. X-A. Gross Anatomy of the Human Eye

PROCEDURE

1. Use Figures X-1, X-2, and X-3 of the eye as self-tests. See Section J, p. 5 (Illustrations as Self-Tests) for a suggested approach.
2. When you have become familiar with the indicated structures on the figures, locate them on the models of the eye and on wall charts.

Ex. X-B. Dissection of the Sheep Eye

DISCUSSION

The size and structures of the sheep eye compare favorably with that of the human eye. This, coupled with their availability, makes them ideal for studying the anatomical structures of the eye.

PROCEDURE

Part 1. External Aspect of the Sheep Eye

1. Note the fat on the surface of the eye. This cushions the eye from shock in its bony orbit.
2. Identify the following structures:
   a. The **sclera**, the very tough, external, white coat.
   b. The **conjunctiva**, a mucous membrane which covers the anterior surface of the eye and lines the eyelids. It is fused with the cornea but can be lifted up from the sclera a short distance from the edge of the cornea.
   c. The **cornea**, the anterior, transparent portion of the sclera. (It is opaque in your specimen, due to the action of the preservative).
   d. The **optic nerve**, located on the posterior surface. The nerve has the appearance of a solid white cord and is approximately 3 mm. thick.

KEY TO FIGURE X-I

1. posterior cavity
   (contains vitreous humor)
2. fovea centralis
3. optic disc
4. retinal blood vessels
5. optic nerve
6. nerve sheath
7. canals of Schlemm

8. posterior chamber
9. anterior chamber
10. anterior cavity
11. aqueous humor
12. pupil
13. cornea
14. crystalline lens
15. iris

16. conjunctiva
17. suspensory
      ligaments
18. ciliary body
19. sclera
20. choroid
21. retina

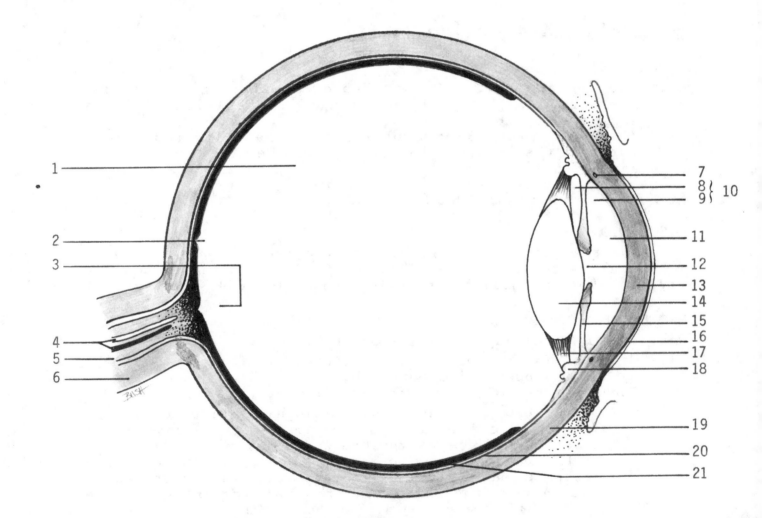

Figure X-1: Midsagittal Section through the Eye

KEY TO FIGURE X-2

1. levator palpebrae superioris
2. pulley
3. superior oblique
4. superior rectus
5. cornea
6. medial rectus
7. lateral rectus
8. sclera
9. inferior oblique
10. inferior rectus

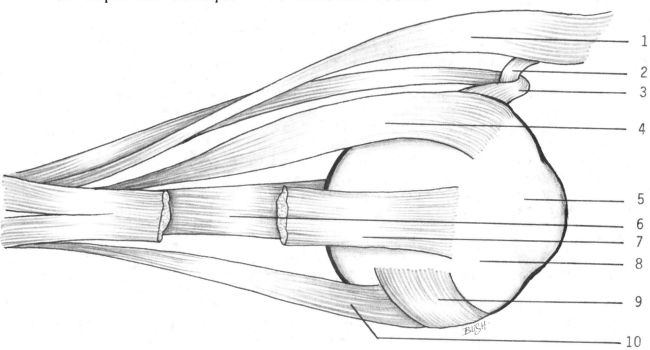

Figure X-2: Extrinsic Muscles of the Right Eye

KEY TO FIGURE X-3

1. superior oblique
2. medial rectus
3. lacrimal duct
4. lacrimal sac
5. puncta lacrimalia
6. nasolacrimal duct
7. superior rectus
8. lacrimal gland
9. excretory ducts
10. lateral rectus
11. sclera
12. pupil
13. iris
14. inferior rectus
15. inferior oblique

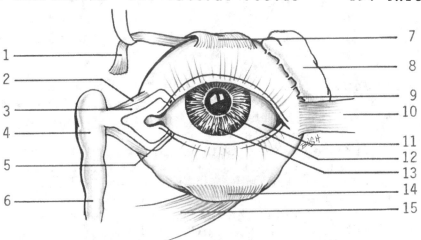

Figure X-3: Anterior View of Left Eye Showing Lacrimal Apparatus

3. Carefully dissect away the connective tissue (fat, etc.) from the posterior surface of the eyeball to free the six **extrinsic eye muscles.** These resemble flattened straps.

Part 2. Internal Aspect of the Sheep Eye

1. Hold the eye so that the cornea is in an inferior position.

2. Make an incision into the eyeball about 1/2 cm. from the edge of the cornea. Cut completely around the eyeball (parallel to and outside the cornea).

3. If the incision was done properly, the cornea should lift off like a lid. It should now be possible to carefully separate the **vitreous humor (vitreous body)** from the **crystalline lens.** Keep the vitreous humor in the posterior portion of the eyeball and the lens in the anterior third of the eye.

4. Examine the interior of the anterior part of the eye.

    a. Observe the **ciliary body,** the black structure which has the appearance of narrow, radial folds.

    b. Locate the **suspensory ligaments,** the very delicate fibers connecting the ciliary body to the lens. They hold the lens in position.

    c. Free the **lens** slowly from the ciliary body and remove it. You should be able to see the suspensory ligaments breaking as you free the lens. Remnants of the suspensory ligaments can be seen attached to the lens.

    d. The **iris** is now visible anterior to the former position of the lens. This also appears black. Try to distinguish between the **circular** and **radial** smooth muscle fibers comprising the iris.

    e. Locate the **pupil,** the hole in the center of the iris.

    f. Hold the lens up to the light. Does any light pass through? The lens in your specimen may be opaque due to the action of the preservative.

5. Examine the external surface of the anterior third of the eye. It is now relatively easy to distinguish the iris, pupil, and cornea.

6. Examine the posterior two-thirds of the eye and observe the following structures:

    a. The **vitreous humor** (in life, this substance is perfectly clear).

    b. The **retina,** the white inner coat that was covered by the vitreous humor. Determine the point at which the retina is attached dorsally. This is called the **optic disc (blind spot),** the point where all the axons exit the retina to form the optic nerve.

    c. The **choroid coat.** The retina covers this coat, and the two are easily separated. The iridescent appearance of the choroid is due to the presence of the **tapetum lucidum,** a special structure not present in the human eye. The function of the tapetum lucidum is to reflect some light back into the retina. This reflecting device is found in vertebrates that live under conditions of low light intensity. This causes the animal's eyes to shine in the dark.

    d. The **sclera,** the outer white coat.

Ex. X-C. Anatomy of the Ear

PROCEDURE

1. Use Figures X-4 and X-5 of the ear as self-tests.
2. Compare the structures indicated on Figures X-4 and X-5 with those found on models of the ear, wall charts, and in references.
3. Using your text or other current references, determine the functions of the structures of the ear.
4. **Demonstration:** Examine the auditory ossicles (**malleus, incus,** and **stapes**) that have been placed under the stereoscopic microscope.
5. Obtain a slide of the **cochlea** labeled Internal Ear, Cochlea. Since the cochlea makes two and a half spiral turns around a pillar of spongy bone, the **modiolus**, the slide contains approximately five views of the canals of the cochlea. Selecting one portion that resembles some model of the cochlea (refer to Figure X-7), diagram a radial section through the canals and label the following structures: **basilar membrane, tectorial membrane, vestibular membrane, scala vestibuli, scala media (cochlear duct), scala tympani, hair cells** of **the Organ of Corti, supporting cells,** and **cochlear nerve.** Indicate the location of **perilymph** and **endolymph**.

KEY TO FIGURE X-4

1. posterior semicircular canal
2. lateral semicircular canal
3. oval window (fenestra ovalis or fenestra vestibuli)
4. round window (fenestra rotunda or fenestra cochlea)

5. superior semicircular canal
6. vestibule
7. cochlea
8. modiolus

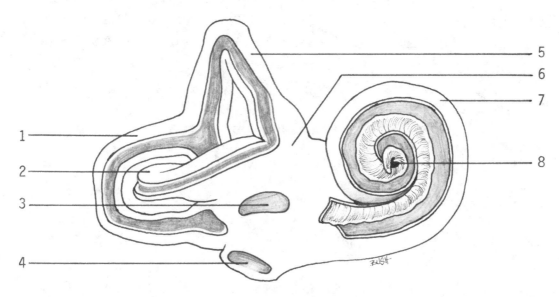

Figure X-4: Osseous Labyrinth

KEY TO FIGURE X-5

1. temporal bone
2. malleus
3. incus
4. tensor tympani (cut)
5. external auditory
   meatus
6. tympanic membrane
7. pinna
8. auditory nerve

9. vestibular nerve
10. cochlear nerve
11. semicircular
    canal
12. ampulla
13. utricle
14. saccule
15. modiolus
16. spiral lamina

17. cochlea
18. fenestra ovalis
19. stapes
20. fenestra rotunda
21. blood vessels
22. styloid process
23. mastoid process
24. eustachian tube

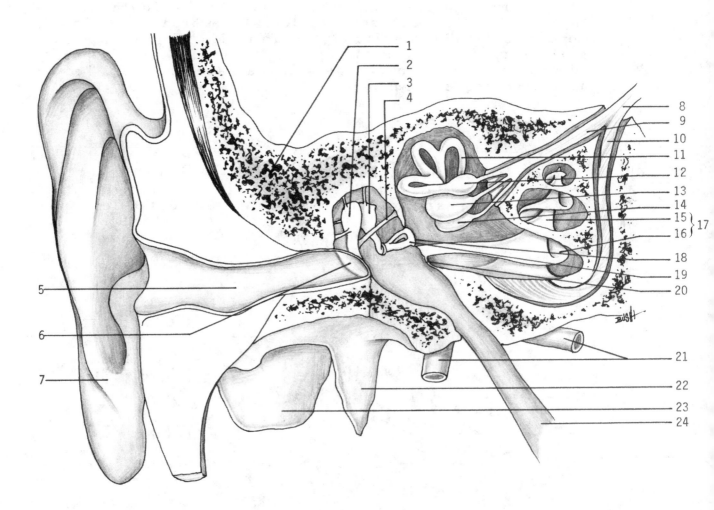

Figure X-5: The Ear

KEY TO FIGURE X-6

1. scala vestibuli
2. vestibular membrane
3. tectorial membrane
4. organ of Corti
5. scala tympani

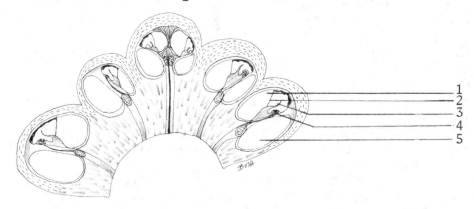

Figure X-6: Axial Section through Entire Cochlea Showing Canals

KEY TO FIGURE X-7

1. hair cells of organ of Corti
2. supporting cells
3. basilar membrane
4. scala tympani
5. scala vestibuli
6. vestibular membrane
7. cochlear duct
8. tectorial membrane
9. cochlear nerve

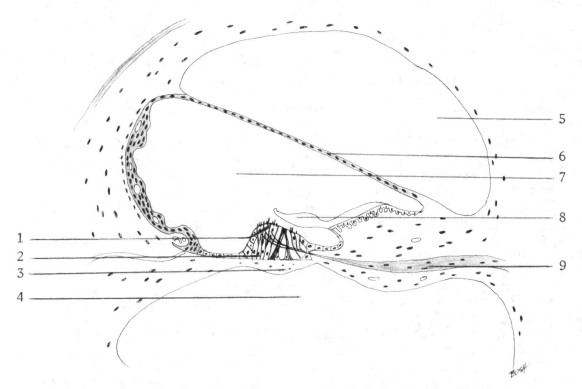

Figure X-7: Radial Section through One Coil of the Cochlea

SELF-TEST: SENSE ORGANS

DIRECTIONS: See Chapter 1, Self-Test, p. 12

1. A **detached retina** occurs when the tissue lining the eyeball is pulled loose in one area and causes blurred vision.
2. **Conjunctivitis** is an inflammation of the membrane which lines the eyelids and covers the cornea.
3. **Glaucoma** is a disease of the eye characterized by increased pressure of aqueous humor and progressive loss of vision.
4. If you look into an eye with an **ophthalmoscope** you may observe the retina, macula lutea, optic disc, and the retinal blood vessels.
5. "Watery eyes" are frequently associated with acute rhinitis because the inflammation of the nasal mucosa causes swelling which closes the **eustachian tube** and blocks tear drainage.
6. **Myopia,** or farsightedness, is caused when the eyeball is too short, or the refractive power too little, which causes the rays to focus behind the retina.
7. The sense of smell diminishes with a cold and causes food to be relatively tasteless. This is because many "tastes" are really **olfactory impressions.**
8. **Otitis media** is usually a complication of a severe cold and sore throat, because the infection ascends through the eustachian tube.
9. **A myringotomy** (an incision of the tympanic membrane) is sometimes performed in severe otitis media to allow pus to escape.
10. Our ears become "stopped up" with sudden changes in altitude because the eustachian tubes are **usually closed;** thus changing air pressure causes bulging of the tympanic membrane.
11. Cutaneous sensations **are equally** distributed over the body.
12. The brushes of Ruffini receive sensations of **heat.**
13. Pressure sensations are received by **Pacinian corpuscles.**
14. The end bulbs of Krause receive **cold** stimuli.
15. Hearing is localized in the **frontal** lobe of the cerebrum.
16. The conscious awareness of heat, cold, and pressure is localized in the **parietal** lobe of the cerebrum.
17. The perception of objects seen is localized in the **occipital** lobe of the cerebrum.
18. Adaptation to odors is a relatively **slow** process.
19. The olfactory cells are **modified hair cells.**
20. Taste buds to detect sweetness are most numerous on the **lateral parts** of the tongue.
21. Injury to the right optic tract behind the optic chiasma would destroy the nasal visual field sight of the **left** eye and the temporal visual field sight of the **right** eye.
22. The shape of the crystalline lens is regulated by the **ciliary muscle.**

23. The **vitreous** humor of the eye circulates through the anterior and posterior chambers and is drained by the canal of Schlemm.
24. The ability of the eye to adapt for near vision and far vision is know as **accommodation**.
25. Astigmatism is due to irregularities in the **cornea**.
26. Conduction deafness may be caused by **cerumen** in the ear canal.
27. The stapes is attached to the **fenestra cochlea or round window**.
28. Hair cells in contact with the **tectorial** membrane (in the inner ear) are stimulated when the membrane vibrates.
29. The receptors for hearing are located on the **organ of Corti** within the inner ear.
30. The utricle is generally associated with **static posture** or the orientation of the body in relation to gravity, while the semicircular canals are concerned with **dynamic equilibrium**.
31. The eustachian tube leads from the pharynx to the **internal** ear.
32. The **semicircular canals** contain hair cells which move when the head is moved.
33. **Ossicles** of the middle ear transmit sound waves to the inner ear.
34. The fluid in the **scala vestibuli** communicates with the round window.
35. The fibers of the cochlear nerve pass through the **modiolus** to reach the organ of Corti.
36. The organ of Corti is located on the **basilar membrane**.
37. The **cornea** is the anterior clear transparent portion of the fibrous layer of the eye.
38. The area where the optic nerve leaves the eye is **devoid of rods and cones** and is, therefore, insensitive to light stimuli.
39. The iris of the eye and ciliary body constitute the **extrinsic** muscles of the eye.
40. The white of the eye is the **choroid** portion of the eye.
41. The area of keenest vision is located at the **fovea centralis**.
42. The blind spot of the eye is located in the **fovea centralis**.
43. The right side of the cerebrum receives the nerve fibers from the **right side** of both eyes.
44. The **rods** are responsible for color vision.
45. The **medial rectus** eye muscle contracts during accommodation, bringing about convergence of the eyes.
46. Vitamin A, frequently associated with night vision, is an essential part of **rhodopsin**.
47. Pink eye is a **very contagious** infection of the conjunctiva.
48. The **pupil** regulates the amount of light entering the eye.
49. When the point of focus of the eyes is in front of the retina, the subject is **near-sighted**.
50. Otoliths are located in the **utricle** of the ear.

51. Accommodation or the focusing of an object on the retina is brought about by the **change of shape in the lens.**
52. With advancing years the lens becomes firmer and the ability to alter its curvature decreases. This condition is called **hypermetropia.**
53. Suspensory ligaments are attached to the **lens.**
54. In vision, accommodation is brought about by action of the **ciliary muscle.**
55. **Cataract** involves opaqueness of the lens.
56. The small air filled chamber which contains the malleus, incus, and stapes is the **tympanum.**
57. The parts of the ear concerned with balance include **otoliths and hair cells.**
58. The process of hearing involves the action of the **tensor tympani** and the **stapedius** muscles.
59. In the order of their occurrence from the outside inward, the bones of the middle ear are the **incus, malleus, and stapes.**

KEY

5. nasolacrimal duct	21. right - left	42. optic disc
6. hyperopia	23. aqueous	44. cones
11. are unequally	27. fenestra ovalis (oval window)	48. iris
15. temporal	31. middle	52. presbyopia
18. rapid	34. scala tympani	56. tympanic cavity
19. neurons	39. intrinsic	59. malleus, incus, and stapes
20. tip	40. sclera	

Chapter XI
THE URINARY SYSTEM

Ex. XI-A. Anatomy of the Human Urinary System

DISCUSSION

The urinary system consists of the **kidneys, ureters, urinary bladder**, and **urethra.** The ureters conduct urine from the kidneys to the bladder; the urethra conducts urine (and sperm in the male) from the bladder to the outside.

The primary function of the kidneys is to preserve **homeostasis.** This term refers to the maintenance of a constant internal environment. The kidneys maintain homeostasis through the excretion of various toxins and metabolic wastes as well as other substances present in the blood in surplus amounts (e.g., sugar eaten in excess or in the disorder known as diabetes mellitus). Fluid and electrolyte balance, as well as acid-base balance, depends primarily upon the proper functioning of the kidneys. Malfunction of these organs results in a failure of homeostasis and, unless corrected, such failure finally results in death.

The structural and functional unit of the kidney is the **nephron**; there are approximately one million of these units in each kidney. The blood is filtered in these units, and urine is produced as a result of selective transport (which is partially under the influence of hormones) of water and other substances from the **uriniferous tubule** of the nephron.

PROCEDURE

1. Using your text, charts, and reference books for orientation, locate the following organs on the dissectable torso. Be prepared to describe the location of each organ in anatomic terms.

    a. Kidneys   c. Urethra
    b. Ureters   d. Urinary bladder

2. On the model of a longitudinal section through the kidney, locate the structures indicated on the keys to Figures XI-1 and XI-2. These figures may be used as self-tests. See Section J, p. 5 (Illustrations as Self-Tests) for a suggested approach.

3. Examine a slide of the kidney showing nephrons. Compare a nephron observed on the slide with Figure XI-3, which depicts a single collecting tubule draining urine from two nephrons, and Figure XI-4 which is an enlargement of the renal corpuscle partially sectioned to show the tuft of capillaries contained within. Figures XI-3 and XI-4 may be used as self-tests.

KEY TO FIGURE XI-1

1. adipose tissue
2. renal pelvis
3. major calyx
4. minor calyx

5. ureter
6. pyramid
7. calyces
8. renal medulla
   (the semicircle
   of pyramids)

9. renal papilla
10. renal cortex
11. renal column
12. renal capsule

KEY TO FIGURE XI-2

1. renal artery
2. renal vein
3. renal pelvis

4. ureter
5. calyces
6. arcuate artery
   and vein

7. interlobar artery
   and vein
8. interlobular artery
   and vein

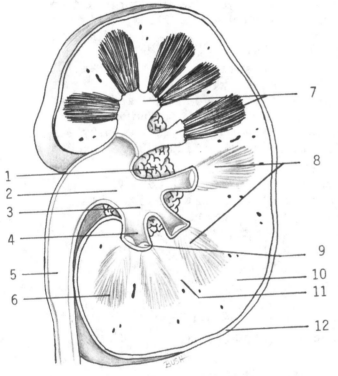

Figure XI-1: Longitudinal Section through the Kidney

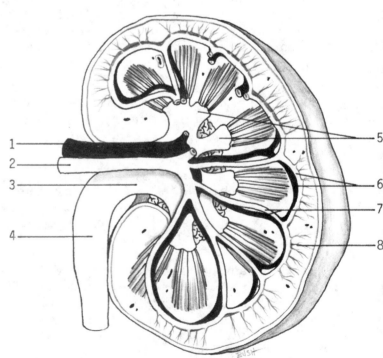

Figure XI-2: Renal Blood Supply

KEY TO FIGURE XI-3

1. distal convoluted tubule
2. proximal convoluted tubule
3. efferent arteriole
4. renal corpuscle
5. afferent arteriole

6. Loop of Henle
   (ascending limb)
7. Loop of Henle
   (descending limb)
8. collecting tubule

KEY TO FIGURE XI-4

1. efferent arteriole
2. efferent arteriole
3. glomerulus
4. Bowman's capsule

5. uriniferous tubule
   (proximal convoluted
   tubule)

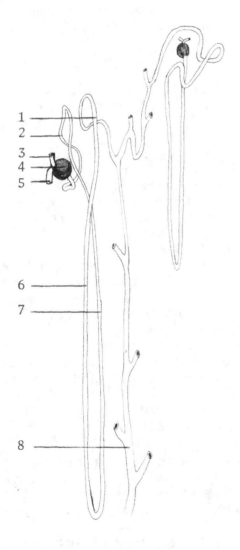

Figure XI-3: The Nephron

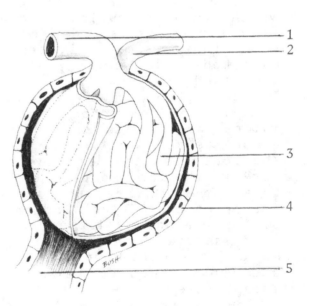

Figure XI-4: Renal Corpuscle

Ex. XI-B. Dissection of the Urinary System of the Cat

DISCUSSION

The organs in the urinary system of the cat are very similar to those in the human. As you dissect the organs, be prepared to trace the path of urine from its site of production to the point at which it passes to the outside. The cat kidney will be sectioned in order to study its internal structure, since it provides a good example of a typical mammalian kidney.

PROCEDURE

1. At the level of the last thoracic and first three lumbar vertebrae, observe the large bean-shaped **kidneys** on the dorsal body wall of the cat. Use Figure XI-5 and Photo 31 as a guide. Each kidney is surrounded by adipose tissue (**perirenal fat**). The right kidney is higher in position than the left in the cat.

2. Remove the adipose tissue and the peritoneum, which covers the ventral surface of the kidney, from the left kidney. Since the kidneys are separated from the abdominal organs by a layer of peritoneum, their location is described as being **retroperitoneal**.

3. Identify the **renal artery** and **renal vein**, which carry blood to and from the kidney.

4. Locate the small **adrenal glands** lying in the connective tissue close to the aorta and just anterior and medial to each kidney. The adrenal glands resemble small lymph nodes in the cat (see Figure XI-5).

5. Observe the **ureter**, the narrow, white, convoluted tube which drains the urine from each kidney. Trace the ureter from the **hilus**, the depression on the medial border of each kidney, freeing it from the peritoneum. The ureters pass behind the urinary bladder to open into the floor of the bladder.

6. The pear-shaped **urinary bladder** is connected to the mid-ventral wall by a **median suspensory ligament** and to the lateral walls by **lateral ligaments**, which contain a large amount of adipose tissue.

7. The **fundus** is the large expanded part of the bladder. The **neck** is the lower part which opens into the urethra.

8. Locate the **urethra**, the duct which conducts urine from the posterior end of the bladder to the outside. The remainder of the urethra will be freed when the reproductive system is dissected.

9. Remove the left kidney and make a longitudinal (coronal) section through it. Locate each of the following structures. (See Figure XI-6).

    a. The **renal capsule** is the thin layer of connective tissue around the outside of the kidney.

    b. The **renal cortex** is the outer light brown layer of the kidney immediately beneath the capsule. This layer contains renal corpuscles.

    c. The next layer of the kidney, the **renal medulla**, contains one large dark **renal pyramid** in the center of the kidney. Other pyramids will be seen as the kidney is dissected (Step e).

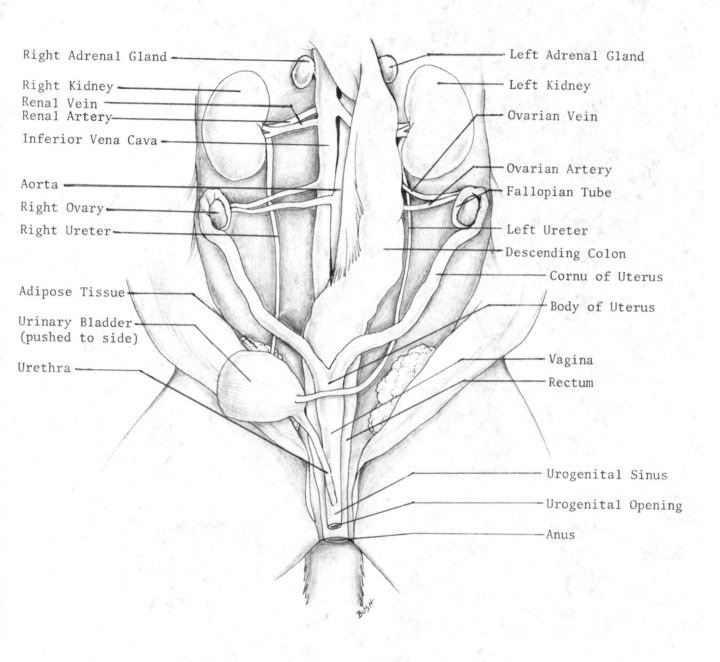

Right Adrenal Gland

Right Kidney
Renal Vein
Renal Artery
Inferior Vena Cava

Aorta
Right Ovary
Right Ureter

Adipose Tissue

Urinary Bladder
(pushed to side)

Urethra

Left Adrenal Gland

Left Kidney
Ovarian Vein

Ovarian Artery
Fallopian Tube

Left Ureter
Descending Colon
Cornu of Uterus
Body of Uterus

Vagina
Rectum

Urogenital Sinus
Urogenital Opening
Anus

Figure XI-5: Dissection of the Female Genitourinary System

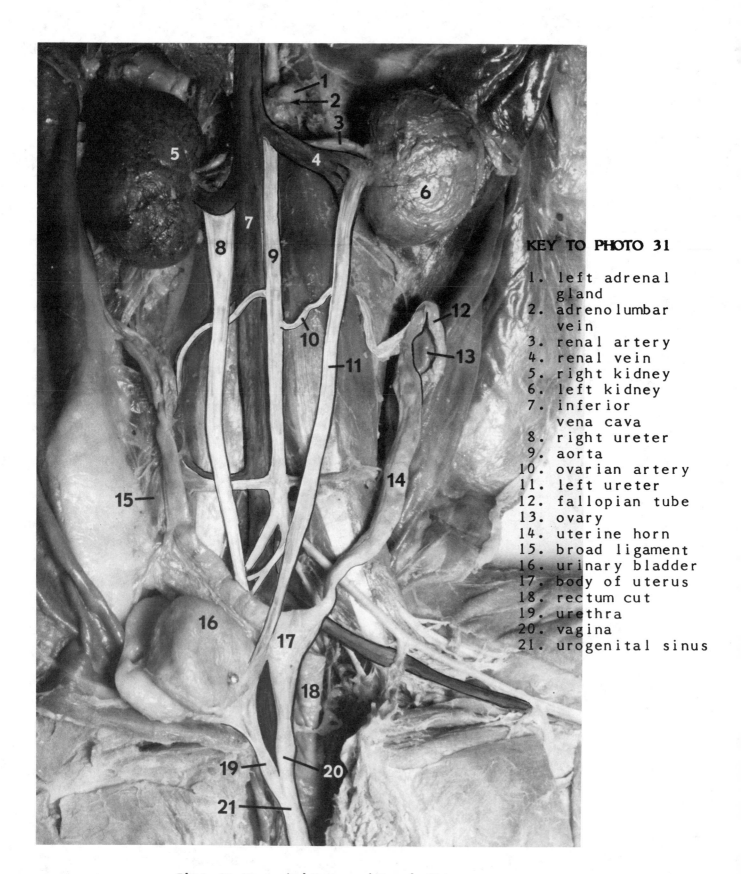

KEY TO PHOTO 31

1. left adrenal
   gland
2. adrenolumbar
   vein
3. renal artery
4. renal vein
5. right kidney
6. left kidney
7. inferior
   vena cava
8. right ureter
9. aorta
10. ovarian artery
11. left ureter
12. fallopian tube
13. ovary
14. uterine horn
15. broad ligament
16. urinary bladder
17. body of uterus
18. rectum cut
19. urethra
20. vagina
21. urogenital sinus

Photo 31: Urogenital System of Female Cat

d. Locate the **renal pelvis,** the funnel-shaped expansion of the ureter inside the **renal sinus,** which is the hollow interior of the kidney. Identify the single **renal papilla,** the tip of the pyramid that projects into the renal pelvis.

e. Trace the renal artery into the kidney. Carefully dissect away the kidney to locate the **interlobar, arcuate** and **interlobular** arteries. The corresponding veins should also be identified. Several small pyramids should now be visible. The interlobar arteries and veins pass between these pyramids in a region of the renal medulla known as the **renal columns.** (Figure XI-2.)

10. Compare the structure of the cat kidney with that of the human kidney (see Figure XI-1 and XI-2).

11. Replace the kidney in the abdominal cavity of the cat.

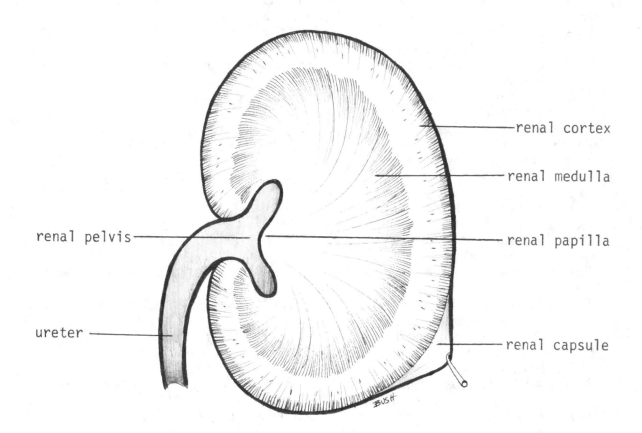

Figure XI-6: Coronal Section through Cat Kidney

SELF-TEST: THE URINARY SYSTEM

DIRECTIONS: See Chapter 1, Self-Test, p. 12

1.   Inflammation of the urinary bladder is called **cystocele**.
2.   The general function of a diuretic drug is to **decrease** the excretion of urine.
3.   The pyramids are located in the renal **medulla** of the kidney.
4.   The renal pelvis opens directly into the **urinary bladder**.
5.   The components of urine enter Bowman's capsule from the blood by the process of **osmosis**.
6.   Urea is formed in the **kidneys**.
7.   If the **pancreas** is malfunctioning, sugar might be found in the urine.
8.   Renal blood vessels enter the kidney at the **hilus**.
9.   The kidneys lie between the **periosteum** and the posterior body wall.
10.   Urination is termed **micturition**.
11.   The smooth muscle in the wall of the bladder is called the **detrusor** muscle.
12.   **Stones** are materials (often albumin) which have taken the form of the tubules in which they are molded.
13.   The kidneys excrete **only a small** amount of the water and other substances they receive from the blood.
14.   The tuft of capillaries in Bowman's capsule is known as the **glomerulus**.
15.   The efferent arteriole has a **larger** diameter than the afferent arteriole.
16.   The **pancreas** is superior in location to each kidney.
17.   The glucose and amino acids are reabsorbed by the part of the nephron known as the **glomerulus**.
18.   The connective tissue surrounding the outside of the kidney is called the **capsule**.
19.   The urinary bladder serves to **concentrate** urine.
20.   The function of the loop of Henle is to reabsorb **water**.
21.   The fundamental microscopic unit of structure of the kidney is the **calyx**.
22.   The kidneys filter approximately **300** quarts of fluid each day.
23.   The pressure of blood in the glomerulus is **higher** than in other systemic capillaries.
24.   The renal **veins** rapidly subdivide to form arterioles.
25.   Bowman's capsule is located in the **renal medulla**.
26.   The **interlobular** arteries form the arcuate arteries.
27.   The part of the renal pelvis surrounding each renal papilla is called the **calyx**.
28.   The **urethra** carries urine from the kidney to the urinary bladder.
29.   The artery branching to form the afferent arterioles is the **arcuate**.
30.   The loop of Henle dips down into the **renal medulla**.
31.   The kidneys are located between the **12th thoracic and 3rd lumbar** vertebrae.

KEY

1. cystitis	15. smaller	22. 190
2. increase	16. adrenal gland	24. arteries
4. ureter	17. proximal convoluted	25. renal cortex
5. filtration	tubule	26. interlobar
6. liver	19. store	28. ureter
9. peritoneum	21. nephron	29. interlobular
12. casts		

Chapter XII
THE ENDOCRINE SYSTEM

Ex. XII-A. Endocrine Glands

DISCUSSION

The secretions of **endocrine glands** (containing hormones) diffuse into the blood which transports them to the structures acted upon. In contrast to these **ductless glands, exocrine glands** have ducts which convey the glandular secretions to some surface either inside or outside of the body. For example, the secretions of the salivary glands are carried by ducts to the buccal cavity.

A compound, to be classed as a hormone, must meet the following criteria: (1) it is produced by a particular endocrine gland; (2) removal of the gland, or the part of the gland producing the compound, results in the failure of some other organ to develop or function normally; (3) in the absence of the endocrine gland, artificial replacement of the hormone in the body restores the target organ to its normal size and functional capacity. Chemically, hormones are either steroids, proteins, or derived from proteins.

In the autonomic nervous system, impulses traveling over preganglionic fibers stimulate the secretion of acetylcholine at the synapses with ganglion cells. This compound is also released at postganglionic parasympathetic terminals and by the postganglionic sympathetic fibers that supply the sweat glands in the skin. All such fibers are known as **cholinergic fibers**; these fibers inhibit the action of certain target organs such as the heart and the sphincters of the gastrointestinal tract, and stimulate the action of others, such as in the muscle in the gastrointestinal tract, bronchioles, urinary bladder, and gall bladder. Norephinephrine (noradrenalin) is released at the postganglionic sympathetic terminals (with the exceptions noted above). These fibers are known as **adrenergic fibers**; they are **excitatory** in certain areas such as the heart, blood vessels in the abdominal viscera, and sphincters, and **inhibitory** in the gastrointestinal tract and urinary bladder. While these fibers are not endocrine glands, the compounds secreted are chemical coordinators which act in a manner similar to hormones. The endocrine and nervous systems are the two main integrating mechanisms of the body. The normal function of these two systems results in the parts of the body working together as an integrated whole.

PROCEDURE

1. Using your text, references, and anatomical charts as resource materials, locate the following glands on the dissectable torso and the model of the brain.

   a. Hypophysis (pituitary)
   b. Ovaries
   c. Pancreas
   d. Parathyroids
   e. Pineal gland
   f. Suprarenals (adrenals)
   g. Testes
   h. Thymus
   i. Thyroid

2. Identify the glands indicated in Figure XII-1 on the dissectable torso, in wall charts, and in illustrations in other reference material. Figure XII-1 may be used as a self-test. See Section J, p. 5 (Illustrations as Self-Tests) for a suggested approach.

Ex. XII-B. Dissection of the Endocrine Glands of the Cat

DISCUSSION

The important endocrine glands of the cat have been identified as they were located in the dissection of other organ systems. Therefore, this exercise will serve as a review of these glands.

PROCEDURE

1. Locate the **thyroid glands** in the neck region (see Figure VII-5). The two lobes of the thyroid lie one on each side of the anterior end of the trachea. The two lobes are connected by a narrow thin isthmus that is often destroyed in the dissection of the trachea.
2. Four tiny **parathyroid glands** are embedded in the dorsal surface of the thyroids. These are not visible with the unaided eye, due to their size.
3. The **adrenal glands** are located anterior and medial to each kidney (see Figure XI-5 in Chapter XI). Each gland resembles a small lymph node.
4. The **pituitary gland (hypophysis)** is located in the sella turcica of the sphenoid bone. It is attached to the hypothalamus by a stalk called the **infundibulum** (see Figure IX-1 in Chapter IX). If you remove the brain of the cat in Ex. IX-B, the pituitary can be seen in the floor of the cranial cavity in the sella turcica. It is not necessary to expose this gland if the brain was not removed.
5. The **pineal gland** may be observed in either the cat or sheep brain above the superior colliculi of the midbrain (see Figure IX-5).
6. The **thymus gland** was observed anterior and ventral to the heart (see Figure VII-5). This gland may have been removed with the pericardium.
7. The **pancreas** is located in the abdominal cavity between the duodenum and the spleen (see Figure VI-9).
8. The location of the **ovaries** and **testes** are described in Chapter XIII, the Reproductive System. (See Figure XI-5 for the location of the ovaries, and Figure XIII-19 for the location of the testes in the cat).

KEY TO FIGURE XII-1

1. pineal gland   4. adrenal gland   7. parathyroid glands
2. thyroid gland   5. testis   8. pancreas
3. thymus gland   6. hypophysis (pituitary   9. ovary
                       gland)

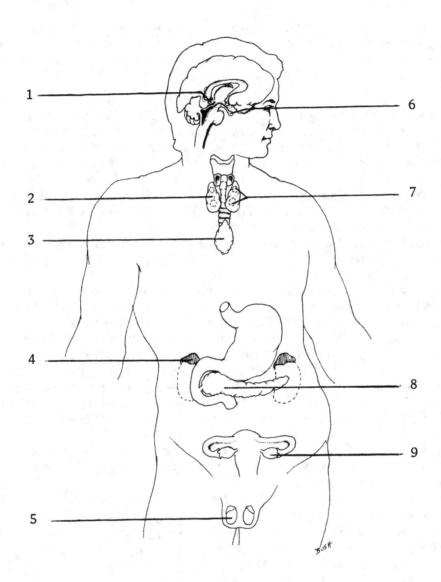

Figure XII-1: Location of Endocrine Glands

SELF-TEST: THE ENDOCRINE SYSTEM

DIRECTIONS: See Chapter 1, Self-Test, p. 12

1. Hypofunction of the thyroid gland in infancy is called **myxedema.**
2. Diabetes insipidus is caused by hypofunction of the **anterior pituitary.**
3. Tetany is caused by hyposecretion of the **thyroid.**
4. The somatotropic hormone is produced by the **anterior pituitary.**
5. Goiter is a condition characterized by excessive growth of the **thymus.**
6. **ADH** stimulates the production of the adrenal cortical hormones.
7. A disease resulting from the failure of the nephrons to reabsorb water is called **diabetes mellitus.**
8. Secretions of the **adrenal** glands control calcium metabolism.
9. An exophthalmic goiter is a result of **hyperthyroidism.**
10. The **pineal** gland is located in the sella turcica.
11. **Hypertrophy** means an increase in the size of a structure.
12. True dwarfism results from a lack of the **parathyroid** hormone.
13. Protruding eyeballs may indicate **hyperthyroidism.**
14. As a person grows older, the thymus **remains the same size.**
15. Adrenalin **decreases** the consumption of oxygen.
16. The PBI is a test of **thyroid** function.
17. The hormone that causes the gall bladder to contract is **secretin.**
18. ACTH is produced by the **adrenal cortex.**
19. Iodine is needed for the production of **parathormone.**
20. Acromegaly is caused by **a lack of thyroxin.**
21. **The lactogenic hormone** causes the ejection of milk from the mammary glands.
22. Oxytocin is stored by the **posterior pituitary.**
23. The hormone controlling male secondary sex characteristics is **FSH.**
24. The adrenal **medulla** is essential for life.
25. A lack of **parathormone** can cause muscle twitches.
26. Dwarfism, gigantism, and acromegaly result from a defect in the **thyroid.**
27. The interstitial cells produce **ICSH.**
28. The hormones of the adrenal medulla have the same function as the **parasympathetic** nervous system.
29. **Cretinism** is more common where there is a lack of iodine in the soil.
30. The **parathyroids** are embedded on the dorsal surface of the thyroid gland.
31. The **thyroid gland** contains the Islets of Langerhans.
32. The adrenal glands are just **inferior** to the kidneys.
33. There are **two pairs** of parathyroid glands.
34. The **pineal body** may become calcified later in life.
35. The thymus is located in the **abdominal** cavity.

KEY

1. cretinism
2. posterior pituitary (or hypothalamus)
3. parathyroids
5. thyroid
6. ACTH
7. diabetes insipidus
8. parathyroid
10. pituitary

12. somatotropic
14. decreases in size
15. increases
17. cholecystokinin
18. anterior pituitary
19. thyroxin
20. an excess of STH

21. oxytocin
23. testosterone
24. cortex
26. pituitary
27. testosterone
28. sympathetic
31. pancreas
32. superior
35. thoracic

Chapter XIII
THE REPRODUCTIVE SYSTEM

Ex. XIII-A. The Human Male Reproductive System

DISCUSSION

The male reproductive system consists of the two male gonads (**testes**), and **ducts** which conduct sperm to the outside, and the accessory structures (**glands** and **penis**). Spermatogenesis begins at puberty under the influence of hormones, and continues throughout the life of the male.

PROCEDURE

1. Examine a slide of a cross section through the human **testis** under both low and high power of the microscope. In order to locate the testis on the slide, compare it with Figure XIII-1 (since some slides contain the epididymis on the same slide which might be mistaken for the seminiferous tubule). The seminiferous tubules should fill the field.
2. Examine the shape of the seminiferous tubules. These are approximately circular, since each is a cross section through a long tubule (see Figure XIII-4).
3. Draw a portion of the field that includes three seminiferous tubules with the interstitial cells in between.
4. Study the wall of one seminiferous tubule. The cells here are in various stages of **meiosis**. The cells near the outside of the tubule are called **spermatogonia**. These cells begin the process of **spermatogenesis** (sperm production) by dividing by **mitosis** several times and enlarging to form **primary spermatocytes**, located closer to the center of the tubule. The primary spermatocytes undergo meiosis and form **secondary spermatocytes**, and finally **spermatids**. (Study Figure XIII-6, which compares spermatogenesis and oogenesis). The spermatids are the cells closest to the lumen of the tubule. These mature into **spermatozoa** (sperm) located in the vicinity of the spermatids. Figure XIII-2 shows an enlargement of part of the wall of the seminiferous tubule.
5. Draw a strip of cells from the outside to the center of one seminiferous tubule on your original drawing of the seminiferous tubule.
6. Study the slide of the **epididymis** (or use the portion of the epididymis on the slide of the testis). Identify each of the parts listed in Figure XIII-3. Note the sperm in the lumen of the tubule. Compare the structure of the wall of the epididymis with the wall of the seminiferous tubule.
7. The testis, the epididymis, and the beginning of the **vas deferens** are located in the **scrotum**. These structures and some of their parts are indicated on Figure XIII-4 which may be used as a self-test. See Section J, p. 5 (Illustrations as Self-Tests) for a suggested approach.

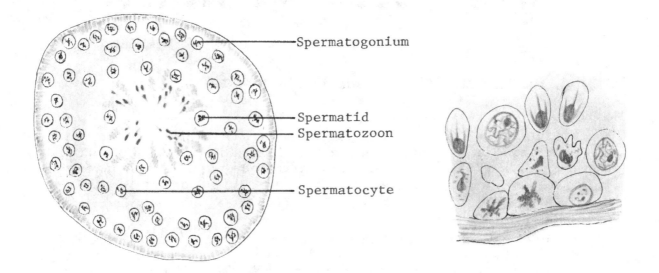

Spermatogonium

Spermatid
Spermatozoon

Spermatocyte

**Figure XIII-1: Cross Section through
a Seminiferous Tubule**

**Figure XIII-2: Cross Section through
a Seminiferous Tubule (enlarged)**

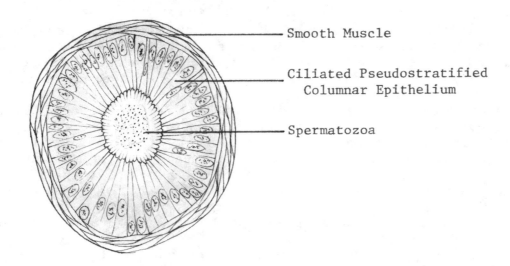

Smooth Muscle

Ciliated Pseudostratified
Columnar Epithelium

Spermatozoa

Figure XIII-3: Cross Section through the Epididymis

8. Using your text or other references, locate the structures on the key to Figure XIII-5 on the dissectable torso and compare them with Figure XIII-5 which may be used as a self-test.

KEY TO FIGURE XIII-4

1. vas efferens
2. epididymis
3. vas deferens

4. seminiferous tubule
5. rete testis

6. septum
7. tunica
   albuginea

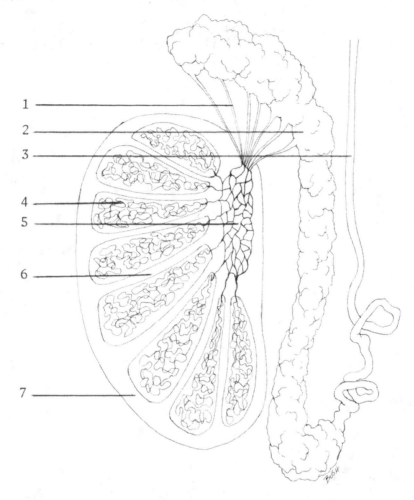

Figure XIII-4: Vertical Section through the Testis & Adjacent Structures

Ex. XIII-B. The Human Female Reproductive System

DISCUSSION

The female reproductive system consists of the female gonads (**ovaries**), the **fallopian tubes, vagina,** and accessory
structures. The process of oogenesis (egg production), which
actually begins before birth, ceases at the time of **climac-
teric,** usually between ages 45 and 50.

PROCEDURE

1. Obtain two slides of the human ovary, one showing the
    Graafian follicle and the other containing the **corpus
    luteum.**

KEY TO FIGURE XIII-5

1. vas deferens
2. pubis
3. prostate gland
4. corpus cavernosum urethrae
5. urethra
6. penis
7. glans penis
8. ureter

9. sacrum
10. urinary bladder
11. seminal vesicle
12. ejaculatory duct
13. rectum
14. Cowper's (bulbourethral gland)

15. external anal sphincter
16. anus
17. tunica vaginalis
18. testis
19. scrotum

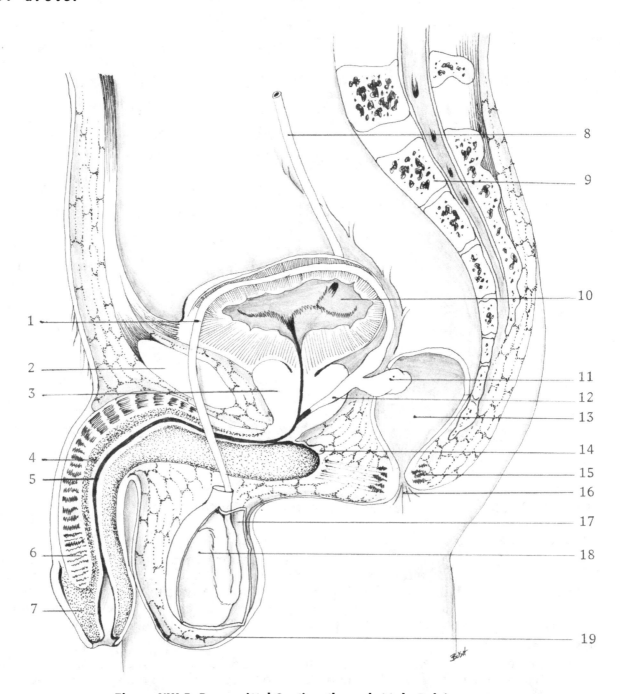

Figure XIII-5: Parasagittal Section through Male Pelvis

2. First study the slide of the ovary showing the Graafian follicle. This slide shows various stages in the development of the follicle. Locate a **primordial follicle** under high power. This structure contains a large immature **ovum** with a conspicuous nucleus, surrounded by a single layer of follicle cells. Mark off a sheet of drawing paper into fourths. Draw the primordial follicle in the first area.

3. Returning to low power, locate an immature follicle. The follicle cells have divided many times and secreted follicular fluid. The immature ovum (which may not be visible, depending on how the follicle was sectioned) is located at one end of the follicle, surrounded by follicle cells. Draw this structure in the second area on your paper.

MEIOSIS

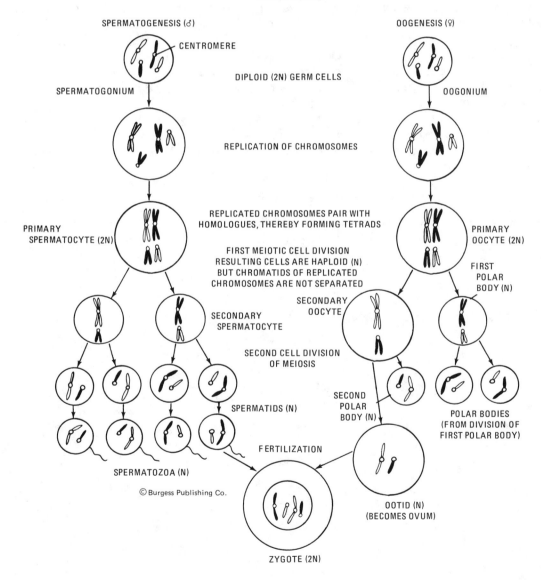

Figure XIII-6: Comparison of Spermatogenesis and Oogenesis

4. On the same slide locate and draw a mature (Graafian) follicle in the third area of your paper. This is a very large follicle filled with clear fluid.

5. On the second slide of the ovary, locate and draw the **corpus luteum**. This structure appears after **ovulation**. The wall of the follicle collapses and is thrown into folds. The cavity assumes an irregular stellate shaped appearance. The cells become filled with a yellow fluid. Draw this structure in the fourth area of your drawing paper.

6. The stages in oogensis are similar to those of spermatogenesis (study Figure XIII-6). The **oogonia** multiply before the birth of a female child. At the time of birth, the primordial follicles contain the **primary oocytes**. These mature at various times during the reproductive years of the woman. Approximately 20 primordial follicles begin to develop each menstrual month; however usually only one matures into a Graafian follicle and releases an egg.

7. Compare the appearance of structures on your slides with Figure XIII-7, which may be used as a self-test.

8. Using your text or other references, locate the structures listed in the key to Figure XIII-8 on the dissectable torso and compare with Figure XIII-8.

9. Using a model, wall chart, your text, or other references, identify each of the structures indicated in the key to Figure XIII-9 and compare with Figure XIII-9 which may be used as a self-test.

KEY TO FIGURE XIII-7

1. primordial follicle
2. blood vessels
3. immature follicle
4. follicular fluid
5. corpus luteum
6. Graafian follicle
7. immature ovum

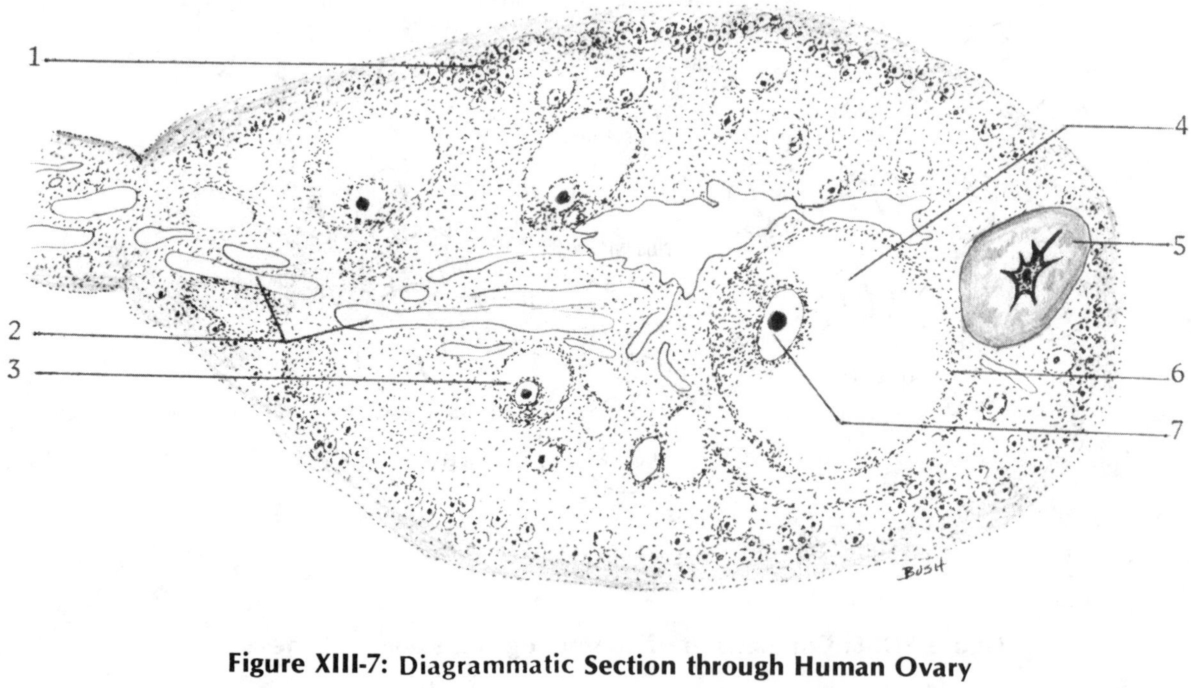

Figure XIII-7: Diagrammatic Section through Human Ovary

KEY TO FIGURE XIII-8

1. fimbriated opening
2. ovary
3. Fallopian tube
4. fundus
5. body cavity
6. urinary bladder

7. urethra
8. labium minus
9. labium major
10. sacrum
11. rectum
12. rectouterine pouch

13. external os
14. fornix
15. vagina
16. external anal
    sphincter
17. anus

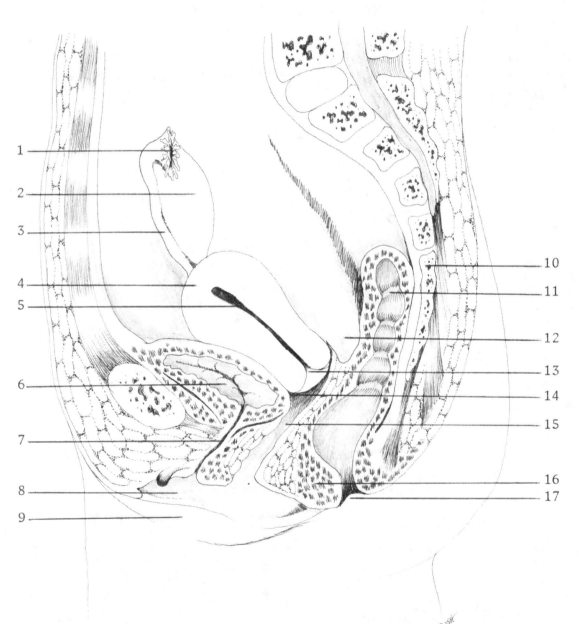

Figure XIII-8: Median Sagittal Section through Female Reproductive Organs

10. Using your text or other references identify each of the structures listed in the key to Figure XIII-10 and compare with Figure XIII-10. This figure may be used as a self-test.

11. Using your text or other references identify each of the structures listed in the key to Figure XIII-11, then compare to Figure XIII-11. The figure may be used as a self-test.

KEY TO FIGURE XIII-9

1. fundus
2. ovary
3. ovarian ligament
4. body cavity
5. myometrium

6. Fallopian tube
7. fimbriated opening
8. ovary (sectioned)
9. internal os

10. cervical canal
11. fornix
12. external os
13. vagina

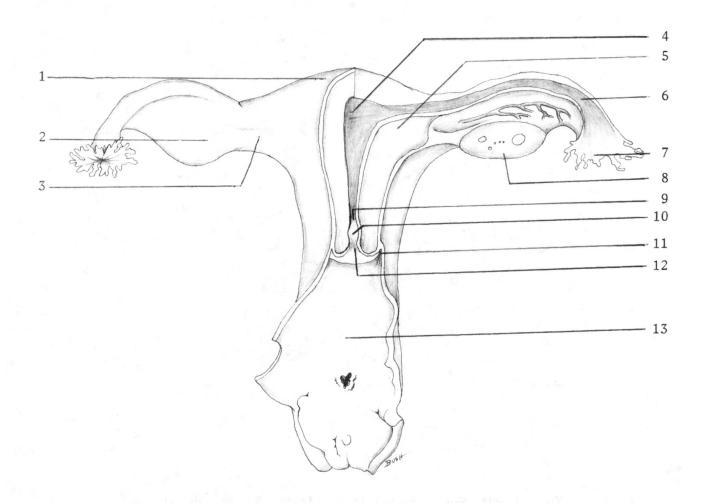

Figure XIII-9: Coronal Section through the Female Reproductive Organs

KEY TO FIGURE XIII-10

1. external urethral
   orifice
2. clitoris
3. vestibule

4. labium minus
5. vaginal orifice
6. labium majus
7. anus

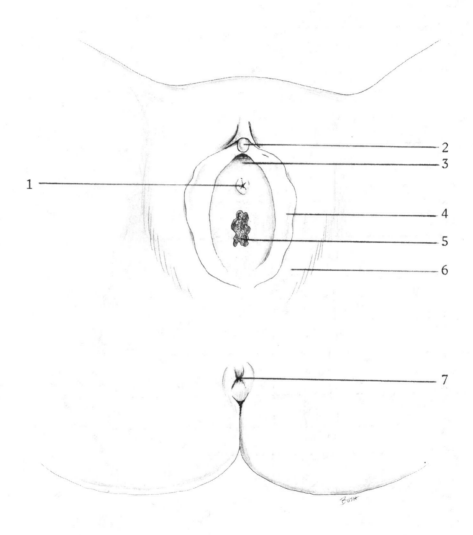

Figure XIII-10: Female External Genital Organs (perineal view)

KEY TO FIGURE XIII-11

1. clavicle
2. pectoralis major
3. adipose tissue
4. skin
5. intercostal muscles

6. rib
7. tubuli lactiferi
8. nipple
9. areola
10. glandular tissue

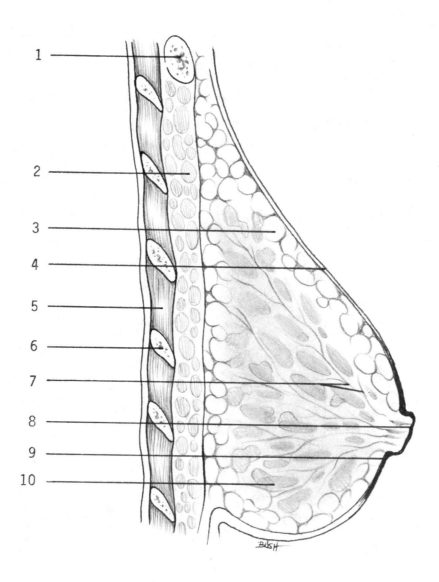

Figure XIII-11: Sagittal Section through the Breast

Ex. XIII-C. The Endometrial (Menstrual) Cycle

DISCUSSION

Menarche, the beginning of a functional menstrual cycle, usually starts at ages 12 to 15. **Menstruation** is the periodic disintegration of the highly vascular **endometrial lining** of the uterus. The endometrial tissue is discharged along with blood through the vagina, in menstruating females, about every 28 days. The period of discharge lasts an average of 4 to 5 days. Normally, menstruation does not occur during pregnancy, and it stops permanently at **menopause** (which usually takes place between 45 and 50 years of age).

In the endometrial cycle (see Scheme XIII-1), the **preovulatory phase** (the time before ovulation) is often days 6 to 13. However, this phase may be much longer. The time of ovulation depends on the duration of the preovulatory phase. For example, in a 32 day cycle the preovulatory phase would probably last until cycle day 17 or 18 and ovulation would then take place on the 18th or 19th cycle day (instead of day 14 or 15). The length of the **postovulatory** or **premenstrual phase,** on the other hand, is fairly constant and usually lasts 14 cycle days. For example, in the 28 day cycle illustrated in the diagram (Scheme XIII-1), the postovulatory phase is from days 15 to 28. Thus, any differences in the length of the total menstrual cycle are due primarily to differences in the duration of the preovulatory, rather than the postovulatory phase.

During the preovulatory phase a follicle containing an immature ovum (egg) begins to develop in response to the presence of **follicle stimulating hormone (FSH),** a secretion of the anterior lobe of the pituitary gland. The follicle soon begins to secrete the hormone **estrogen** which stimulates the initial formation of the endometrium. After ovulation (during the postovulatory phase), the anterior pituitary secretes **luteinizing hormone (LH)** which causes the follicle to thicken into the **corpus luteum.** This structure produces the hormone **progesterone** (and estrogens) which continues the development of the endometrium and maintains it for about 7 or 8 months in the event of pregnancy. An ovum will die if it is not fertilized within 24 hours after ovulation. If fertilization does not occur, the pituitary gland (a few days after ovulation) does not provide enough hormones (e.g., LH) to maintain the corpus luteum which, in turn, ceases to provide hormones for maintaining the endometrium. The result is **menses.**

PROCEDURE
1. Using your text and/or some other references, define each of the following:
   a. Menses _____
   b. Preovulation _____
   c. Premenstrual _____
   d. Postovulation _____
   e. Endometrium _____
   f. Graafian follicle _____

g. Corpus luteum _____

h. Anterior pituitary _____

i. Ovulation _____

2. Determine which hormones are secreted during the preovulatory phase and record them on Scheme XIII-1 (Diagram of the Endometrial Cycle).

3. Determine which hormones are secreted during the postovulatory phase and record them on the diagram below.

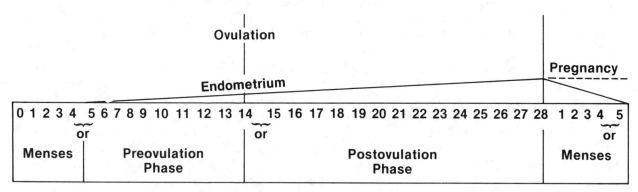

Scheme XIII-1. Diagram of the Endometrial Cycle

The slanted line between days 5-28 represents the buildup of the endometrium. The slanted line between days 1-5 represents the disintegration of the endometrium. The dotted line with the word pregnancy on it represents the maintenance of the endometrium during pregnancy.

Ex. XIII-D. The Placenta

DISCUSSION

The placenta serves as an organ of nutrition, espiration, and excretion for the developing individual. It also serves as a temporary endocrine gland. The chorionic portion (see Figure XIII-12) of the placenta secretes **chorionic gonadotrophin,** a hormone which maintains the functioning of the corpus luteum. The placenta also produces estrogens and progesterone.

PROCEDURE

1. Use Figure XIII-12, showing a section of the placenta, as a self-test.

2. Compare Figure XIII-12 with the model of the placenta, the preserved fetus, and with drawings of this organ in your text and/or other references. As you study the placenta, note the following:

   a. The **trophoblast,** which develops an outer and an inner layer.

   b. The **placental villi,** which grow from the inner layer of the trophoblast.

   c. The **chorion,** which includes the trophoblast and its villi; it is the outer fetal membrane.

   d. The **umbilical arteries,** which lead into capillaries in the chorionic villi, and which carry waste materials from the embryo to the placenta.

KEY TO FIGURE XIII-12

1. marginal sinus
2. chorion
3. amnion
4. trophoblast

5. maternal arterioles
6. maternal venules
7. placental septum
8. villus

9. intervillous space
10. umbilical arteries
11. umbilical vein
12. umbilical cord

Figure XIII-12: Section of Placenta Showing Scheme of Circulation

e. The **marginal sinuses** and **intervillous spaces**, where the mother's blood surrounds the villi.

f. The **maternal arterioles** and **venules**, which carry blood to and from the marginal sinuses and intervillous spaces.

g. The **umbilical vein**, which carries oxygenated blood from the placenta to the embryo.

h. The **umbilical cord**, which contains the umbilical blood vessels. Note that it does not contain any nerves.

i. The **amnion**, which is a fetal membrane that rests against the chorion. The amnion is filled with amnionic fluid in which the embryo floats.

Ex. XIII-E. Embryology

DISCUSSION

The stages in early embryology will be studied in the starfish. The stages in human embryology are similar, although not identical.

PROCEDURE

1. Obtain three slides of starfish embryology (cleavage stages, blastula, and gastrula). Compare all structures observed with Figure XIII-13.

2. After fertilization occurs, the fertilized egg divides repeatedly by mitosis. These cells normally remain attached together. The slide entitled **"cleavage stages"** contains the fertilized egg and the early cleavage stages. Locate the zygote, the 2, 4, 8, and 16 cell stages. Observe the **fertilization membrane** surrounding the fertilized egg in the early stages of cleavage. Observe the size of the fertilized eggs and the size of the young embryo.

3. After a number of cleavage divisions, a solid ball of cells (the **morula**) is formed. Locate the structure on the slide.

4. The cells in the solid ball soon move to the outside, forming a hollow ball or **blastula**. On the slide entitled "starfish blastula" locate a sectioned blastula showing the cavity in the center.

5. Soon after the formation of the blastula, the ball becomes indented at one end. This invagination produces a two-layered embryo. Locate this stage (**gastrula**) on the slide entitled "starfish gastrula."

6. Study the stages of human development exemplified by specimens present in the laboratory. Note the age at which the nails and hair develop. Study Figures XIII-14 through XIII-17, which show stages in human development.

7. Examine Figure XIII-18 which shows the position of a full term fetus in the uterus.

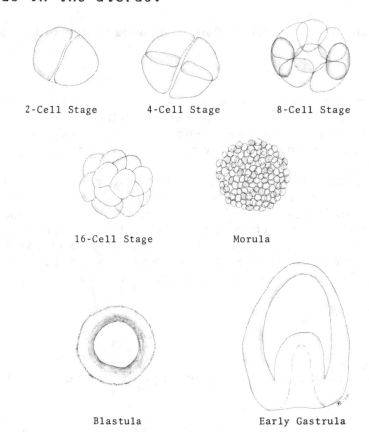

2-Cell Stage   4-Cell Stage   8-Cell Stage

16-Cell Stage   Morula

Blastula   Early Gastrula

Figure XIII-13: Stages of Starfish Embryology

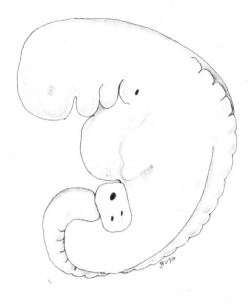

Figure XIII-14: Twenty-Six Day
Old Human Embryo

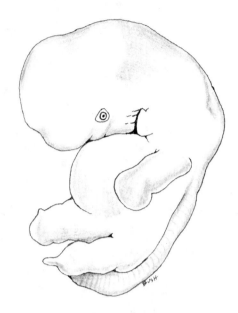

Figure XIII-15: Thirty-Four Day
Old Human Embryo

Figure XIII-16: Forty-Three Day
Old Human Embryo

Figure XIII-17: Fifty-Six Day
Old Human Embryo

KEY TO FIGURE XIII-18

1. chorion   3. uterus wall   5. umbilical cord
2. amnion   4. placenta   6. cervix
                                    7. vagina

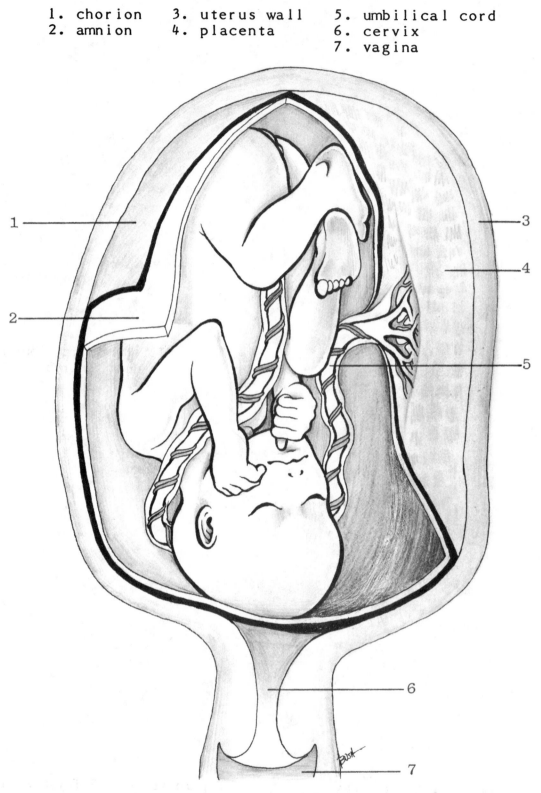

Figure XIII-18: Full Term Human Fetus

Ex. XIII-F. Dissection of the Reproductive System in the Cat

DISCUSSION

The reproductive organs of the cat are similar to those of the human. Note, however, the differences in the structure of the uterus in the female and the absence of the seminal vesicle glands and ejaculatory ducts in the male. Although you will dissect the reproductive system of only one sex, you are responsible for that of both sexes. Therefore, carefully study the reproductive structures on a cat of the opposite sex.

Part 1. The Female Reproductive System

PROCEDURE

1. Use Figure XI-5 (in Chapter XI) and Photo 32 in this chapter as a guide in your dissection. Identify the **ovaries,** a pair of small light-colored oval bodies located posterior to the kidneys.

2. The **uterine tubes (Fallopian tubes)** are very small, highly convoluted tubes. Each one begins close to the posterior end of the ovary, goes anteriorly and then posteriorly, completely encircling the ovary. The expanded end (**infundibulum**) of the Fallopian tube partially covers the ovary and receives eggs (**ova**) through the opening (**ostium**) at the end of the tube. Find the end of the Fallopian tube and try to insert a dull probe into the ostium.

3. Trace the Fallopian tubes until a larger tube is reached immediately next to each ovary. These tubes, the **uterine horns** or **cornua,** are the beginning of the uterus. The eggs are carried through the Fallopian tubes to the uterine horns where they develop. The fetuses tend to be equally spaced throughout the two horns. A specialization of the parietal peritoneum, the **broad ligament,** supports the uterine horns and body of the uterus, extending from the cornua and body to the lateral body walls.

4. The two horns unite in the midline to form the **body of the uterus** which lies dorsal to the urethra.

5. To dissect the rest of the female reproductive system, the pelvic cavity must be exposed. In the midventral line cut through the pelvic muscles with a scalpel and the pubic symphysis with bone shears. Cut with care since the urethra lies immediately beneath the pubis. Open the area further by pushing back on the thighs to crack the bone.

6. Locate the **urethra,** the tube carrying urine from the urinary bladder.

7. Dorsal to the urethra, identify the **vagina,** the tube leading from the posterior end of the uterus.

8. Separate the urethra from the vagina. Toward the posterior end, the vagina and urethra unite to form a common passage called the **urogenital sinus** or **vestibule.** The opening to the outside is called the **urogenital opening.**

9. Examine the **vulva,** the external genitalia. The **labia majora,** the large lips surrounding the opening of the urogenital sinus, are visible.

10. Locate the **rectum,** the continuation of the large intestine, dorsal to the vagina.

KEY TO PHOTO 32

1. urinary bladder
2. vas deferens
3. right ureter
4. left ureter
5. vas deferens
6. testicular artery & vein
7. internal opening of inguinal canal
8. urethra
9. large intestine
10. right testis in tunica vaginalis
11. superficial opening of inguinal canal
12. spermatic cord
13. prostate gland
14. testicular artery & vein
15. vas deferens
16. bulbourethral gland
17. glans penis
18. epididymis
19. left testis
20. scrotum

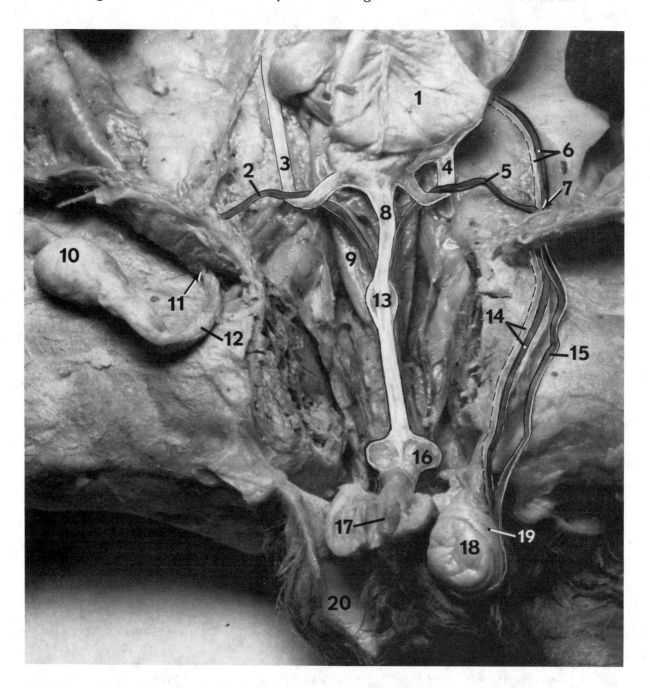

Photo 32: Reproductive System of the Male Cat

Part 2.   The Male Reproductive System

PROCEDURE

1. Use Figure XIII-19 and Photo 33 as a guide in your dissection. Locate the **scrotum,** the double sac ventral to the anus. Early in fetal development, the testes are located below the kidneys; before birth they migrate through the inguinal canal into the scrotum. The scrotum is covered with skin on the outside and lined with peritoneum. It is divided into two compartments by a median septum.

2. Cut open the scrotum on each side and examine the two **testes.** They are oval bodies covered with peritoneum; this covering is called the **tunica vaginalis.** Open the tunica vaginalis around one testis to more clearly see the testis and associated structures.

3. Next locate the **epididymis** along the anterior and lateral side of each testis. This is a long coiled tube which receives sperm from the testis. It begins at the cranial end of the gonad and extends to its caudal end.

4. Locate the **inguinal canals,** two openings in the abdominal wall, by tracing the internal spermatic arteries posteriorly from the aorta until they pass through the inguinal canals.

5. The **vas deferens (ductus deferens)** carries the sperm from the epididymis through the inguinal canal to empty into the urethra. Trace the vas deferens as it passes along the outside of the pelvic region to the inguinal canal. It is accompanied by the testicular artery, vein, and nerve and collectively these structures, covered with peritoneum and connective tissue, are called the spermatic cord. Follow the vas deferens through the inguinal canal to the urethra, noting how it loops over the ureter and enters the dorsal surface of the urethra.

6. To dissect the rest of the male reproductive system, the pelvic cavity must by exposed. In the midventral line cut through the pelvic muscles with a scalpel and the pubic symphysis with bone shears. Cut with care since the urethra lies immediately beneath the pubis. Open the area further by pushing back on the thigh to crack the bone.

7. The **urethra** should now be visible emerging from the urinary bladder. Trace this down to the penis. Observe the opening of the vas deferens into the dorsal surface of the urethra. Locate the **prostate gland,** a small swelling on the urethra, at the point where the vas deferens opens into the urethra. In the human the prostate is immediately adjacent to the urinary bladder; in the cat the prostate gland surrounds the urethra about one inch posterior to the urinary bladder.

8. The urethra is divided into three parts: the **prostatic urethra** surrounded by the prostate gland; the **membranous urethra** passing through the pelvic floor; and the **spongy urethra** passing through the penis.

9. Beneath the cut pubic symphysis, carefully dissect away the tissue to locate the two **bulbourethral (Cowper's) glands.** These prominent swellings lie on either side of the membranous urethra.

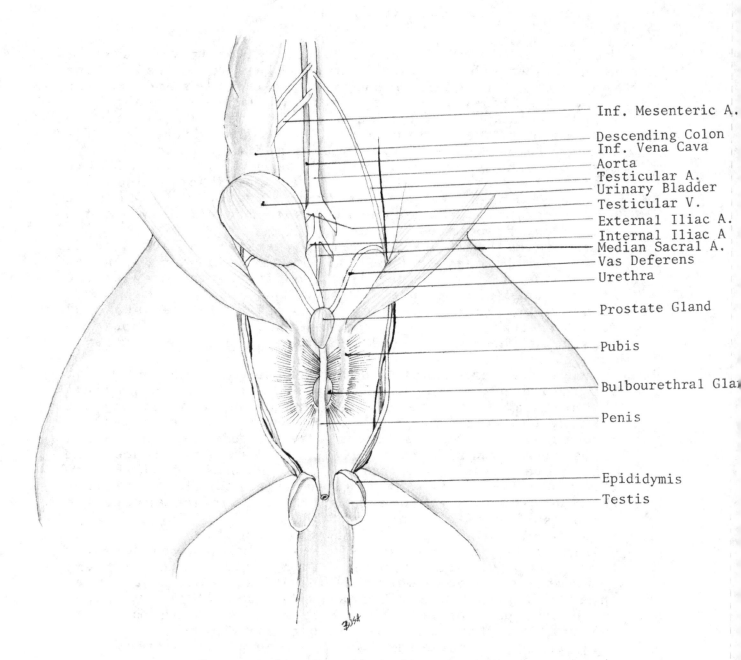

Inf. Mesenteric A.

Descending Colon
Inf. Vena Cava
Aorta
Testicular A.
Urinary Bladder
Testicular V.
External Iliac A.
Internal Iliac A
Median Sacral A.
Vas Deferens
Urethra

Prostate Gland

Pubis

Bulbourethral Gla...

Penis

Epididymis
Testis

Figure XIII-19: Reproductive System of the Male Cat

10. Locate the **penis** ventral to the scrotum. Remove the over-
    lying skin so that the penis is exposed. The **glans penis**
    is the enlargement at the distal end of the organ. The
    prepuce or **foreskin** covers the glans penis. Remove the
    overlying skin so that the penis is exposed.
11. Observe the **rectum** dorsal to the urethra.

KEY TO PHOTO 33

1. left adrenal gland
2. renal artery
3. renal vein
4. right kidney
5. left kidney
6. inferior vena cava

7. aorta
8. ovarian artery
9. fallopian tube
10. ovary
11. broad ligament
12. right ureter
13. left ureter

14. uterine horn
15. urinary bladder
16. body of uterus
17. rectum (cut)
18. vagina
19. urethra
20. urogenital sinus

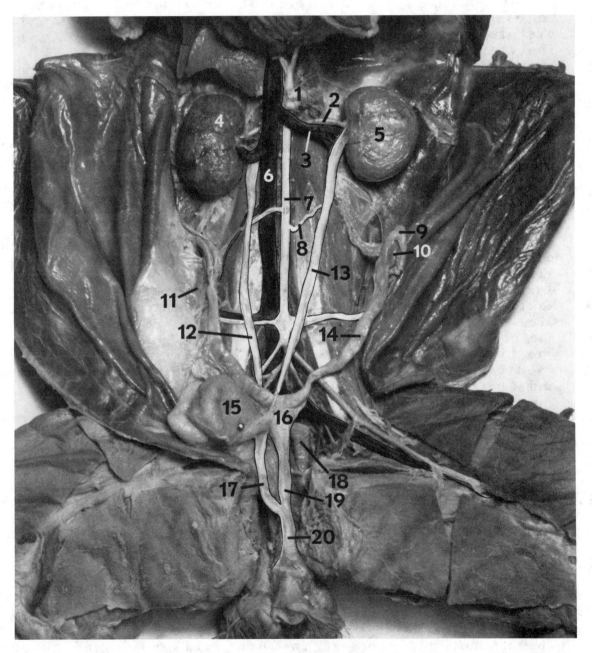

Photo 33: Urogenital System of Female Cat

SELF-TEST: THE REPRODUCTIVE SYSTEM

DIRECTIONS: See Chapter 1, Self-Test, p. 12

1. The sperm cell on its way to the exterior of the body of man follows this course: **seminiferous tubule, vas deferens, epididymis, and urethra.**
2. An ovum on its way to the exterior of the body follows this course: **ovary, oviduct, uterus, and vagina.**
3. A zygote is a **follicle.**
4. The term **"implantation"** means: blastula embedding in the mucous lining of the uterus.
5. The **menopause** is the cessation of menstruation.
6. Unless fertilization occurs, the human ovum usually **disintegrates** before reaching the uterus.
7. The vagina normally has an **acid** pH.
8. Spermatozoa are formed in the **epididymis.**
9. **Androgens** are produced by the interstitial cells.
10. Ovulation involves the rupture of the **corpus luteum** with the release of the egg.
11. The upper rounded part of the uterus is called the **fundus.**
12. The female homologue of the penis is the **clitoris.**
13. The seminal vesicles produce a secretion giving an **acid** pH to the semen.
14. Testosterone is produced by the **follicle** cells.
15. The mucosa of the pregnant uterus is called the **decidua.**
16. Another name for the womb is the **uterus.**
17. The placenta serves for **transport** of material between mother and child.
18. Salpingitis is an inflammation of the **uterus.**
19. A **mastectomy** is surgical removal of the uterus.
20. **Rectocele** is the protrusion of the rectum into the vagina.
21. Cleavage of the zygote begins in the **uterus.**
22. The notochord is the precursor of the **spinal cord.**
23. The first division of the fertilized ovum results in **two identical cells,** each containing the same amount of male and female chromosome elements.
24. The skin is formed from the **entoderm.**
25. Progesterone is secreted by **both the corpus luteum and the placenta.**
26. The **areola** is the pigmented area around the nipple.
27. The **rectouterine pouch** is the pocket between the **rectum** and the uterus.
28. Circumcision is the surgical excision of the **prepuce or foreskin.**
29. The testes descend through the **inguinal canal** before birth.
30. The umbilical **artery** contains deoxygenated blood.
31. The **chorion** is the inner of the two fetal membranes.
32. The cervix is the lower part of the **Fallopian tube.**
33. Pregnancy is not possible after a hysterectomy, **but ovulation still occurs.**
34. The normal position of the uterus is with the fundus tilted **forward over the urinary bladder.**
35. Sperm cells are produced in the **vasa efferentia.**

36. A mature sperm cell contains the **haploid** number of chromosomes as a result of **meiosis**.
37. The **diploid** number of chromosomes results from the fertilization of an ovum by a sperm cell.
38. Sperm cells are stored in the **epididymis and the vas deferens**.
39. Failure of the male gonads to descend into the scrotum is known as a **hernia**.
40. The erectile tissue of the ventral portion of the penis is called the **corpus cavernosum**.
41. The common passageway for both sperm and urine is the **ureter**.
42. The secretion of the **bulbourethral (Cowper's)** glands lubricates the urethra in males during sexual excitation.
43. Another name for the birth canal is the **uterine cavity**.
44. Progesterone is produced in the nonpregnant body by **only the corpus luteum**.
45. In the nonpregnant body, estrogens are produced by the **follicle only**.

KEY

1. seminiferous tubule, epididymis, vas deferens, urethra	17. exchange	35. seminiferous tubules
	18. Fallopian tubes	39. cryptorchidism
3. fertilized egg	19. hysterectomy	40. corpus urethrae (corpus spongiosum)
8. seminiferous tubules	21. Fallopian tube	
10. Graafian follicle	22. vertebral column	41. urethra
13. alkaline	24. ectoderm	43. vagina
14. interstitial cells	31. amnion	45. corpus luteum & follicle
	32. uterus	

Name _____

QUESTIONS FOR CHAPTER I.

EX. I-A. ORGANIZATION OF THE BODY AS A WHOLE

Part 1. Cavities of the Body:

In the blanks provided indicate the specific body cavity in which each of the following is located (dorsal and ventral are not answers):

1. stomach _____
2. spinal cord _____
3. urinary bladder _____
4. uterus _____
5. Fallopian tubes _____
6. large intestine _____
7. prostate gland _____
8. tongue _____
9. pancreas _____
10. aortic arch _____
11. brain _____

12. lungs _____
13. heart _____
14. kidneys _____
15. teeth _____
16. ovaries _____
17. appendix _____
18. small intestine _____
19. adrenal glands _____
20. spleen _____

Part 2. Regions of the Body:

1. A surgeon would make an incision through what region of the body to perform an appendectomy? _____
2. To perform surgery on the right kidney, an incision would be made through what region of the body? _____

EX. I-B. ANATOMIC TERMINOLOGY

Part 1. Using Directional Terms:

1. Write the number preceding the statement in Column II in Column I. Some of the statements may describe or define more than one term and may, therefore, be used more than once.

Column I	Column II
___ a. anterior	1. Term for the back side of the body.
___ b. caudal	2. Term meaning towards the head end of the body.
___ c. cranial	3. Term describing the location of a structure located in the middle of another structure, such as the arm.
___ d. distal	4. Away from the center of the body; towards the outside.
___ e. dorsal	5. Layer of a membrane lining the walls of a cavity.
___ f. dorsum	6. Layer of a membrane covering the organs within a cavity.
___ g. inferior	7. Sole of the foot.
___ h. lateral	8. Palm of the hand.
___ i. medial	9. Superior surface of the foot.

___ j. median

10. Term describing the location of the little toe with respect to the big toe.

___ k. parietal

11. Term meaning farther away from a point of reference, such as the trunk.

___ l. peripheral

12. Term meaning towards the tail end of the body.

___ m. plantar

13. Term meaning the lower portion of the body.

___ n. posterior

14. Term for the front side of the body.

___ o. proximal

15. Term meaning closer to a point of reference such as the trunk.

___ p. superior

16. Term meaning towards the midline of the body.

___ q. ventral

___ r. visceral

___ s. volar

Part 2. Planes of the Body

1. Distinguish between the terms sagittal and midsagittal.

    _____

    _____

2. Dividing the body to expose the coronal plane through the thorax would expose what structures? (Use the dissectable torso and anatomic charts to aid you in answering this question.) _____

    _____

3. Is the transverse plane limited to one specific area of the body or is this a general term that can be applied to many parts of the body? _____ Explain your answer giving examples. _____

    _____

EX. I-C. MAJOR ORGAN SYSTEMS

1. In the following table indicate the specific cavity in which each of the structures listed are located (dorsal & ventral are not answers). In the second column, list the major organ system to which the organ belongs.

Name _____

Structures	Cavity	Organ System
a. stomach		
b. thalamus		
c. small intestine		
d. uterus		
e. esophagus		
f. bronchioles		
g. spinal cord		
h. kidney		
i. tooth		
j. Fallopian tube		
k. adrenal glands		
l. prostate gland		

2. What is the name given to the fundamental unit of structure and function in the body? _____

3. What is the name given to several tissues grouped into one structure performing one or more general functions?
_____

4. Which organ system has the function of conducting air?
_____

5. Which organ system eliminates body wastes?
_____

6. Which organ system synthesizes hormones?
_____

7. Sweat glands are found in which organ system?
_____

8. Leukocytes are part of which organ system?
_____

9. Lymph nodes are part of which organ system?
_____

10. Gastric juice is a secretion of which organ system?
_____

Name _____

QUESTIONS FOR CHAPTER II

EX. II-A. STRUCTURE OF THE MICROSCOPE

1. What is the function of slide clips? _____

2. What is the function of the iris diaphragm? _____

3. Why should the coarse adjustment knob never be used to focus downward when the high power objective is used? _____
   _____

4. A word that refers to objectives or lenses that focus at the same position is: _____

5. The magnification obtained with the microscope is the product of the magnification indicated on the ocular (usually 10X) times that on the objective (10X for low power). Determine the magnification obtained with the low power objective in position. _____

6. Give total magnificaation when the high power objective is in position. _____

7. If the magnification of the ocular is 15X and that of the objective is 20X, what is the total magnification? _____

8. The diameter of the low power field in a microscope is 1.5 mm. Express this diameter in micrometers. _____

9. Size of cells may be calculated from the formula:

$$\frac{\text{diameter of field}}{\text{no. of cells visible}} = \text{size of cell}$$

   If 10 cells are visible across the width of the microscope field (diameter 0.6 mm.), and 4 visible down the length of the microscope field, what are the dimensions of one cell in millimeters? _____

10. What are the dimensions of one cell (in No. 9) in micrometers? _____

11. What is the area of one cell (in No. 9) in square micrometers? _____

EX. II-C. ORIENTATION OF IMAGES VIEWED THROUGH THE COMPOUND MICROSCOPE

1. Draw the letter "p" as it would appear through the microscope. _____

2. In Part 1 and/or Part 2, No. 5, in which directions did you move the paper slide (or microscope slide) in order to center the letter? _____

EX. II-D. THREAD SLIDE

1. In this exercise, which gave the best results, low or high power objectives? _____

2. Relate this exercise (Ex. II-D) to the procedure necessary to follow when observing the parts of a cell. _____
   _____

Name _____

QUESTIONS FOR CHAPTER III

EX. III-A. STRUCTURE OF A CELL OBSERVED UNDER THE LIGHT MICROSCOPE COMPARED TO THAT OBSERVED WITH AN ELECTRON MICROSCOPE

1. Give the primary function of each of the following structures:

   a. Vacuole _____

   b. Nucleus _____

   c. Chromosomes _____

   d. Centrioles _____

   e. Mitochondria _____

   f. Nucleolus _____

   g. Inclusions _____

   h. Endoplasmic reticulum _____

   i. Ribosomes _____

   j. Cytoplasmic membrane _____

   k. Lysosomes _____

   l. Pinocytic vacuole _____

   m. Golgi apparatus _____

2. Which of the structures listed under No. 1 can only be observed with an electron microscope? (Write the letter preceding any structures in answering this question). ____
_____

EX. III-B. MITOSIS

1. What is the significance of mitosis? _____
_____

2. In the spaces provided, indicate the phase of mitosis described in each of the following statements:

   a. Nuclear membrane present; two centrioles in a single centrosphere; chromosomes not visible. _____

   b. Chromatids have completely separated into individual chromosomes, and begin moving to opposite poles. _____
_____

   c. The cleavage furrow has just made its appearance. ____
_____

   d. The chromosomes are oriented along the equator. _____
_____

   e. Centrioles begin moving to opposite poles. _____
_____

   f. Nuclear membrane disappears; distinct chromosomes first observed. _____

3. Where does mitosis occur in the human body? _____
_____

4. What cells in the human body do not undergo mitosis? _____
_____

EX. III-C. EPITHELIAL TISSUE

1. For each of the tissues listed below give (a) two **loca-tions**; (b) **two functions**; and (c) **two identifying** charac-teristics:

Simple squamous: (a) _____ _____
                  (b) _____ _____
                  (c) _____ _____
Simple columnar: (a) _____ _____
                  (b) _____ _____
                  (c) _____ _____
Ciliated columnar: (a) _____ _____
                  (b) _____ _____
                  (c) _____ _____
Simple cuboidal: (a) _____ _____
                  (b) _____ _____
                  (c) _____ _____
Stratified squamous: (a) _____ _____
                  (b) _____ _____
                  (c) _____ _____

2. Which of the preceding tissues contain blood vessels? ____
_____

EX. III-D. CONNECTIVE TISSUE

Part 1. Areolar (Loose) Connective Tissue

1. Where is areolar connective tissue located? _____
_____

2. What is the function of collagenous fibers? _____
_____

3. What is the function of elastic fibers? _____
_____

4. Give two functions of areolar connective tissue. _____
_____

Part 2. Adipose Tissue

1. List three functions of adipose tissue. _____
_____

2. What is the matrix of adipose tissue. _____
_____

Part 3. Hyaline Cartilage

1. List four locations of hyaline cartilage. _____
_____

2. What is the function of hyaline cartilage? _____
_____

3. How does hyaline cartilage differ from fibrous and elastic cartilage? _____

Name _____

Part 4. Osseous (Bony) Tissue
  1. What is the function of the Haversian canal? _____
      _____
  2. What is the function of a canaliculus? _____
      _____
  3. The bony matrix is deposited by what cells? _____
  4. The preceding cells are located in depressions called ____
      _____

Part 5. Blood
  1. What is the major function of erythrocytes? _____
  2. What is the major function of leukocytes? _____
  3. What is the major function of thrombocytes? _____
  4. Where are erythrocytes manufactured in adults? _____
  5. Where are erythrocytes produced before birth? _____
      _____
  6. Where are leukocytes produced? _____
  7. What kind of blood cell is anucleate? _____
  8. In a normal human, what is the rarest kind of leukocyte?
      _____
  9. In a normal human, what is the most common type of
      leukocyte? _____

EX. III-E. MUSCULAR TISSUE

  1. Where is skeletal muscle tissue located in the body? _____
      _____
  2. Why is skeletal muscle tissue also called voluntary
      muscle? _____
  3. Why is visceral muscle tissue also called smooth muscle?
      _____
  4. Where is visceral muscle located? _____
  5. What does cardiac muscle tissue have in common with
      skeletal muscle? _____
  6. What does cardiac muscle tissue have in common with
      visceral muscle? _____
  7. Give an identifying characteristic of cardiac muscle
      tissue. _____

EX. III-F. NERVE TISSUE

  1. What is the function of myelin? _____
  2. What is the function of the neurilemma? _____
  3. In what parts of the nervous system is myelin found? _____
      _____
  4. What general subdivision of the nervous system lacks a
      neurilemma? _____

EX. III-G. THE SKIN

1. Where, within the skin, is melanin located? _____
2. What is the function of melanin? _____
3. What causes a suntan? _____
4. Give the function of the arrector pili muscle. _____
   _____
5. What part of skin is stratified squamous epithelium? _____
   _____
6. What is the function of a sudoriferous gland? _____
   _____
7. What is the function of a sebaceous gland? _____
   _____
8. Where, within the skin, are Pacinian corpuscles located?
   _____
9. Where, within the skin, are Meissner's corpuscles? _____
   _____
10. Is a hair alive or dead? _____ How is it nourished? ____
    _____
11. What is the function of the stratum germinativum? _____
    _____

Name _____

QUESTIONS FOR CHAPTER IV

EX. IV-A.   COMPOSITION AND STRUCTURE OF BONE

1. What is the scientific term used for the shaft of a long bone? _____

2. The slides of bone used in Ex. III-D, part 4, were obtained from which part of the long bone? _____

3. What is the function of the organic material in bone? _____

4. What is the function of the inorganic material in bone? _____

5. Name the cells that form bone. _____

6. Where are the bone-forming cells located in bone? _____

7. Describe the appearance of the bone soaked in acid. _____ _____

8. Describe the appearance of the bone subjected to intense heat. _____

9. Name the most abundant inorganic salts in bone. _____ _____

10. Define a "green-stick" fracture. _____

11. In what age group does a "green-stick" fracture occur most commonly? _____ Explain why: _____

12. What is the function of each of the following:

    a. Haversian canals _____
    b. Canaliculi _____
    c. Volkmann's canals _____
    d. Periosteal blood vessels _____
    e. Nutrient foramen _____

EX. IV-B.   THE APPENDICULAR SKELETON

1. Name the bones comprising the shoulder girdle. _____

2. Name the bones comprising the pelvic girdle. _____

3. Name the bones comprising the pelvis. _____

4. How does the female pelvis differ from the male pelvis?

    _____

    _____

    _____

5. Define Colles' fracture. _____

6. What is a common cause of Colles' fracture? _____

7. Why is the clavicle particularly likely to fracture if a person falls on his shoulder? _____

8. What is the common name of each of the following?

    a. Clavicle _____   d. Phalanges _____
    b. Scapula _____   e. Femur _____
    c. Os coxae _____   f. Calcaneus _____

9. How many carpals in the entire adult skeleton? _____

10. How many tarsals in the entire adult skeleton? _____

11. What is the "funny bone"? _____

12. What is the "elbow bone"? _____

13. What is the "ankle bone"? _____

14. Name the bone of the forearm that is lateral when the individual stands in anatomical position. _____

15. Name the socket in which the head of the femur articulates. _____

16. Name the socket in which the head of the humerus articulates. _____

17. Name the leg bone which is lateral in position. _____

18. Define:

    a. Pelvic brim _____
    b. Pelvic inlet _____
    c. True pelvis _____
    d. False pelvis _____
    e. Carpus _____
    f. Tarsus _____
    g. Phalanx _____
    h. Obturator foramen _____

EX. IV-C. THE AXIAL SKELETON

1. Define:

    a. Lordosis _____
    b. Kyphosis _____
    c. Scoliosis _____

2. What is another name for the first cervical vertebra? _____

3. What is another name for the second cervical vertebra? _____

4. What is meant by a "slipped disc"? _____

5. What is the cause of spina bifida? _____

6. Name the bones making up each of the following structures:

    a. Nasal septum _____
    b. Hard palate _____
    c. Orbit _____

7. List the bones possessing paranasal sinuses. _____

8. Into what structures does the paranasal sinuses drain? _____

9. List the five regions of the vertebral column and the distinguishing characteristics of each region.

Region	No. of Vertebrae	Distinguishing Characteristics
cervical	7	
thoracic	12	
lumbar	5	
sacral	5	
coccygeal	4	

Name _____

10. Name the bones united by the following sutures:
    a. Lambdoidal _____
    b. Sagittal _____
    c. Coronal _____
    d. Squamosal _____
11. Name the bones forming the thorax. _____
12. What distinguishes true ribs from false ribs? _____
    _____
13. What distinguishes floating ribs from other false ribs?
    _____
14. What is a cleft palate? _____
    _____
15. Name the bones containing the teeth. _____
    _____
16. Name the auditory ossicles. _____
    _____
17. What are wormian bones? _____
    _____

EX. IV-D. THE FETAL SKELETON

1. Compare the fetal and adult skeletons by filling in the following table.

	Description of Bone in Fetal Skeleton
frontal bone	
sternum	
patella	
os coxae	
spinous processes of vertebrae	
carpals	
proximal epiphysis of humerus	

2. What is a fontanel? _____
3. List the bones that border each of the following fontanels:
    a. Anterior _____
    b. Anterolateral _____
    c. Posterior _____
    d. Posterolateral _____
4. How many bones are there in the typical fetal skeleton?
    _____
5. What is the sex of the fetal skeleton? _____
6. What characteristics of the fetal skeleton enabled you to determine its sex? _____

EX. IV-E. THE JOINTS

1. Fill in the following table concerning the joints.

Name of Joint	Bones Comprising Joint	Types of Movement Possible at Joint
hip joint		
knee joint		
elbow joint		
wrist joint		
interphalangeal joint		

2. How does the hip joint differ from the shoulder joint? Discuss both the structure of the joint and the range of movement. _____

3. What is the function of synovial fluid? _____

4. What is a meniscus? _____

5. What is the function of a ligament? _____

6. What is the function of the patella? _____

7. What is a sesamoid bone? _____

8. Define the ligamenta flava. _____

9. What type of joint (classified as to structure **and** as to amount of movement possible) is found between:

    a. the bodies of vertebrae? _____

    b. the articular processes of the vertebrae? _____

    c. the os coxae bone and the sacrum? _____

Name _____

QUESTIONS FOR CHAPTER V

1. Complete the following chart concerning muscle action. In the column headed Chief Antagonist, list a muscle that has an action antagonistic to the major action listed in the middle column.

Muscle	Major Action	Chief Antagonist
pectoralis major		
biceps brachii		
deltoid		
external intercostals		
gluteus medius		
gastrocnemius		
triceps brachii		
brachialis		
quadriceps femoris		
gluteus maximus		
latissimus dorsi		
rectus abdominis		

2. Contraction of which muscle will produce each of the following facial expressions?
    a. Smiling _____ c. Pouting _____
    b. Frowning _____ d. Contempt _____
3. Which muscle is involved in the following actions?
    a. Closing the eyes _____ b. Opening eyes _____
4. Which muscle wrinkles the forehead to produce the expressions of fright, horror, and surprise? _____
5. Which muscle is called the:
    a. trumpeter's muscle _____
    b. muscle of kissing _____
6. Contraction of which muscle pulls down the corners of the lips? _____
7. Name the muscles of mastication. _____
    _____
8. Contraction of which muscle flexes the head laterally? ___
    _____

9. Contraction of which muscle would raise the head from a position of lateral flexion back to the vertical position? _____

10. Describe the principal difference between the cleidomastoid and sternomastoid muscles in the cat and man. _____

11. Describe the exact location in the cat of the large lymph gland that lies close to the salivary glands. _____

12. Name a muscle which lies parallel and ventral to most of the trachea. _____

13. Name five muscles that insert on the scapula in the cat.

    _____   _____

    _____   _____

    _____

14. Which muscle attached to the scapula shows its interdigitations most clearly? _____

15. How do the pectoralis muscles of the cat differ from those of man? _____

16. Name the muscles that attach the forelimb of the cat and the pectoral girdle to the vertebral column. _____

17. Name the two largest muscles that insert on the humerus in the cat. _____

18. What is the difference between a tendon and a ligament? _____

19. Name two small muscles with origins on the scapula and insertions of the humerus in the cat. _____

20. Name the lateral abdominal wall muscles in order, from the outside in. _____

21. In what direction do the muscle fibers of each of these muscles extend? _____

22. Discuss the advantage in the way these muscle fibers lie in reference to each other. _____

23. Name the longitudinal muscle of the anterior abdominal wall. _____

24. How is adipose tissue (fat) arranged in reference to the abdominal muscles? _____

25. Name the innermost layer of the abdominal wall. _____

26. Define the term "retroperitoneal." _____

27. What is the linea alba? _____

28. Define the term "aponeurosis." _____

Name _____

29. Sometimes hard objects that cannot be chewed are found in bacon. What are these hard objects? _____

30. Name five superficial muscles of the hip and lateral thigh in the cat.

_____   _____

_____   _____

_____

31. Give a description of the structure of the tensor fasciae latae muscle. _____

32. Name the two narrow and almost parallel structures that lie deep to the biceps femoris muscle in the cat.

_____   _____

33. Name the two large superficial muscles on the ventral surface of the thigh in the cat.

_____   _____

34. State the principal differences between the gluteal muscles of the cat and man. _____

35. Compare the sartorius muscles of the cat and man. _____

_____

36. Name the muscles making up the calf of the leg. _____

_____

37. What muscles insert on the calcaneus by way of the tendon of Achilles? _____

Name _____

QUESTIONS FOR CHAPTER VI

EX. VI-A.   ANATOMY OF THE HUMAN DIGESTIVE SYSTEM

1.   The dental formula for deciduous teeth is? _____
2.   The dental formula for permanent teeth is? _____
3.   What is another name for the cuspids? _____
4.   What is another name for the premolars? _____
5.   What is the function of the cecum? _____
6.   Trace the path of food through the digestive tract from the point of ingestion to the point of absorption of the food into the blood stream. _____
     _____
     _____
7.   Name the three regions of the small intestine. _____
     _____
8.   In which layer of a tooth are nerves and blood vessels found? _____
9.   Define each of the following:
     a.   third molar _____
     b.   dentin _____
     c.   gingiva _____
     d.   periodontal membrane _____
     e.   lingual frenulum _____
     f.   uvula _____
     g.   hard palate _____
     h.   cardiac sphincter _____
     i.   chief cells _____
     j.   fundus _____
     k.   pyloric sphincter _____
     l.   rugae _____
     m.   mucosa _____
     n.   Stensen's duct _____
     o.   lacteal _____
     p.   villi _____
     q.   pancreatic duct _____
     r.   haustra _____
     s.   sigmoid colon _____
     t.   vermiform appendix _____
     u.   greater omentum _____
     v.   mesentery _____
     w.   palatine tonsils _____
     x.   adenoids _____
     y.   tunica serosa _____

EX. VI-B. DISSECTION OF THE DIGESTIVE SYSTEM OF THE CAT

1. Compare the dental formula for the mature cat with that of the human adult.

    _____   _____
                    Cat   Human
2. A cat contains how many teeth in a complete set? _____
3. Name the bones that comprise the hard palate. _____

4. What is the posterior extension of the soft palate called in humans? _____
5. Does the cat have this structure? _____
6. What is the function of the Eustachian tubes? _____

7. What is the function of the common bile duct? _____

8. How many lobes are in the human liver? _____
9. How many lobes in the liver of a cat? _____
10. List three possible functions of the greater omentum.

    _____

    _____
    _____

11. What is the function of the gall bladder? _____
12. What sphincter surrounds the opening of the common bile duct? _____
13. Name the sphincter between the small and large intestine. _____

14. List the functions of the large intestine. _____

15. Name the microscopic fingerlike projections present in the lining of the small intestine. _____
16. What is the function of the structures in No. 15? _____

17. Name the blood vessel that absorbs digested food from the digestive tract. _____
18. The pyloric sphincter is a thickening of which layer of the wall of the stomach? _____
19. To which curvature of the stomach is the greater omentum attached? _____
20. The small arteries in the mesentery are branched from which larger artery? _____
21. What is the function of the cecum in herbivorous animals? _____

22. What is meant by the term retroperitoneal? _____

23. List the retroperitoneal organs you have identified in the abdominal cavity. _____

24. Which excavation (vesicouterine or rectouterine) is deeper in the human female? _____
25. Name the most abundant tissue in the tongue. _____
26. What is a diaphragmatic hernia? _____

    _____

Name _____

QUESTIONS FOR CHAPTER VII

EX. VII-A.   ANATOMY OF THE HUMAN RESPIRATORY SYSTEM

1. Name the bones in the skull that possess paranasal sinuses. _____
2. Into which part of the respiratory tract do these sinuses open? _____
3. What is the function of the paranasal sinuses? _____ _____
4. Name the specific cartilage(s) in the larynx:
    a. that serves as a lid for the larynx. _____
    b. to which the vocal folds are attached. _____
    c. shaped like a signet ring.   _____
    d. shaped like a shield.   _____
    e. that forms the Adam's apple.   _____
5. What are the functions of the larynx? _____ _____
6. What is the name for the opening between the vocal folds? ___
7. Describe the location of the trachea with respect to the esophagus. _____ _____
8. Trace the path of air from a point outside the nose to the point of exchange of gases with the pulmonary capillaries. _____ _____
9. Define or give an important function of each of the following:
    a. cilia _____
    b. glottis _____
    c. external intercostals _____
    d. diaphragm _____
    e. terminal bronchiole _____
    f. bronchus _____
    g. intrapleural space _____
    h. interpleural space _____
    i. phrenic nerves _____

EX. VII-B.   DISSECTION OF THE RESPIRATORY SYSTEM OF THE CAT

1. What is the common name for the trachea? _____
2. What is the function of the cartilage in the wall of the trachea? _____
3. Are the rings of cartilage in the trachea incomplete dorsally or ventrally? _____
4. What is the common name for the larynx? _____
5. What is the function of the thymus gland? _____ _____
6. What is the function of the thyroid gland? _____ _____

7. Name three serous membranes. _____
_____

8. What is the name given to the space in between the lungs?
_____

9. Name five structures located in this space. _____
_____

10. What is the function of the phrenic nerve? _____

11. Compare the number of lobes in the lungs of the cat with
the number present in the human lungs. _____

12. What is the function of the esophagus? _____

13. Does the trachea divide into two bronchi dorsal or
ventral to the heart? _____

14. Name the muscle visible between the ribs beneath the
parietal pleura. _____

QUESTIONS FOR CHAPTER VIII

EX. VIII-A. STRUCTURE OF AN ARTERY, VEIN, AND LYMPH VESSEL VALVE

1. What is the function of each of the following in the wall of an artery?
   a. Endothelium _____
   b. Elastic Connective Tissue _____
   c. Vasa Vasorum _____
2. Which type of vessel contains valves? _____
3. Explain the cause of the difference in shape of the interior of the artery and the vein. _____
_____
4. Which contains proportionally more muscle, a large or small artery? _____
5. Briefly describe, in the table below, the distinguishing characteristics of the following vessels:

Vessel	Structure	Function
Artery		
Capillary		
Vein		

EX. VIII-B. GROSS ANATOMY OF THE HUMAN CIRCULATORY SYSTEM

1. List the major organ(s) supplied by each of the following arteries:
   a. Brachial _____
   b. Internal mammary _____
   c. Celiac _____
   d. Inferior mesenteric _____
   e. Lumbar _____
   f. Internal iliac _____
   g. Anterior tibial _____
   h. Inferior phrenic _____
   i. Renal _____
   j. Hepatic _____
2. Trace the path of a molecule of glucose from the small intestine to the right arm and name all blood vessels and chambers of the heart passed through. _____
_____
_____

3. Trace the path of a drop of blood from the left fingers to the dorsum of the foot, following the same directions as for No. 2. _____
_____

_____

4. Blood that flows away from the heart is always carried by blood vessels called _____. Is this blood always oxygenated? _____. Explain: _____
_____

5. Blood that flows toward the heart is carried by blood vessels called _____. Is this blood always deoxygenated? _____. Explain: _____
_____

6. Explain why the heart is considered a double pump. _____

_____

7. What is the function of the portal system? _____
_____

EX. VIII-C. THE DISSECTION OF THE SHEEP HEART

1. Describe the location of the parietal layer of the pericardium. _____
_____

2. Describe the location of the visceral layer of the pericardium. _____
_____

3. Name the major tissue in the myocardium. _____
4. What is the function of the myocardium? _____
_____

5. What is the function of the pulmonary artery? _____
_____

6. What is the function of the blood vessels in the anterior longitudinal sulcus? _____
_____

7. Which ventricle has thicker walls? _____
8. Which chamber makes up the apex of the heart? _____
9. How many pouches are present in the pulmonary semilunar valve? _____
10. Are chordae tendineae attached to these semilunar valve pouches? _____
11. Does the semilunar valve open during systole or diastole of the right ventricle? _____
12. Is there a valve visible at the entrance of the superior vena cava into the heart? _____
13. What is the function of the coronary sinus? _____
14. What is the function of the chordae tendineae? _____
15. What is the function of the pulmonary valve? _____
16. Are chordae tendineae attached to the bicuspid valve? _____
17. Is a moderator band visible in the interior of the left ventricle? _____

Name _____

18. How many pouches are visible in the aortic semilunar valve? _____

19. Name the three blood vessels branching from the aortic arch in humans. _____

20. What is the internal layer of the artery wall called? _____
_____

21. In No. 20, what type of tissue forms the lining of this layer? _____

22. What type of tissue would be found in largest amounts in the tunica media of the aorta? _____

23. **Based on your observations of the sheep heart,** what is the easiest way to distinguish between an artery and a vein?
_____

24. What is the function of the ductus arteriosus before birth? _____

25. What is the name of the structure containing cartilage in the walls dorsal to the aorta? _____

26. Trace a drop of blood through the heart from the superior vena cava to the aorta. _____
_____
_____

EX. VIII-D. THE DISSECTION OF THE CIRCULATORY SYSTEM OF THE CAT

1. To what structures was the pericardium attached? _____
_____

2. Name the branches of the celiac artery. _____
_____

3. Name the remnant of the ductus arteriosus after birth. ___
_____

4. Compare the aortic arch in man and in the cat. _____
_____

5. Is there a common iliac artery in the cat? _____

6. Describe the base of the aorta (the inferior portion) in the cat. _____

7. What is the special importance of the azygos vein? _____
_____

8. Name the vein which drains the digestive organs. _____

9. Compare the formation of the brachiocephalic veins in cat and man. _____
_____

10. What is the relationship of the inferior vena cava to the peritoneum? _____

11. Where does the vertebral artery eventually terminate? _____
_____

12. With respect to the inferior vena cava, does the aorta lie to the right or to the left? _____

13. List arteries that you have seen in the circulatory system that are not paired with corresponding veins. _____
_____

14. Which type of blood (oxygenated or deoxygenated) is located in each of the following in the adult cat?
   a. Pulmonary artery _____   d. Renal artery _____
   b. Pulmonary vein _____   e. Hepatic vein _____
   c. Aorta _____

15. Trace the path of a drop of blood from the ankle of the human fetus to the right side of the fetal brain; name all blood vessels and chambers of the heart passed through.
   _____
   _____

16. Which type of blood (oxygenated, deoxygenated, or mixed) is located in each of the following in the fetal cat? (Study the coloring carefully in the model of human fetal circulation).

a. Aorta _____   f. Pulmonary artery _____
b. Ductus arteriosus _____   g. Superior vena cava _____
c. Ductus venosus _____   h. Umbilical artery _____
d. Inferior vena cava _____   i. Umbilical vein _____
e. Internal iliac artery _____

17. Trace the path of a drop of blood from the fetal brachial artery to the stomach. _____
   _____

18. List several causes of a "blue baby." _____
   _____

Name _____

QUESTIONS FOR CHAPTER IX

EX. IX-A.   ANATOMY OF THE NERVOUS SYSTEM

Part 1.   Structure of a Nerve

1. How is it possible to distinguish between an axon and a dendrite in the slide of the cross section of a nerve? ___
    _____

2. Define each of the following:
    a. Nerve _____
    b. Tract _____
    c. Ganglion _____
    d. Vasa Nervorum _____
    e. Neuron _____
    f. Neurilemma _____
    g. Myelin sheath _____

Part 2.   The Spinal Cord

1. What is the function of each of the following?
    a. Dorsal horn _____
    b. Lateral horn _____
    c. Ventral horn _____
    d. White matter _____
    e. Dorsal root ganglion _____
    f. Dorsal root _____
    g. Ventral root _____

2. Figure IX-6 is an outline of a cross section through the spinal cord. Complete the diagram by drawing the roots and the beginning of the spinal nerve. Add to the diagram a simple reflex arc and label its components.

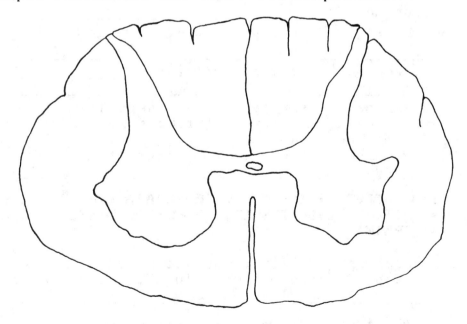

Figure IX-6: Cross Section of Spinal Cord

3. What is the function of each of the following tracts and where does each cross over?

Tracts	Site of crossing over	Function
Posterior columns		
Lateral spinothalamic tract		
Spinocerebellar tract		
Lateral corticospinal tract		

4. How many pairs of spinal nerves emerge from the cord? ____
5. What is the cauda equina? _____
6. Name the major plexuses of spinal nerves and list which spinal nerves form each plexus. _____
_____
_____
7. Classify the neuron whose cell body was visible in the dorsal root ganglion as to structure _____ and function. _____
8. Classify the neuron whose cell body was located in the ventral horn as to structure _____ and function. _____
9. Where does the spinal cord terminate? _____

Part 3. The Gross Structure of the Brain
1. What is the function of each of the following?
    a. Cerebellum _____
    b. Hypothalamus _____
    c. Thalamus _____
    d. Pons _____
    e. Superior colliculi _____
2. Name the lobes of the cerebral cortex. _____
_____
3. Name the three parts of the forebrain. _____
_____
4. Which cranial nerves emerge from the medulla? _____
5. Name one example of commissural fibers seen in the sagittal section of the brain. _____
6. Name the three layers of the meninges that surround the brain and cord. _____

EX. IX-B. THE DISSECTION OF THE SHEEP BRAIN (THESE QUESTIONS MAY ALSO BE USED FOR EX. IX-C. THE DISSECTION OF THE CAT BRAIN)

1. Where is cerebrospinal fluid manufactured? _____
2. Trace the path of cerebrospinal fluid through the brain.
_____
_____
3. What is the advantage of having convolutions in the cerebral cortex? _____

Name _____

4. Describe the composition of white matter in the cord.
   _____
5. Of what is gray matter composed? _____
6. What is the function of cerebrospinal fluid? _____
7. Where is a spinal tap usually made? _____
8. What is the cause of hydrocephalus? _____
9. Compare the structure of the dura mater of the brain with
   that of the cord. _____

EX. IX-D. THE DISSECTION OF THE CAT PERIPHERAL NERVOUS SYSTEM

1. Injury to which nerve produces each of the following?
   a. Wrist drop _____
   b. Ankle drop _____
   c. Inability to extend leg _____
   d. Tic douloureux _____
   e. Ptosis of upper eyelid _____
   f. Lack of facial expression _____
   g. Persistently dilated pupil _____
2. Name two important muscles supplied by the radial nerve.
   _____
3. The phrenic nerve emerges from which plexus in humans?
   _____
4. Examine a cat skeleton and describe the location of the
   supracondyloid foramen. _____
5. Name the largest spinal nerve. _____
6. What is the function of the phrenic nerve? _____
   _____
7. What is the difference between the composition of the
   brachial plexus in the cat and that in man? _____
   _____

Name _____

QUESTIONS FOR CHAPTER X

EX. X-A. GROSS ANATOMY OF THE EYE

1. Indicate, in the blanks provided, whether the following structures are part of the outer, middle, or inner coat of the eye.

   a. Rods and cones _____   c. Cornea _____

   b. Ciliary body _____   d. Iris _____

2. Identify the structures having the following functions (a structure may be used more than once since it may have several functions):

   a. Protects and gives form and shape to the eyeball. _____

   b. An outer, transparent structure which refracts light and thus aids in focusing light rays. _____

   c. Essential in accommodation of the eye. The contraction of its muscle fibers results in change of the shape of the lens. _____

   d. Contains many blood vessels to provide for the nourishment of the retina. _____

   e. Provides place of attachment of extrinsic eye muscles. _____

   f. Contains a pigment which prevents internal reflection of light rays. _____

   g. Contraction results in dilation of the pupil. _____

   h. Contraction results in constriction of the pupil. _____

   i. Contains the light receptors. _____

3. Give the primary functions of each of the following:

   a. Rods _____

   b. Cones _____

   c. Fovea centralis _____

   d. Vitreous humor _____

4. Answer the following questions:

   a. What is the location of the aqueous humor? _____

   _____

   b. Which humor is more gelatinous? _____

   c. Which one of the three eye coats is complete anteriorly? _____

   d. At what point is the retina attached dorsally? _____

   e. Which cranial nerves supply the extrinsic eye muscles?

   _____

5. Describe the location of the optic nerve. _____

_____

6. Name the intrinsic eye muscles: _____

7. Name the extrinsic eye muscles and, after each, give its function.

Muscle	Function
_____	_____
_____	_____
_____	_____
_____	_____
_____	_____

EX. X-B. DISSECTION OF THE SHEEP EYE

1. List any structures you were unable to observe in this dissection and briefly explain why this was not possible.

_____

_____

2. List any structures present in the sheep eye that are lacking in the human eye. _____

3. What is the function of the tapetum lucidum? _____

_____

EX. X-C. ANATOMY OF THE EAR

1. Give the function of each of the following structures:
   a. Tympanic membrane _____
   b. Ear ossicles _____
   c. Eustachian tube _____
   d. Semicircular canals _____
   e. Cochlear nerve _____
   f. Vestibular nerve _____
   g. Organ of Corti _____
   h. Endolymph _____
   i. Fenestra ovalis (oval window) _____
   j. Fenestra rotunda (round window) _____
2. Name the ear ossicles. _____
3. Which ossicle is attached to the tympanic membrane? _____

_____

4. Which ossicle is attached to the fenestra ovalis (oval window)? _____
5. What are otoliths and where are they located? _____

_____

Name _____

6. Identify and define each of the following:
   a. Modiolus _____
   b. Tectorial membrane _____
   c. Basilar membrane _____
   d. Utricle _____
   e. Saccule _____
   f. Vestibule _____
   g. Cochlea _____
   h. Scala tympani _____
   i. Scala vestibuli _____
   j. Osseous labyrinth _____
   k. Membranous labyrinth _____
   l. Cerumen _____

Name _____

QUESTIONS FOR CHAPTER XI

EX. XI-A. ANATOMY OF THE HUMAN URINARY SYSTEM

1. What is the function of each of the following?
    a. Glomerulus _____
    b. Uriniferous tubule _____
    c. Renal pelvis _____
    d. Ureter _____
2. What is the function of the adipose tissue which surrounds the kidney? _____
3. Into which blood vessel does the renal vein empty? _____
4. What is the name given to the portion of the renal cortex which is located between the pyramids? _____
5. What is the name given to the layer of the kidney which contains the pyramids? _____
6. What name is given to the apex of the pyramid? _____
7. In which body cavity are each of the following organs located?
    a. Kidneys _____ c. Ureters _____
    b. Urinary bladder _____
8. What is the trigone of the bladder? _____
9. Which subdivision of the autonomic nervous system prevents elimination of urine? _____

EX. XI-B. DISSECTION OF THE URINARY SYSTEM OF THE CAT

1. Trace the path of urine from its site of formation to the outside of the body. _____
    _____
2. Define the term retroperitoneal. _____
    _____
3. Which parts of the nephron are located in the renal cortex? _____
    _____
4. Which parts of the nephron are located in the renal medulla? _____
    _____
5. Name the structure located in the renal sinus. _____
6. Trace the path of blood from the renal artery to the glomerulus. _____
    _____
7. Trace the path of blood from the glomerulus to the renal vein. _____
    _____
8. Compare the internal structure of the cat kidney with that of the human kidney. _____
    _____
9. Compare the location of the adrenal glands in the cat with those in man. _____
    _____

QUESTIONS FOR CHAPTER XII

Name _____

EX. XII-A.   ENDOCRINE GLANDS

1. Define an endocrine gland. _____
2. Which endocrine glands are considered to be mixed glands?

   _____
3. Which endocrine gland is embedded in the dorsal surface of the thyroid gland? _____
4. Fill in the following chart concerning functions of hormones.

Function of Hormone	Hormone
Adsorption of glucose into cell	
Regulates BMR	
Regulates thyroid gland	
Stimulates spermatogenesis	
Regulates calcium balance	
Regulates reabsorption of water in kidney	
Stimulates contraction of pregnant uterus	
Stimulates ovulation	
Regulates mental development	
Regulates sodium and potassium balance	
Increases heart rate and blood pressure	

5. The table on the following page contains a list of symptoms resulting from endocrine disorders. In the spaces provided, write the name of the specific part of the gland (wherever possible), the name of the hormone involved and the disease, and place a check mark under hyposecretion or hypersecretion.

Symptoms of Endocrine Dysfuncton	Gland (or Part of Gland)	Hormone	Name of Disease	Hypo-secretion	Hyper-secretion
Failure of physical, sexual, and mental development					
Muscle spasms due to increased irritability of nerves and muscles					
Precocious sexual development					
Continued growth of bones in children					
Shock, convulsions, marked decrease in blood sugar					
Copious excretion of urine					
Loss of vigor, falling hair, puffy skin, lowered BMR					
Development of secondary char. of male in adult female					
Obesity, sexual infantilism, often sub-normal intelligence	both ant. and post. pituitary	all hormones	Frölich's syndrome		
Coma, marked increase in blood sugar					
Demineralization of bones, with spontaneous fractures					
Bulging eyeballs, goiter, loss of weight, nervousness, rapid pulse					
Lower jaw, hands, and feet become larger in adults					

6. Name two hormones produced by the ovary. _____
_____

7. Which gland is called the master gland? _____
8. What is the function of the pineal gland? _____
_____

9. Which hormone is sometimes called an emergency hormone?
_____

10. Which two glands are called "glands of childhood". _____
_____

11. What is the common name of the somatotropic hormone? _____
_____

Name _____

EX. XII-B.   THE ENDOCRINE GLANDS IN THE CAT

1. Give a brief, precise anatomical description of the location of each of the following glands in the cat.

    a. Hypophysis (pituitary) _____

    b. Ovaries _____

    c. Pancreas _____

    d. Parathyroids _____

    e. Suprarenals (adrenals) _____

    f. Testes _____

    g. Thymus _____

    h. Thyroid _____

    i. Pineal Body _____

2. Compare the location of the adrenal glands in the cat and man. _____

    _____

Name _____

QUESTIONS FOR CHAPTER XIII

EX. XIII-A. THE HUMAN REPRODUCTIVE SYSTEM

1. Was there any evidence of spermatogenesis in the wall of the epididymis? _____ Should there be? _____
2. What is the function of each of the following?
    a. Epididymis _____
    b. Vas deferens _____
    c. Prostate gland _____
    d. Cowper's gland _____
    e. Urethra _____
    f. Seminal vesicle _____
    g. Seminiferous tubules _____
    h. Interstitial cells _____
3. Define cryptorchidism. _____
    What is the significance of this condition? _____
    _____
4. Trace the path of sperm from the site of production to the outside. _____
5. Name the three male accessory reproductive glands. _____
    _____
6. Define semen. _____
7. What is the spermatic cord? _____
8. Why would enlargement of the prostate gland interfere with the passage of urine? _____
    _____
9. Where are the Cells of Sertoli located? _____
    What is their function? _____
10. What structure in the male is homologous to the labia majora? _____

EX. XIII-B. THE HUMAN FEMALE REPRODUCTIVE SYSTEM

1. Describe the location of each of the following:
    a. Broad ligament _____
    b. Round ligament _____
    c. Ovarian ligament _____
2. What is the endometrium? _____
3. Trace the path of the egg (ovum) from the site of production to the outside. _____
4. What type of muscle is located in the wall of the uterus?
    _____
5. What is meant by salpingitis? _____
6. Would pregnancy be possible in case of a bilateral salpingectomy? _____ Explain. _____
    _____
    Would menstruation be possible in this case? _____
    Explain. _____
7. Define the hymen. _____
8. Name the two parts of the uterus. _____
9. What is a retroverted uterus? _____

10. How many mature Graafian follicles are produced by the ovary at one time? _____

11. What is the mons pubis? _____

12. Define the perineum. _____
    What is the obstetrical perineum? _____

13. What is the name of the erectile tissue located near the anterior junction of the labia minora? _____

14. What is an oophorectomy? _____

EX. XIII-C. THE ENDOMETRIAL (MENSTRUAL) CYCLE

1. Name the hormone secreted by the follicle. _____

2. What is the function of this hormone? _____

3. In which phase (see diagram in Procedure) is this hormone active? _____

4. What is the name of the hormone that stimulates the growth of the follicle? _____

5. Which gland produces the hormone in Question 4? _____

6. Which gland produces the luteinizing hormone? _____

7. In which phase of the menstrual cycle is this hormone active? _____

8. What is the function of the luteinizing hormone? _____

9. Name the hormones secreted by the corpus luteum. _____
   _____

10. On which day of a 40 day menstrual cycle does ovulation usually occur? _____

11. On which day of a 28 day menstrual cycle does ovulation usually occur? _____

12. How long will an ovum survive if not fertilized? _____

13. Lack of which hormone causes the endometrium to break down? _____

14. Failure of the fertilized ovum to become embedded in the endometrium results in cessation of the secretion of _____; this in turn results in the disintegration of the endometrium, a process called _____
    or _____

15. Fill in the following chart concerning the hormones in the menstrual cycle.

Hormone	Gland Secreting Hormone	Stimulus for Production of Hormone	Function of Hormone in Menstrual Cycle
a. FSH			
b. Estrogen			
c. LH			
d. Progesterone			

Name _____

EX. XIII-D.   THE PLACENTA

1. Name the two human fetal membranes. _____
2. Define the decidua basalis. _____
3. What is the origin of the placenta? _____
4. What is the function of the placenta? _____
   _____
5. What are the major components of the afterbirth? _____
   _____

EX. XIII-E.   EMBRYOLOGY

1. Compare the blastula stages of the starfish with that of humans. _____
2. Compare the gastrula stage in the starfish with that of humans. _____
3. When does implantation of the fertilized egg occur? _____
   _____
4. What is the vernix caseosa? _____
5. What is the average duration of a pregnancy? _____
6. Name the three germ layers of the developing embryo and two structures produced from each layer.

Germ Layers	Structures Produced
ectoderm	
entoderm (endoderm)	
mesoderm	

EX. XIII-F.   DISSECTION OF THE REPRODUCTIVE SYSTEM OF THE CAT

1. List any differences noted between the reproductive organs of the human and the cat. _____
   _____
2. What is the function of the urogenital sinus in the female cat? _____
3. Compare the place of development of the fetus in the human with that in the cat. _____
4. Trace the path of sperm from the site of production to the outside in the cat. _____
   _____
5. List the accessory reproductive glands in the male cat.
   _____

Student Survey

Barbara H. Kalbus, Kenneth G. Neal, Margaret A. Wilson

A LABORATORY MANUAL & STUDY GUIDE FOR HUMAN ANATOMY
Third Edition

Students, send us your ideas!

The author and the publisher want to know how well this book served you and what can be done to improve it for those who will use it in the future. By completing and returning this questionnaire, you can help us develop better textbooks. We value your opinion and want to hear your comments. Thank you.

Your name (optional) _____ School _____

Your mailing address _____

City _____ State _____ ZIP _____

Instructor's name (optional) _____ Course title _____

1. How does this laboratory manual compare with others you have used? (Check one)

   ☐ Superior   ☐ Better than most   ☐ Comparable   ☐ Not as good as most

2. Circle those chapters you especially liked:

   Chapters: 1   2   3   4   5   6   7   8   9   10   11   12   13

   Comments:

3. Circle those chapters you think could be improved:

   Chapters: 1   2   3   4   5   6   7   8   9   10   11   12   13

   Comments:

4. Please rate the following. (Check one for each line)

	Excellent	Good	Average	Poor
Readability of text material	( )	( )	( )	( )
Logical organization	( )	( )	( )	( )
Up-to-date treatment of subject	( )	( )	( )	( )
Match with instructor's course organization	( )	( )	( )	( )
Illustrations that clarify the text	( )	( )	( )	( )
Selection of topics	( )	( )	( )	( )
Explanation of difficult concepts	( )	( )	( )	( )

(Over, please)

5. List any chapters that your instructor did not assign. _____

_____

6. What additional topics did your instructor discuss that were not covered in the text?_____

_____

7. Did you buy this book new or used?   ☐ New   ☐ Used

   Do you plan to keep the book or sell it?   ☐ Keep it   ☐ Sell it

   Do you think your instructor should continue to assign this book?   ☐ Yes   ☐ No

   Did you purchase the study guide for the text?   ☐ Yes   ☐ No

8. After taking the course, are you interested in taking more courses in this field?   ☐ Yes   ☐ No

   Did you take this course to fulfill a requirement, or as an elective?   ☐ Required   ☐ Elective

9. What is your major? _____

   Your class rank?   ☐ Freshman   ☐ Sophomore   ☐ Junior   ☐ Senior   ☐ Other, specify:

10. GENERAL COMMENTS:

May we quote you in our advertising?   ☐ Yes   ☐ No

Please remove this page and mail to: Marketing Department
                                          Burgess Publishing
                                          7110 Ohms Lane
                                          Edina, MN 55435

THANK YOU!